EUGLENOID FLAGELLATES

Prentice-Hall Biological Science Series

William D. McElroy and Carl P. Swanson, *Editors*

Actions of Chemicals on Dividing Cells, BENGT A. KIHLMAN

Biochemical Systematics, RALPH E. ALSTON AND B. L. TURNER

Biological Phosphorylation: Development of Concepts, HERMAN M. KALCKAR

The Cellular Functions of Membrane Transport, JOSEPH F. HOFFMAN, ED.

Classic Papers in Genetics, JAMES A. PETERS

Experimental Biology, RICHARD W. VAN NORMAN

Foundations of Experimental Embryology, BENJAMIN H. WILLIER AND JANE M. OPPENHEIMER

General and Comparative Physiology, WILLIAM S. HOAR

An Introduction to Animal Behavior: Ethnology's First Century, PETER H. KLOPFER AND JACK P. HAILMAN

Introduction to Molecular Biological Techniques, L. JACK BRADSHAW

Mechanisms of Body Functions, DEXTER M. EASTON

Milestones in Microbiology, THOMAS D. BROCK

Molecular Architecture in Cell Physiology, TERU HAYASHI AND ANDREW SZENT-GYORGYI, EDS.

Papers on Human Genetics, SAMUEL H. BOYER, IV

Poisonous Plants of the United States and Canada, JOHN M. KINGSBURY

Principles of Biology, NEAL D. BUFFALOE

Principles of Microbial Ecology, THOMAS D. BROCK

Radiotracer Methodology in Biological Science, C. H. WANG AND DAVID L. WILLIS

Readings in Ecology, EDWARD J. KORMONDY, ED.

Selected Botanical Papers, IRVING W. KNOBLOCH

Selected Papers on Virology, NICHOLAS HAHON

The Specificity of Cell Surfaces, BERNARD DAVIS AND LEONARD WARREN, EDS.

A Synthesis of Evolutionary Theory, HERBERT H. ROSS

BIOLOGICAL TECHNIQUES SERIES

Alexander Hollaender, *Editor*

Autoradiographic Techniques: Localization of Radioisotopes in Biological Material, WILLIAM D. GUDE
Introduction to Research in Ultraviolet Photobiology, JOHN JAGGER

CONCEPTS OF MODERN BIOLOGY SERIES

Behavioral Aspects of Ecology, PETER H. KLOPFER
Euglenoid Flagellates, GORDON F. LEEDALE
Molecular Biology: Genes and the Chemical Control of Living Cells, J. M. BARRY
The Organism As an Adaptive Control System, JOHN M. REINER
Processes of Organic Evolution, G. LEDYARD STEBBINS

FOUNDATIONS OF MODERN BIOLOGY SERIES

Adaptation, 2nd ed., BRUCE WALLACE AND A. M. SRB
Animal Behavior, 2nd ed., VINCENT DETHIER AND ELIOT STELLAR
Animal Diversity, 2nd ed., EARL D. HANSON
Animal Physiology, 2nd ed., KNUT SCHMIDT-NIELSEN
The Cell, 2nd ed., CARL P. SWANSON
Cell Physiology and Biochemistry, 2nd ed., WILLIAM S. McELROY
Chemical Background for the Biological Sciences, EMIL H. WHITE
Growth and Development, 2nd ed., MAURICE SUSSMAN
Heredity, 2nd ed., DAVID M. BONNER AND STANLEY E. MILLS
The Life of the Green Plant, 2nd ed., ARTHUR W. GALSTON
Man in Nature, 2nd ed., MARSTON BATES
The Plant Kingdom, 2nd ed., HAROLD C. BOLD

PRENTICE-HALL INTERNATIONAL, INC. *London*
PRENTICE-HALL OF AUSTRALIA, PTY. LTD. *Sydney*
PRENTICE-HALL OF CANADA, LTD. *Toronto*
PRENTICE-HALL OF INDIA PRIVATE LTD. *New Delhi*
PRENTICE-HALL OF JAPAN, INC. *Tokyo*

EUGLENOID FLAGELLATES

GORDON F. LEEDALE

Department of Botany
University of Leeds
England

PRENTICE-HALL, INC., *Englewood Cliffs, N. J.*

Current printing (last digit):
10 9 8 7 6 5 4 3 2 1

273439

Library of Congress Catalog Card Number: 67–19494

Printed in the United States of America

For Hazel, Wanda, Sian and Jonathan

PREFACE

Euglena is one of biology's most intensively studied organisms, important both as a basic type in teaching and as the preferred living cell for numerous lines of research. Elementary courses in biology feature *Euglena* as the classic "plant-animal"; courses at a more advanced level present the euglenoid flagellates in dual guise as algae and protozoa. In research, euglenoid species have been much used in studies on photosynthesis, chloroplast structure, carbon metabolism, enzyme biosynthesis, lipid chemistry and metabolism, phototaxis and flagellar movement. In medicine, *Euglena gracilis* is important as an assay organism for the anti-pernicious anæmia factor, vitamin B_{12}.

In recent years euglenoid physiology has been more intensively investigated than euglenoid structure, with *Euglena* (particularly strain Z and var. *bacillaris* of *Euglena gracilis*) being studied to the virtual exclusion of all other genera. This book aims to redress the balance by placing *Euglena* in its taxonomic setting and by providing a modern account of euglenoid cell structure. Certain aspects of physiology are briefly discussed at appropriate points, but the deliberate emphasis of this account is on taxonomy, phylogeny and cell organisation.

The book is in two parts, the first dealing with the organisms and the second with their organelles. The organisms are considered mainly at the generic level within the framework of a revised scheme of classification, with representative species selected for illustration and special comment. The survey of organelles is a study in correlation: Light microscopy of living cells is correlated with electron microscopy of fixed cells, and aspects of structure thereby revealed are correlated with known aspects of cell function. It is hoped that this approach will aid the profitable study of a key group of organisms and help define the most inviting areas for future research.

Acknowledgments

It is a very real pleasure to record my grateful thanks to all who have helped in the production of this book: to Prof. I. Manton, F. R. S., and Prof. Dr. E. G. Pringsheim for their invaluable advice on my research and for critically reading the entire manuscript; to my research assistant, Miss Jane Stoker, B. Sc., for her help at all stages of preparation of the manuscript and, in particular, for ferreting out the originals of every publication listed in the bibliography; to Mr. K. Oates for his technical

ix

assistance in electron microscopy; to Prof. M. B. E. Godward who supervised my first chromosome studies; to Mr. E. A. George, Dr. W. Koch, Dr. H. E. Christen, Dr. E. Paasche and others for sending me cultures of euglenoids; to Dr. J.-P. Mignot for supplying me with original prints and permission to reproduce Figs. 122 and 173–175; to Dr. J. O. Corliss and Mr. Ross for advice on problems of nomenclature, and to Mr. Ross for providing the Latin diagnoses given on pp. 204–205; to Mr. D. Lawson of Prentice-Hall, Inc. for his friendly help and advice; to the British Phycological Society for permission to reproduce Figs. 85, 86–88 and 92 [which first appeared in *British Phycological Bulletin*, **2** (5), 291–306 (1964)]; to Springer-Verlag for permission to reproduce Figs. 69, 70, 73, 75, 76, 79 and 81 [which first appeared in *Archiv für Mikrobiologie*, **32**, 32–64 (1958), Springer-Verlag, Berlin, Göttingen, Heidelberg], Fig. 84 [which first appeared in *Archiv für Mikrobiologie*, **42**, 237–245 (1962), Springer-Verlag, Berlin, Göttingen, Heidelberg], and Figs. 85, 94, 111, 135 and 140 [which first appeared in *Archiv für Mikrobiologie*, **50**, 68–102 (1965), Springer-Verlag, Berlin, Heidelberg, New York]; to the Science Research Council for providing grants for light microscopy equipment and for the employment of a research assistant; and, most gratefully of all, to my wife for her support and encouragement and to my daughters for providing me with (occasional) peace and quiet.

GORDON F. LEEDALE

CONTENTS

Part I THE ORGANISMS

Chapter 1 The Position of Euglenoid Flagellates in the Biological
Hierarchy   3

Chapter 2 Diagnostic Features of the Euglenophyta (Euglenida)   6

Chapter 3 Taxonomy I. Classification   8

Chapter 4 Taxonomy II. Characters of Orders, Genera and Species   11

*Order 1. Eutreptiales, 11.   Order 2. Euglenales, 16.   Order
3. Rhabdomonadales, 46.   Order 4. Sphenomonadales, 52.
Order 5. Heteronematales, 59.   Order 6. Euglenamorphales,
66.   Genera of uncertain affinity or validity, 69.*

Chapter 5 Phylogeny   72

Part II CELL COMPONENTS AND CELL INCLUSIONS

Chapter 6 Introduction   79

Chapter 7 The Nucleus   81

*The interphase euglenoid nucleus, 81.   Euglenoid mitosis, 83.
Amitosis, 92.   Euglenoid meiosis, 92.*

Chapter 8 The Pellicle   96

*Organisation of the pellicle: associated organelles, 96.   Eu-
glenoid movement, 99.   Ornamentation, 100.   Cell symmetry,
102.   Cell cleavage and pellicular growth, 104.*

Chapter 9 Muciferous Bodies   108

Chapter 10   Endoplasmic Reticulum, Ribosomes and Cytoplasmic Matrix   115

Endoplasmic reticulum and ribosomes in the euglenoid cell, 115.

Chapter 11   Canal and Reservoir   120

Structure, 120.   Function, 121.

Chapter 12   Flagella   127

General considerations of function and structure, 127.   Flagella in euglenoid cells, 128.

Chapter 13   Eyespot and Flagellar Swelling   143

The euglenoid eyespot, 143.   The flagellar swelling, 145. Photoreception, 146.

Chapter 14   The Contractile Vacuole   148

The contractile vacuole in euglenoid flagellates, 149.

Chapter 15   Golgi Bodies   155

Golgi bodies in the euglenoid cell, 158.

Chapter 16   Mitochondria   160

Mitochondria in euglenoid cells, 163.

Chapter 17   Phospholipid Vesicles and Lysosomes   166

Chapter 18   Chloroplasts and Pyrenoids   169

Euglenoid chloroplasts and pyrenoids, 171.

Chapter 19   Paramylon   185

Chapter 20   Ingestion Organelles   190

Appendix 1   Key for the Identification of the Genera of Euglenoid Flagellates   196

Appendix 2 Notes on the Collection, Cultivation, Nutrition and
Microscopical Examination of Euglenoid Flagellates   199

*Collection, 199.   Cultivation, 199.   Nutrition, 201.   Micro-
scopical examination, 202.*

Appendix 3 Latin Diagnoses of Euglenoid Orders   204

Bibliography   206

Index   223

Part I

THE ORGANISMS

Chapter 1

THE POSITION OF EUGLENOID
FLAGELLATES IN THE
BIOLOGICAL HIERARCHY

The consensus of taxonomic opinion places euglenoid flagellates as a division or class of the algae at the base of the plant kingdom, or as a class or order within the phylum *Protozoa* at the base of the animal kingdom.

In Fritsch's (1935) classification of the algae the *Euglenineae* are a class equal in status to the groups predominated by flagellates (*Dinophyceae*, *Chrysophyceae*) and also to the main algal classes (*Chlorophyceae*, *Xanthophyceae*, *Phaeophyceae*, *Bacillariophyceae*, *Rhodophyceae*, *Myxophyceae*), whereas in more recent taxonomic systems euglenoid flagellates (*Euglenophyta*) and other algal groups appear as divisions (phyla), equal in rank to the divisions of higher plants (see Bold, 1964). In the scheme of classification recently proposed by Christensen (1962, 1966), the euglenoids once more feature as a class (*Euglenophyceae*; see Table 1).

The world of protozoology, where euglenoid flagellates have for a long time figured as a class of the division *Flagellata* within the phylum *Protozoa* (as *Euglenida* or *Euglenineae*), has likewise recently produced a revised classification of the *Protozoa* (Honigberg *et al.*, 1946; see Table 2).

There is little to discuss in the position accorded to the *Euglenida* within the *Protozoa*, since the new scheme is still a tentative one and its artificiality is recognised. Christensen's classification of the algae, on the other hand, is based on phylogenetic grounds, and significant points are raised by the position allocated to the *Euglenophyceae*. Photosynthetic pigments are selected as the major taxonomic criterion, euglenoid flagellates being placed near to the green algae and higher plants because of their mutual possession of chlorophylls *a* and *b*. Nevertheless, it should be noted that on most other characters (discussed in detail later) the euglenoids lie closer to classes of Christensen's *Chromophyta* than to his *Chlorophyta*: the carbohydrate storage product, paramylon, is a β-1:3-linked glucan, as are laminarin of the *Phaeophyceae* and leucosin (chrysolaminarin) of the *Chrysophyceae* and *Bacillariophyceae*; muciferous bodies, trichocysts, flagellar grooves and nuclear division are all similar to those in some *Dinophyceae*; the locomotory flagella bear rows of long hairs as appendages, a feature common to the *Chryso-*

Table 1

Position of the Euglenoid Flagellates in the Algal
Taxonomic System Proposed by Christensen (1962)

A. *PROCARYOTA*	Cellular organisms without a true nucleus (and with no delimitation of subunits of cellular function as membrane-bounded organelles)
I. CYANOPHYTA	
Class 1. *Cyanophyceae*	(Blue-green algae)
B. *EUCARYOTA*	Cellular organisms with a true nucleus (and with subunits of cellular function enclosed within membranes)
a. *ACONTA*	No evolution of flagella
I. RHODOPHYTA	
Class 1. *Rhodophyceae*	(Red algae)
b. *CONTOPHORA*	Flagella or flagellated stages present
I. CHROMOPHYTA	Chlorophyll *a* present, but no chlorophyll *b*
Class 1. *Cryptophyceae*	
Class 2. *Dinophyceae*	(Dinoflagellates)
Class 3. *Rhaphidophyceae*	
Class 4. *Chrysophyceae*	
Class 5. *Haptophyceae*	
Class 6. *Craspedophyceae*	
Class 7. *Bacillariophyceae*	(Diatoms)
Class 8. *Xanthophyceae*	
Class 9. *Phaeophyceae*	(Brown algae)
II. CHLOROPHYTA	Chlorophylls *a* and *b* present
⟹ Class 1. *Euglenophyceae*	
Class 2. *Loxophyceae*	
Class 3. *Prasinophyceae*	
Class 4. *Chlorophyceae*	(Green algae)

phyceae, *Xanthophyceae* and *Phaeophyceae;* neither the periplast nor the extracellular envelope contains cellulose, an important constituent of cell walls in *Chlorophyceae* and higher plants.

In the present account, therefore, the practice is followed of according the status of division (phylum) to each major algal group, including the euglenoid flagellates. In such a system, in comparison with Table 1, the phylum *Euglenophyta* might stand equal in rank to the phyla *Cyanophyta*, *Rhodophyta*, *Pyrrophyta* (= *Dinophyta*), *Chrysophyta*, *Bacillariophyta*, *Xanthophyta*, *Phaeophyta* and *Chlorophyta*.

Table 2

Position of the Euglenoid Flagellates in the Phylum
Protozoa (Extracted from Honigberg *et al.*, 1964)

Phylum *PROTOZOA*

    Subphylum I. *SARCOMASTIGOPHORA* (Flagellates and amoebae)

        Superclass I. MASTIGOPHORA   (Flagellates)

           Class 1. *Phytomastigophorea*   (Phytoflagellates)

               Order   1. *Chrysomonadida*

               Order   2. *Silicoflagellida*

               Order   3. *Coccolithophorida*

               Order   4. *Heterochlorida*

               Order   5. *Cryptomonadida*

               Order   6. *Dinoflagellida*

               Order   7. *Ebriida*

⟹   Order   8. *Euglenida*

               Order   9. *Chloromonadida*

               Order 10. *Volvocida*

            Class 2. *Zoomastigophorea*   (Zooflagellates)

        Superclass II. OPALINATA   (Opalinids)

        Superclass III. SARCODINA   (Amoeboid forms)

    Subphylum II. *SPOROZOA*

    Subphylum III. *CNIDOSPORA*

    Subphylum IV. *CILIOPHORA*   (Ciliates)

Chapter 2

DIAGNOSTIC FEATURES OF THE
EUGLENOPHYTA (EUGLENIDA)

The euglenoid flagellates are a well-defined group of closely related organisms. Within the group are placed very few species whose natural inclusion is less than certain, while hardly any forms are known which appear to be intermediate between the *Euglenophyta* (*Euglenida*) and other algal phyla or protozoan orders (see p. 71).

Diagnostic features of the group may be summarised as follows, terminology being explained in subsequent chapters:

1. The flagella arise anteriorly within an invagination of the cell; the invagination consists of a tubular portion, the canal, and a pyriform chamber, the reservoir; the flagellar bases are inserted in the wall of the reservoir.

2. The basic number of flagella is two per cell, one or both emerging from the canal as organelles of locomotion; in some genera with only one locomotory flagellum there is known to be a second flagellum ending within the invagination; in other "uniflagellate" genera it is probable that a second flagellum (or basal body) will be demonstrated by electron microscopy; a few parasitic species have more than two flagella per cell.

3. The emergent portion of each locomotory flagellum bears a unilateral row of fine hairs.

4. Helical (screw) symmetry is exhibited by the pellicle and associated cytoplasmic structures.

5. The carbohydrate storage product is paramylon, a β-1:3-linked glucan which is deposited as solid granules with helical organisation.

6. Nuclear division is a peculiar form of mitosis in which the chromosomes lie parallel to the division axis at metaphase, the endosome (nucleolus) persists and divides, and various features suggest a mitotic mechanism which does not involve a spindle.

7. The eyespot, when present, is independent of the chloroplasts.

8. The photoreceptor, when present, is a swelling on the non-emergent portion of the main flagellum.

9. The contractile vacuole, when present, discharges into the reservoir.

Any cell combining all or most of these features must be a euglenoid flagellate, and, on present knowledge, the characters listed as 3, 5, 6 (in detail) and 7 are unique to this group of organisms. Additional features which may prove to be diagnostic and/or unique when more is known are the following:

1. The pellicle is composed of interlocking proteinaceous strips which fuse into one another at each end of the cell.

2. The muciferous bodies are formed from the peripheral portion of the endoplasmic reticulum.

3. The mitochondrial cristae are constricted at the base.

4. Sexuality seems to be absent throughout the group.

5. Meiosis occurs only rarely, apparently following a non-sexual process of autogamy.

Chapter 3

TAXONOMY I. CLASSIFICATION

The euglenoid flagellates present a series of problems to the taxonomist: problems of duplication at the specific level, demarcation at the generic level and grouping at the ordinal level.

Huber-Pestalozzi (1955) recognises more than 800 species of euglenoids, the majority of which fall into six genera, *Trachelomonas* (235 spp.), *Phacus* (150 spp.), *Euglena* (100 spp.), *Petalomonas* (45 spp.), *Strombomonas* (40 spp.) and *Lepocinclis* (40 spp.). There is no doubt that many of these species are invalid, duplications occurring where size varieties and ecological forms have been described as separate species. For example, Pringsheim (1956) has reduced the number of valid species of *Euglena* to less than 50 by removing synonyms and forms insufficiently described to be recognisable. What is now needed is a similar reappraisal of the other euglenoid genera through studies based upon cells in culture. As Pringsheim has shown, the range of variability of a species can be established only by growing material under controlled conditions. When this is done it is often found that the delimitation of a species embraces several forms previously given specific status when described from nature.

Another important point is the probable absence of sexuality in euglenoid flagellates (p. 92), carrying with it the implication that many natural populations are asexual clones. If a viable clone is produced by a euglenoid cell with a major morphological peculiarity (acquired, say, through mutation or misdivision), the clone can legitimately be described as a new "species," though the somatic variation on which the diagnosis is based might not have survived in an organism with sexual reproduction. The situation is similar to that in apogamous flowering plants; whether it is useful or convenient to give the variant specific status may depend upon the particular circumstances of its discovery. The species concept in euglenoid flagellates is thus very different from that in sexual organisms; euglenoid "species" are delimited on morphology alone, without recourse to interbreeding capabilities as a criterion.

Demarcation at the generic level is often difficult, and several genera recognised today are probably polyphyletic in origin (see p. 75). Furthermore, major evolutionary steps (loss of chloroplasts, adoption of phagotrophy) have certainly taken place more than once (p. 73). The biological ideal of a natural taxonomic system (one that reflects exactly the phylogeny of its taxa) is thus even less approachable with the euglenoids than with many other groups of organisms. However, what can be reasonably hoped for is a rational taxonomic scheme which obscures none of the main known relationships and reflects what are coming to be recognised as the major evolutionary trends within the group.

The system proposed by Klebs (1883) and followed by many subsequent authors, though convenient, fulfills neither of these aims. He distinguishes three groups on the basis of nutrition: the green, phototrophic genera (Family *Euglenaceae*, Section I. *Euglenae*), the colourless, saprotrophic genera (Family *Euglenaceae*, Section II. *Astasiae*) and the colourless, phagotrophic genera (Family *Peranemeae*). Such a system masks the close relationship between certain green and colourless forms and obscures the probability that phagotrophy has arisen several times. Subsequent taxonomic systems which agree closely with that of Klebs, though usually establishing the three groups as equivalent families, have been reviewed by Pringsheim (1948, 1963) and need not be considered here. Of great importance, however, is the scheme in which Hollande (1942, 1952) more accurately reflects natural relationships by basing his primary classification on flagellar organisation. Such a system has been notably followed in the studies of Pringsheim (1948) and Christen (1963).

In the light of the most recent knowledge, though much remains to be clarified, I have felt constrained to go further than any of these authors in revising euglenoid classification. For phylogenetic reasons discussed elsewhere (pp. 72–75), the features of euglenoid diversity upon which a taxonomic scheme must be based* have been considered in the following order of precedence (again, terminology will be explained in subsequent chapters):

1. FLAGELLA: number per cell; relative lengths; emergent or non-emergent from the canal; path traced during swimming.

2. CHLOROPLASTS: present or absent (see also 10, below).

3. EYESPOT and **FLAGELLAR SWELLING:** present or absent.

4. INGESTION APPARATUS: present or absent; form if present.

5. NUTRITION: related to points 2 and 4; normal nutrition phototrophic, phagotrophic or exclusively osmotrophic.

6. CELL: rigidity (pellicle rigid or elastic); shape (especially degree of flattening).

7. CANAL and **RESERVOIR:** canal opening apical or subapical.

8. ENVELOPE: present or absent.

9. COLONIAL HABIT: present or absent.

10. CHLOROPLASTS: number, shape, size; presence or absence of pyrenoids; form of pyrenoids if present.

11. PARAMYLON: regular position and shape of large granules.

12. MUCIFEROUS BODIES: shape and distribution; whether or not cell forms cysts and palmellae.

13. CONTRACTILE VACUOLE: present or absent; position, size and activity.

* Other features which would certainly be used taxonomically if more details were known include chromosome numbers and trichocysts. Physiological characteristics such as optimal growth temperature, drug resistance and special nutritional requirements are used to delimit different strains of one species.

14. CELL: size.

15. NUCLEUS: shape and size; number of endosomes.

16. ECOLOGY: fresh-water or marine; free-living or parasitic.

The application of these criteria in comparative cytological studies has permitted the inference of close and less close intergeneric relationships among present-day euglenoid flagellates. This in turn has led to the erection of a phylogenetic scheme (p. 75), sectors of which have been named as orders of the phylum *Euglenophyta* in the taxonomic system adopted for this book. These are the orders *Eutreptiales, Euglenales, Rhabdomonadales, Spheno-monadales, Heteronematales* and *Euglenamorphales*. In the protozoological classi-fication (p. 5), these major groupings will appear as the suborders *Eutreptiina, Euglenina, Rhabdomonadina, Sphenomonadina, Heteronematina* and *Euglenamorphina,* of the order *Euglenida.*

Chapter 4

TAXONOMY II. CHARACTERS OF ORDERS, GENERA AND SPECIES

Further taxonomic consideration of the euglenoid flagellates will be confined, in the present account, to a characterisation of each order and genus and the illustration of representative species. The illustrations are based upon what can be seen in the living organism by light microscopy (especially anoptral contrast; see p. 202) and are mostly a diagrammatic combination of two optical sections: the median focal plane (for nucleus, flagellar apparatus, etc.) and a peripheral level (for chloroplasts, mitochondria, etc.). In the interests of clarity, three-dimensional representation has rarely been attempted, and components which are not normally visible in living cells have been omitted. Notes on locomotion and other features of cytological and biological interest are added to assist in the study of the organisms and, wherever possible, the illustrations are of species which are available for teaching and research from permanent culture collections.* Authorities are given for the original descriptions and nomenclature of all genera and species cited; references to further species can be traced through Huber-Pestalozzi (1955). An artificial key to the genera is given as Appendix 1 (p. 196).

Order 1. Eutreptiales [= Suborder (1) Eutreptiina]

Four genera: *Eutreptia, Eutreptiella, Distigmopsis* and *Distigma*. Ordinal characters:†

1. Two flagella; both emergent from the canal; both of the same thickness; heterodynamic;‡ **one directed anteriorly and the other laterally or posteriorly during swimming; highly mobile, not held straight.**

* A considerable number of euglenoids are maintained in permanent culture collections and are available for teaching and research. The largest collections (which include all the species listed as available on the ensuing pages) are Die Sammlung von Algenkulturen, Pflanzenphysiologisches Institut der Universität, (34) Göttingen, Nikolausberger Weg 18, Germany, and the Culture Collection of Algae and Protozoa, Botany School, Downing Street, Cambridge, England. Many of the cultures are maintained also in the Culture Collection of Algae of Indiana University, Bloomington, Indiana, U. S. A., and elsewhere.

† On this and the following pages, the most *distinctive* features of each order and genus are printed in boldface. Latin diagnoses of the six orders are given on pp. 204–205.

‡ Reference should be made to Part II of this book for definitions of unfamiliar terms.

2. Green or colourless, **never phagotrophic.***

3. Cell non-rigid; euglenoid movement* usually very pronounced.

4. Cell elongated and unflattened.

5. Cell solitary; envelope lacking.

Genus 1. Eutreptia   Perty 1852

Generic characters:

1. The two flagella equal in length or nearly so; heterodynamic; both highly mobile during swimming.

2. Green; phototrophic; the numerous chloroplasts discoid or ribbon-shaped; chloroplasts without individual pyrenoids.

3. Paramylon centre* present in all species where cell structure is known, usually with a rigid sphere of paramylon granules surrounding it.

4. Eyespot present; flagellar swelling present on one flagellum only.

5. Canal opening subapical.

6. Muciferous bodies small; copious mucilage produced, a palmelloid state being characteristic for material in biphasic culture.*

7. Contractile vacuole present in brackish forms, apparently absent (or non-functional) in marine forms.

8. Only a few species known; typically brackish or marine.

The genus has been recently reviewed by Pringsheim (1953a).

EUTREPTIA PERTYI   Pringsheim 1953

Figures 1, 2, 161. Cultures available. **Notes:** Swimming involves cell gyration with anterior end of cell tracing a wide circle, giving the appearance of swaying from side to side; flagellar swelling presumably on anteriorly-directed flagellum (see p. 145); pellicular striations delicate, with an S-helix (not shown in figure; see p. 102); euglenoid movement violent in non-swimming, non-palmelloid cells (Fig. 2); muciferous bodies small (not shown in figure); chromosomes in interphase nucleus show clearly as relationally-coiled chromatids (p. 85); chromosome number 90, in *Eutreptia viridis* Perty 1852, 44–45 (suggesting a polyploid relationship); mitochondria confined between pellicle and chloroplasts (not shown in figure); Golgi bodies not visible in living cell; recorded from various brackish and marine eutrophic waters, such as the Grand Canal of Trieste and the Adriatic Ocean.

Genus 2. Eutreptiella da Cunha 1913

Generic characters:

1. The two flagella unequal in length; heterodynamic; one directed anteriorly and the other laterally or posteriorly during swimming.

* Reference should be made to Part II of this book for definitions of unfamiliar terms.

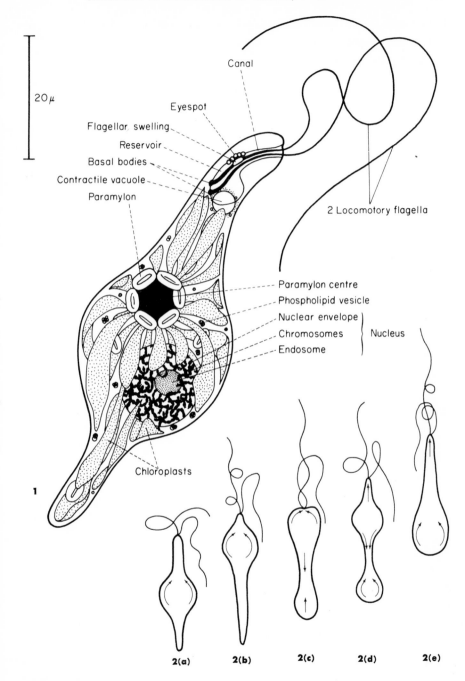

Fig. 1 *Eutreptia pertyi:* living cell, lateral aspect. Original drawing.

Figs. 2(a)-2(e) *Eutreptia pertyi*: stages in euglenoid movement; *arrows* indicate directions of cytoplasmic flow. Original drawing.

2. Green; phototrophic; discoid chloroplasts without pyrenoids.

3. Eyespot present; flagellar swelling present on one flagellum only.

4. Canal opening subapical.

5. Contractile vacuole apparently absent, although a vesicular region is present in the anterior end of the cell.

6. Few species known; all marine.

The genus was redescribed by Schiller (1925) under the name *"Gymnastica."*

EUTREPTIELLA MARINA da Cunha 1913

Figure 3. No cultures available. **Notes:** Description by da Cunha meagre; cell stated to have violent euglenoid movement; one flagellum three times as long as other, but no description given of swimming; named by da Cunha (1913), description in da Cunha (1914); recorded only from the open sea as a planktonic organism. Recent study* of a **new species** (as yet undescribed), isolated by Jahn Throndsen and Sidsel Saetrang of the Institutt for Marin Biologi, Blindern-Oslo, has produced two observations of potential taxonomic importance. (a) Swimming cells have the shorter flagellum extended anteriorly and the longer one directed posteriorly. (N.B. Other species are recorded as having the longer flagellum directed anteriorly, as in *Distigma*.) (b) There is no paramylon, carbohydrate reserves being stored in liquid form, usually in one large vesicle between reservoir and nucleus. (N.B. This observation is unique for euglenoid flagellates, but see p. 53. Demonstration that the reserve is leucosin would be of great taxonomic interest; see pp. 3 and 185.)

Genus 3. Distigmopsis   Hollande 1942

Generic characters (from Hollande, 1942):

1. The two flagella unequal in length; heterodynamic.

2. Colourless; osmotrophic.

3. Leucostigma present; flagellar swelling not recorded.

4. Semi-rigid cell; lethargic euglenoid movement.

5. Canal opening subapical.

6. Contractile vacuole not recorded.

7. Only one species known; isolated from horse dung, possibly a parasitic organism.

* Of living material sent to me from Oslo by Dr. E. Paasche.

Fig. 3 *Eutreptiella marina:* living cell. Freely redrawn from da Cunha, 1914.

Fig. 4 *Distigmopsis grassei:* living cell stained with neutral red. Freely redrawn from Hollande, 1942.

Fig. 5 *Distigma proteus:* living cell, lateral aspect.   Original drawing.

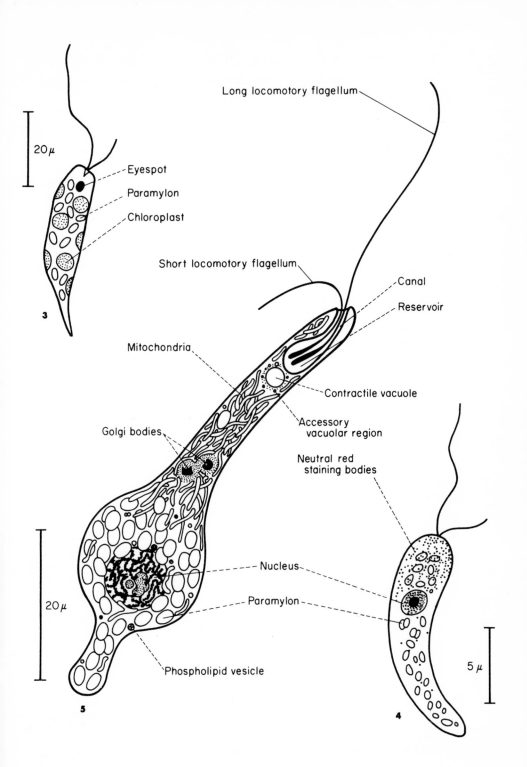

Long locomotory flagellum

20μ

Eyespot

Paramylon

Chloroplast

3

Short locomotory flagellum

Canal

Reservoir

Mitochondria

Contractile vacuole

Accessory
vacuolar region

Golgi bodies

Neutral red
staining bodies

Nucleus

20μ

Paramylon

Phospholipid vesicle

5μ

5

4

DISTIGMOPSIS GRASSEI Hollande 1942

Figure 4. No cultures available. **Notes:** Swimming rapid, with wide rotation of anterior end of cell; longer flagellum directed anteriorly, shorter flagellum curving laterally during swimming; eyespot said to be stroma only, no carotenoid pigment (needs reinvestigation in the light of fine structural studies on the euglenoid eyespot; see p. 143); numerous bodies in anterior end of cell stain with neutral red (muciferous bodies?); validity of this genus and species questioned by some authors.

Genus 4. Distigma   Ehrenberg 1838

Generic characters:

1. The two flagella unequal in length; one less than half the length of the other, directed laterally or posteriorly during swimming, sometimes so short as to be a barely emergent stub.

2. Colourless; osmotrophic.

3. Eyespot and flagellar swelling absent.

4. Canal opening fractionally subapical, appearing apical in a few species.

5. Muciferous bodies small, spherical; cysts known.

6. Contractile vacuole large and conspicuous.

7. Several species known; all fresh-water.

The genus has been reviewed in part by Pringsheim (1942).

DISTIGMA PROTEUS   Ehrenberg 1838

Figures 5, 121, 137. Cultures available. **Notes:** Cell exhibits violent euglenoid movement, *even when swimming* (a rare feature, not seen in slightly more rigid *Distigma* spp.); during swimming the long anteriorly-directed flagellum is lashed about with great mobility, though basically having waves travelling from base to tip; shorter flagellum has a more "cilium-like" beat, with straight stroke backwards and relaxed recovery stroke; long mitochondrial threads are violently moved during euglenoid movement of the cell, so that they lie along the axis of a stretched cell (Fig. 5) and across the axis of a rounded one; two or three large Golgi bodies lie posterior to the reservoir, but no structures are seen to account for the "two eyes" described and figured for this genus by Ehrenberg (1829, full diagnosis 1838); widespread species, characteristic of acid fresh-water habitats such as bogs; important papers in the study of this species are those by Lackey (1934), Hollande (1937) and Pringsheim (1942).

Order 2. Euglenales   [= Suborder (2) Euglenina]

Thirteen genera: *Euglena, Khawkinea, Astasia, Euglenopsis, Cyclidiopsis, Trachelomonas, Strombomonas, Klebsiella, Ascoglena, Colacium, Lepocinclis, Phacus* and *Hyalophacus.* Characters of the order:

1. Two flagella, one of which emerges from the canal as the locomo-

tory flagellum, whereas the other is so short as to be non-emergent from the reservoir; the locomotory flagellum highly mobile throughout its emergent length.

2. Green or colourless; phototrophic or osmotrophic; one genus (*Euglenopsis*) phagotrophic, no special ingestion apparatus.

Genus 1. Euglena   Ehrenberg 1838

Generic characters:

1. Green; phototrophic; chloroplasts discoid, shield-shaped or ribbon-shaped, entire or dissected, with or without pyrenoids, pyrenoids naked, double-sheathed or inner (see p. 171); each chloroplast type characteristic of a group of species.

2. Eyespot and flagellar swelling present.

3. Cell non-rigid or semi-rigid, **never completely rigid;** euglenoid movement pronounced, slight or manifested only in response to extreme stimuli.

4. Cell flattening apparent in some species.

5. Canal opening subapical.

6. Cell free-swimming; solitary; no envelope, but cysts and palmelloid stages known.

7. Contractile vacuole present, even in marine forms.

8. Many species known; mostly fresh-water; a few marine species also recorded.

Euglena was named by Ehrenberg (1830a) and diagnostically defined by him in 1838. Referred to many times in the present book, this widely studied genus is the subject of an excellent monograph by Pringsheim (1956). Important earlier references are Dangeard (1901), Chadefaud (1937), Hollande (1942), Chu (1946), Conrad and van Meel (1952) and Gojdics (1953). Pringsheim divides the genus into six subgenera, selected species from each of which are considered below.

Subgenus I. Rigidae   Pringsheim 1956*

Subgeneric characters:

1. Chloroplasts numerous, small, discoid/lenticular; pyrenoids absent.

2. Cell almost completely rigid; non-swimming movements normally restricted to slow bendings of the cell, although lethargic euglenoid movement can be induced by extreme heat and by chemical stimuli.

3. Cell elongated, posterior spine present.

* To accord with the rules of biological nomenclature, the name of one subgenus (that containing the type species) should be changed to be the same as the genus (i.e., *Euglena* subgenus *Euglena* Ehrenberg 1838). However, Professor E. G. Pringsheim feels that this would now lead to confusion, and at his request I have retained his (1965) names for the subgenera.

4. Two large paramylon granules present in most species, one anterior to and one posterior to the nucleus.

5. Muciferous bodies small; slime sheath produced, but cysts and palmelloid stages unknown; cells often stick to a substratum by the posterior spine.

EUGLENA SPIROGYRA   Ehrenberg 1831

Figures 6, 72, 80, 83, 85–87, 91, 92, 94, 97, 104–106, 111, 112, 127, 129, 135, 136, 138–140, 145, 164, 171. Cultures available. **Notes:** Size varieties of this species range from 45 to 250 μ in length; cell slightly flattened and twisted, so that cross-section is oval; chromosome number is 86 (in a 100 μ-long strain); amitosis known (p. 92); common species with worldwide distribution, occurring particularly in ditches and iron-containing pools; the cytology and biology of this species are the subjects of a recent detailed study (Leedale, Meeuse and Pringsheim, 1965).

EUGLENA ACUS   Ehrenberg 1830

Figures 7, 81, 82, 107, 163. Cultures available. **Notes:** Size varieties known, but smaller range than *E. spirogyra* (only 80 to 150 μ); swims with emergent flagellum held like a spinning lasso,* with rapid gyration of the cell; eyespot variable, sometimes many small droplets, sometimes a few large droplets; the several endosomes divide separately during mitosis (p. 84); amitosis known (p. 92); species named by Ehrenberg (1830a); worldwide distribution, typically a planktonic species of acidic ponds and lakes, sometimes found in water with pH as low as 4; colourless form (see p. 73) known and available in culture ("*Euglena acus* var. *hyalina*," Figs. 108, 144, 169; strictly referable to the genus *Khawkinea* and not to be confused with *Cyclidiopsis*).

Subgenus II. Lentiferae   Pringsheim 1956

Subgeneric characters:

1. Chloroplasts as in *Euglena* subgenus *Rigidae*.

2. Cell non-rigid or semi-rigid; euglenoid movement slight to pronounced under normal conditions, violent contortion on irritation.

3. Cell elongated, no posterior spine.

4. Paramylon deposited as small, oval, flattened granules, with occasional larger granules scattered in the cell.

5. Muciferous bodies small; cysts known.

* This simile, though not exact, is a useful means of referring to the path of locomotory flagellum found in many euglenoids. The proximal part of the flagellum describes a funnel shape in front of the cell; the distal part is looped at right angles to the direction of swimming.

Fig. 6 *Euglena spirogyra:* living cell, lateral aspect. Original drawing.

Fig. 7 *Euglena acus:* living cell, lateral aspect. Original drawing.

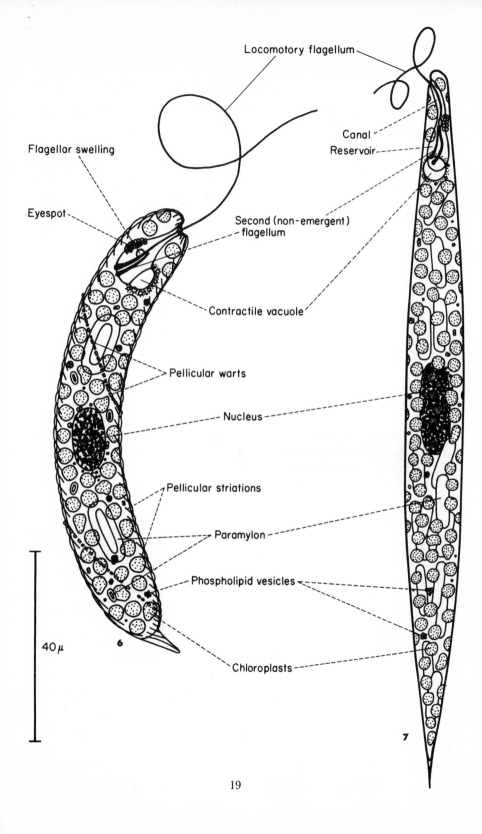

Locomotory flagellum

Canal

Reservoir

Flagellar swelling

Eyespot

Second (non-emergent) flagellum

Contractile vacuole

Pellicular warts

Nucleus

Pellicular striations

Paramylon

Phospholipid vesicles

Chloroplasts

40μ

6

7

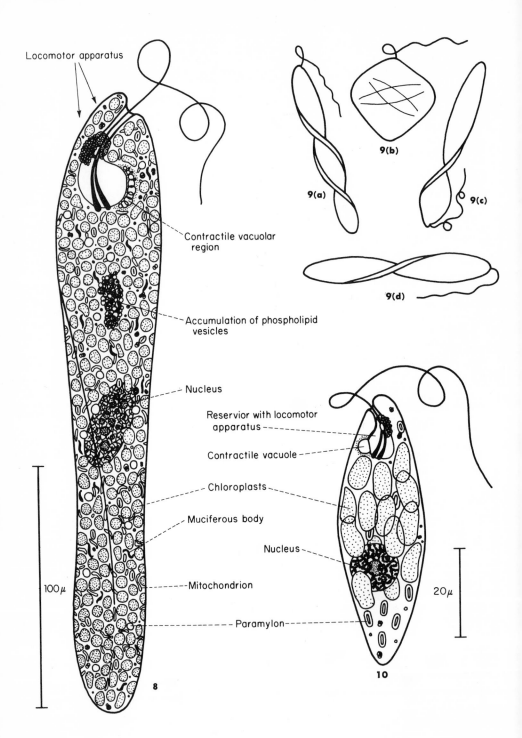

Locomotor apparatus

Contractile vacuolar region

Accumulation of phospholipid vesicles

Nucleus

Reservior with locomotor apparatus

Contractile vacuole

Chloroplasts

Muciferous body

Nucleus

Mitochondrion

Paramylon

100 μ

20 μ

8

10

9(a)

9(b)

9(c)

9(d)

20

EUGLENA EHRENBERGII   Klebs 1883

Figures 8, 9, 70. Cultures available. **Notes:** One of the largest euglenoids; swimming cell always flattened, usually with one or two twists in it [Figs. 9(a), 9(c), 9(d)]; size varieties range from 100 to 400 μ in length; flagellum directed posteriorly during swimming, cells rotating slowly to either left or right (often with a change in rotational direction after checking); paramylon small solid spheres or minute oval links, the large granules figured by most authors rare; muciferous bodies few, 4 μ long and spindle-shaped; no cysts, but visible mucilaginous sheath on all cells; cells often lose locomotory flagellum and creep on a surface; phospholipid vesicles frequently accumulate anterior to nucleus; cytoplasmic streaming a marked feature of all cells, apparently random currents carrying along mitochondria and small inclusions; rare but widespread species, usually found in small bodies of water (ponds, hoofmarks) where pollution occurs.

EUGLENA PROXIMA   Dangeard 1901

Figures 10, 103. Cultures available. **Notes:** Type variety illustrated, several morphological varieties known; chloroplasts characteristically concentrated in anterior two-thirds of cell; muciferous bodies small (not shown in figure), but copious mucilage production results in frequent cyst and palmella formation; forms of this one species known from fresh-water, brackish and marine habitats.

Subgenus III. Catilliferae   Pringsheim 1956

Subgeneric characters:

1. Chloroplasts large, flat, often shield-shaped; each with a central pyrenoid covered on both sides by a watchglass-shaped cap of paramylon.

2. Cell fusiform in most species; non-rigid; various degrees of euglenoid movement, usually pronounced.

3. Paramylon present as pyrenoid caps and small ovals scattered in the cell.

4. Muciferous bodies of shapes and sizes characteristic for particular species; cysts and palmellae known.

EUGLENA GRACILIS   Klebs 1883

Figures 11, 71, 73, 74, 77, 98, 116, 117, 125, 130. Maintained in culture in many laboratories as an experimental organism (see below); cultures available either biphasic or bacteria-free. **Notes:** Swimming rapid, with anterior end of the gyrating cell tracing a wide circle; euglenoid movement pronounced after shedding of locomotory flagellum, but cells never creep or glide; chloroplasts 6 to 12(+) per cell; cells in old cultures become packed with phospholipid vesicles so that

---

Fig. 8 *Euglena ehrenbergii:* living cell, lateral aspect; components of the locomotor apparatus as labelled in Figs. 6 and 7. Original drawing.

Figs. 9(a)-9(d) *Euglena ehrenbergii:* various shapes adopted by swimming cells [9(a), 9(c), 9(d)] and by a rounded, non-swimming cell [9(b)]. Original drawings.

Fig. 10 *Euglena proxima:* living cell, lateral aspect; components of the locomotor apparatus as labelled in Figs. 6 and 7. Original drawing.

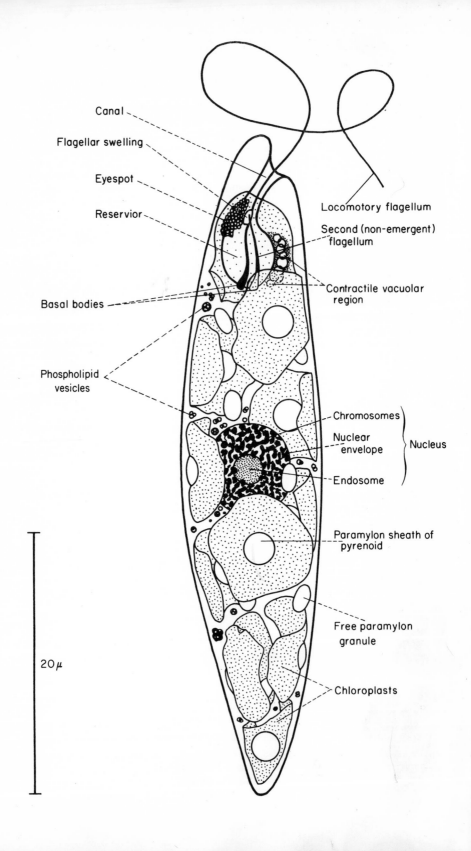

Canal

Flagellar swelling

Eyespot

Reservior

Basal bodies

Phospholipid
vesicles

Locomotory flagellum

Second (non-emergent)
flagellum

Contractile vacuolar
region

Chromosomes

Nuclear
envelope   } Nucleus

Endosome

Paramylon sheath of
pyrenoid

Free paramylon
granule

Chloroplasts

20 μ

culture looks brown; palmelloid colonies form on mud (and on agar in culture); chromosome number 45; relatively rare species in nature, characteristically found in ponds and ditches containing rotting leaves; forms with no chloroplasts (*"Euglena gracilis* var. *hyalina,"* see Figs. 114, 124) and no chloroplasts or eyespot can be produced experimentally (p. 183); these are also available from culture collections; numerous other physiological strains have been isolated by Pringsheim, and most of the recent experimental work on *Euglena* is based upon two of these—*Euglena gracilis* Z and *Euglena gracilis* var. *bacillaris*; references to the major experimental studies will be found on pp. 116, 146, 165, 179 and 181–184.

EUGLENA PISCIFORMIS   Klebs 1883

Figures 12, 88, 89. Cultures of several strains available. **Notes:** Cell shape variable, particularly the posterior end which may be pointed, rounded, blunt or lobed; swimming rapid, with wide gyration of cell and abrupt changes of direction; chloroplasts two per cell (sometimes three, rarely one or four), usually unequal in size and placed either side by side (Fig. 12), obliquely or (rarely) one behind the other; cosmopolitan, common species of many fresh-water habitats; a taxonomically confused species with many forms; see Pringsheim (1956) for synonymy and varieties; the closely related *Euglena archaeoplastidiata* Chadefaud 1937, which always has a single, cup-shaped, perforated chloroplast with two pyrenoids, can perhaps be regarded as the basic (simple or reduced?) Catilliferous type.

EUGLENA OBTUSA   Schmitz 1884

Figure 13. No cultures available. **Notes** (from wild material): Neither flagellum emergent, the longer one ending within canal above flagellar swelling (Fig. 13); locomotion always by creeping; reservoir tapers into canal which is almost closed anteriorly (sometimes with a second, blind canal opening off main one); large spherical muciferous bodies (not shown in figure) produce copious mucilage, presumably in connection with creeping locomotion; typically a species of estuarine mud flats, salt marshes or mud margins of fresh-water ponds, creeping to mud surface when emersed, disappearing when mud is flooded; despite abundant material and much trial, this species has not yet been reared in culture.

EUGLENA MAGNIFICA   Pringsheim 1956

Figures 14, 96, 159, 167. Cultures available. **Notes:** Chloroplasts 20 to 25 per cell, shape varying according to the metabolic state of the cell: the two extremes are (a) chloroplasts condensed, individualised, appearing as flat plates, much dissected, the arms radiating from each double-sheathed pyrenoid (Fig. 14), (b) chloroplasts greatly expanded, the arms fewer, longer, becoming arranged helically in rows parallel to the pellicular striations, with plastid individuality obscured (Fig. 159); muciferous bodies numerous, fusiform, lying side by side in helical rows (Figs. 14, 96), copious mucilage produced on irritation; species recorded only once, from a fresh-water pool.

Related species with this complex chloroplast organisation are *E. sanguinea*

Fig. 11 *Euglena gracilis:* living cell, lateral aspect; as in most of the drawings, the delicate pellicular striations are omitted even though visible in the living cell. Original drawing.

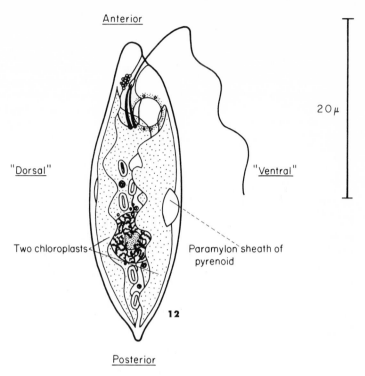

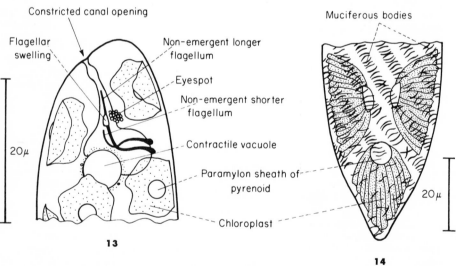

Fig. 12 *Euglena pisciformis:* living cell, lateral aspect; organelles as labelled in Fig. 11. Original drawing.

Fig. 13 *Euglena obtusa:* anterior end of a living cell, showing that both flagella are non-emergent; lateral aspect. Original drawing.

Fig. 14 *Euglena magnifica:* posterior end of a living cell, with chloroplasts in the condensed state. Original drawing.

Ehrenberg 1831, *E. laciniata* Pringsheim 1956 and *E. splendens* Dangeard 1901. The fluidity of the chloroplasts in these forms is not fully understood. The chloroplasts are expanded when light intensity is optimal for photosynthesis, but contract immediately when placed in bright light; in addition, *Euglena sanguinea* accumulates carotenoid pigment which moves to the surface and turns the cell red under certain conditions (Heidt, 1934; Johnson and Jahn, 1942).

Subgenus IV. Radiatae   Pringsheim 1956

Subgeneric characters:

1. Chloroplast system of ribbons radiating from one to several paramylon centres; the ribbons can dissociate into discoid chloroplasts which have no pyrenoids.

2. Cell elongated to fusiform; non-rigid; euglenoid movement more or less pronounced.

3. Paramylon granules small, some scattered in the cell and others grouped around the paramylon centre.

4. Muciferous bodies often large; palmellae and cysts known, being the predominant state in some species.

EUGLENA VIRIDIS   Ehrenberg 1830

Figure 15. Cultures available. **Notes:** Selected as example of *Euglena* subgenus *Radiatae* with one paramylon centre per cell; type variety illustrated, morphological varieties known; swimming rapid, with jerky rotation of cell; euglenoid movement consists of cell contortions, not regular flowing activity; species difficult to identify when chloroplast ribbons dissociate into discoid plastids (usual condition in cells in culture); chromosome number 42; amitosis known (p. 92); muciferous bodies spherical (not shown in figure), whereas those of closely related *Euglena stellata* Mainx 1926 are long, fusiform and discharged like trichocysts on irritation; cysts and palmellae common, on mud surfaces and in culture; common species of polluted habitats, often the species producing green pools in farmyards, also common in sluggish streams and stagnant pools and ditches.

EUGLENA GENICULATA   Dujardin 1841

Figures 16, 162. Cultures available. **Notes:** Selected as example of *Euglena* subgenus *Radiatae* with two or more paramylon centres per cell; swimming as *E. viridis*, but *E. geniculata* differs in often progressing on a substratum by gliding; chloroplast ribbons shorter than those of *E. viridis*, with anterior group usually larger than posterior group; muciferous bodies of different forms in different varieties; palmellae known, not common; ecology similar to that of *E. viridis*, but a less common species, perhaps because of being much less resistant to desiccation and cold; composite species with many forms, named by Dujardin (1841) but typified by Perty's (1852) redescription.

Subgenus V. Serpentes   Pringsheim 1956

Subgeneric characters:

1. Chloroplasts medium-sized, flat, each with a central "naked" pyrenoid (not covered with a paramylon cap).

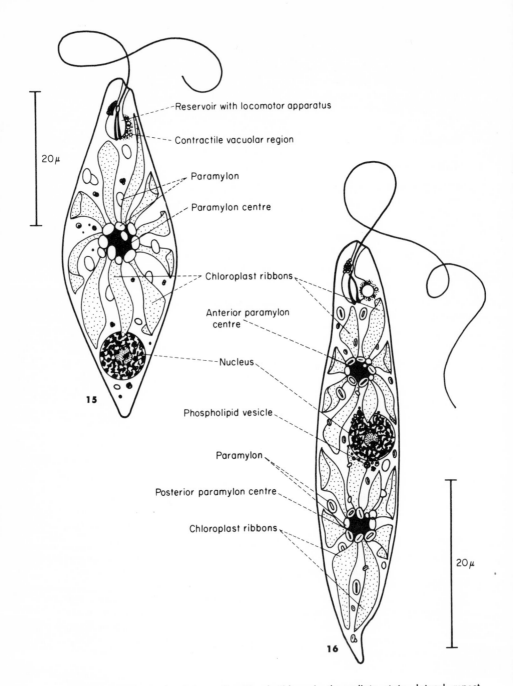

Reservoir with locomotor apparatus

Contractile vacuolar region

Paramylon

Paramylon centre

Chloroplast ribbons

Anterior paramylon centre

Nucleus

Phospholipid vesicle

Paramylon

Posterior paramylon centre

Chloroplast ribbons

20μ

20μ

15

16

Fig. 15 *Euglena viridis:* living cell with plastidome in the radiate state, lateral aspect. Original drawing.

Fig. 16 *Euglena geniculata:* living cell with plastidome in biradiate state, lateral aspect; unlabelled organelles as in Fig. 11. Original drawing.

2. Locomotory flagellum short and readily shed, sometimes non-emergent so that locomotion is by creeping only.

3. Cell elongated, usually unflattened, serpentine, continually changing shape by coiling.

4. Paramylon granules small, scattered in the cell.

5. Muciferous bodies small.

EUGLENA DESES   Ehrenberg 1833

Figures 17, 93, 95. Cultures available. **Notes:** A collective species, embracing many strains and size varieties (see Pringsheim, 1956); size varieties range from 60 to 200 μ in length; swimming slow and intermittent; cells frequently shed emergent flagellum and creep in mud (some strains never produce an emergent flagellum); swimming cells elongated and cylindrical, creeping cells flattened, shorter, wider anteriorly; euglenoid movement pronounced on irritation; eyespot varies in size in different strains; muciferous bodies not visible in living cell, but considerable slime sheath produced; cysts and palmellae not formed; cell cleavage much delayed in biphasic culture, resulting in many stages of arrested normal cleavage and many cleavage monsters (Fig. 95); world-wide distribution, common, especially as a mud-creeping species in shallow bodies of fresh and brackish water.

EUGLENA MUTABILIS   Schmitz 1884

Figures 18(a)–18(c). Cultures available. **Notes:** Closely related to *E. deses*, but with fewer chloroplasts and narrower cell; very short locomotory flagellum, often non-emergent, locomotion by creeping; cell movement very pronounced, consisting of coiling, wriggling and looping (Fig. 18); characteristic species of acid habitats.

Subgenus VI. Limpidae   Pringsheim 1956

This subgenus was erected by Pringsheim (1956) to accommodate species which appear to be colourless derivatives of known species of *Euglena*. In the present account, most of these forms are considered under the genus *Khawkinea* (p. 29). *Astasia longa* Pringsheim 1936 (p. 32) is a special case, being a naturally occurring form similar to experimentally "bleached" *Euglena gracilis* (p. 183).

Finally, mention must be made of the recently discovered *Euglena pringsheimii* Iyengar 1962. This species is described as having band-shaped chloroplasts with inner pyrenoids of the form characteristic for many species of *Trachelomonas* and *Colacium* (pp. 36, 41 and 171). It will consequently have to be placed in a new subgenus of *Euglena*, to which *E. mucifera* Mainx 1926 may also belong.

Genus 2. Khawkinea   Jahn et McKibben 1937

Generic characters:

1. Colourless; osmotrophic.

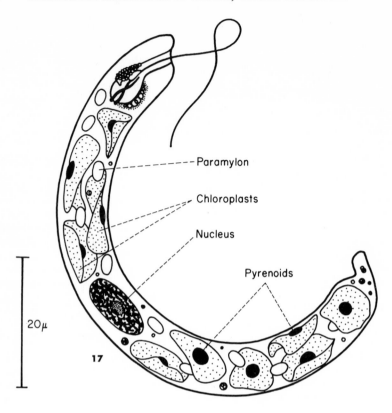

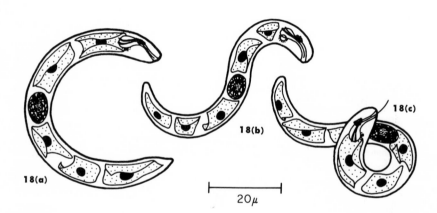

Fig. 17 *Euglena deses:* living cell, lateral aspect; unlabelled organelles as in Fig. 11. Original drawing.

Figs. 18(a)-18(c) *Euglena mutabilis:* coiling shapes adopted by living cells. Original drawings.

2. Eyespot and flagellar swelling present.

3. Cell non-rigid; euglenoid movement usually pronounced.

4. Most species fusiform; no pronounced flattening of the cell.

5. Canal opening subapical.

6. Cell free-swimming; solitary; no envelope, but palmelloid stages known.

7. Contractile vacuole present in non-parasitic forms, apparently absent in some parasitic species.

8. Several species known; all fresh-water or parasitic in fresh-water animals.

The genus was established by Jahn and McKibben (1937) to accommodate a new euglenoid species having an eyespot and flagellar swelling but no chloroplasts, together with similar forms previously described as species of *Euglena* or *Astasia*. It is desirable to confine the genus to *Astasia*-like forms with eyespot, in accordance with the generic characters outlined above (excluding species of *Cyclidiopsis*, *Hyalophacus* and "*Hyalotrachelomonas*," q.v.). Some species of *Khawkinea* are almost certainly colourless derivatives of particular species of *Euglena* (Pringsheim, 1956, 1963); endoparasitic species are known from fresh-water flatworms, copepods and annelids (including *Stenostomum*, *Catenula*, *Cyclops* and *Chaetogaster*). The genus is undoubtedly polyphyletic.

KHAWKINEA QUARTANA (Moroff 1904) Jahn et McKibben 1937

Figures 19, 115, 131, 132, 143. Cultures available [in some cases listed as "*Astasia quartana* (Moroff) Pringsheim"]. **Notes:** Size variable, from 40 to 60 μ in length; emergent flagellum readily shed; non-swimming cells exhibit violent euglenoid movement; contractile vacuole larger than reservoir when full, good species for observing contractile vacuolar activity; muciferous bodies small (not shown in figure), numerous, spherical, in closely packed rows along the delicate pellicular striations; palmellae known; originally recorded from water with a high sulphur content.

Genus 3. Astasia   Dujardin 1841

Generic characters:

1. Colourless; osmotrophic.

2. No eyespot or flagellar swelling.

3. Cell non-rigid; euglenoid movement moderate or pronounced.

4. Cells fusiform or elongated; slight flattening of the cell apparent in some species.

5. Canal opening apical or subapical.

6. Cell free-swimming; solitary; no envelope.

7. Contractile vacuole always present, though records to the contrary are frequent.

8. Numerous species known; typically fresh-water, but marine species have been recorded.

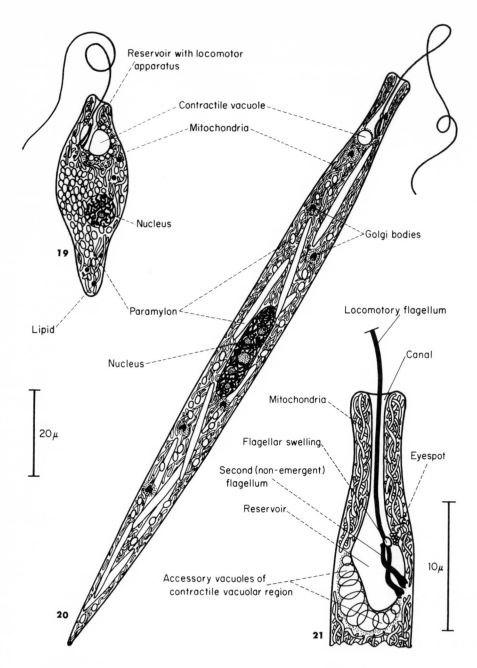

Fig. 19 *Khawkinea quartana*: living cell, lateral aspect. Original drawing.

Fig. 20 *Cyclidiopsis acus*: living cell, lateral aspect. Original drawing.

Fig. 21 *Cyclidiopsis acus*: anterior end of a living cell, showing details of canal shape and components of the locomotor apparatus; lateral aspect. Original drawing.

The genus was named by Ehrenberg (1830b) but first defined as colour-less by Dujardin (1841). Christen (1958, 1963) proposes three subgenera, as below.

Subgenus I. Euastasia   Christen 1963*

Distinguishing subgeneric characters:

1. Canal opening apical.
2. Osmotrophic, never phagotrophic.

   * Strictly, this should be *Astasia* Dujardin 1841; see footnote on p. 17.

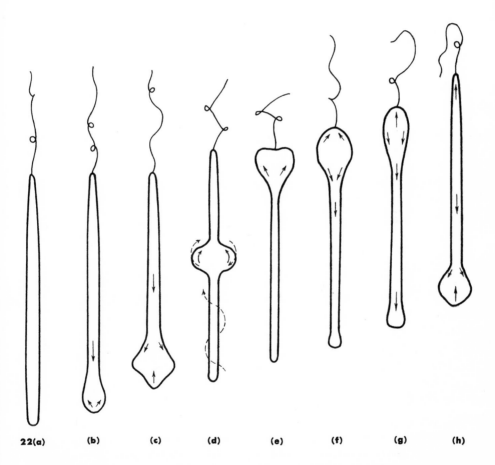

22(a)   (b)   (c)   (d)   (e)   (f)   (g)   (h)

Figs. 22(a)-22(h) *Astasia klebsii:* successive stages in euglenoid movement; *solid arrows* indicate directions of cytoplasmic flow, *dotted arrows* indicate "winding" of cell. Original drawing.

ASTASIA KLEBSII   Lemmermann 1910

Figures 22, 23, 69. Cultures available. **Notes:** Size varieties occur, but most discrepancies of measurement are due to not measuring cells when fully stretched; cell slightly flattened; euglenoid movement pronounced, even when cell is swimming; each "pulse" of euglenoid movement involves (a)passage along the cell of a groove lying across the bulge which spirals its way from posterior to anterior (Fig. 22), and (b) subsequent "unwinding" of the rest of the cell through several turns; nucleus moved violently about cell by euglenoid movement; chromosomes few (approximately 18) and large (Fig. 69), appearing in living cells as short lengths consisting of several large granules; apparently two kinds of mitochondria, large spheres or ovals ($2 \times 3\,\mu$) and many fine threads; one very large Golgi body lies anteriorly, apparently in association with contractile vacuole but moved about cell by euglenoid movement; lipid droplets conspicuous in anterior half of cell, with paramylon usually confined to posterior half; widespread species of polluted waters.

Subgenus II. Euglenoidea   Christen 1963

Distinguishing subgeneric characters:

1. Canal opening subapical, as in genus *Euglena*.
2. Osmotrophic, never phagotrophic.

ASTASIA LONGA   Pringsheim 1936

Figure 24. Cultures available. **Notes:** Originally described from the wild (Pringsheim, 1936, 1942); morphologically similar forms can now be produced by experimental "bleaching" of *Euglena gracilis* (pp. 73 and 183); because of this and because some strains of the wild form can be grown in pure culture (whereas no other species of *Astasia* can), Pringsheim (1963) now calls the wild form *Pseudastasia longa* (see Christen, 1963) to avoid placing it in either of the genera *Astasia* or *Euglena*; however, closely related wild forms with slight cytological differences must be referred to the genus *Astasia* (e.g., *Astasia concinna* Christen 1959) and, for the present, I prefer to retain the binomial, *Astasia longa*; natural habitats characteristically rather acidic, such as drainage channels in peaty land or *Sphagnum* hollows.

Subgenus III. Phytophaga   Christen 1963

Christen's third subgenus, *Phytophaga* or *Astasia devorantes*, contains species which are phagotrophic but otherwise similar to members of *Astasia* subgenus *Euglenoidea*. In the present account these are dealt with as species of the genus *Euglenopsis*.

Fig. 23 *Astasia klebsii:* living cell, lateral aspect. Original drawing.

Fig. 24 *Astasia longa:* anterior end of a living cell, showing the subapical canal opening (compare with Fig. 23); lateral aspect. Original drawing.

Fig. 25 *Euglenopsis edax:* living cell, lateral aspect. Composite redrawing of Christen's "*Astasia edax*," from Christen, 1959.

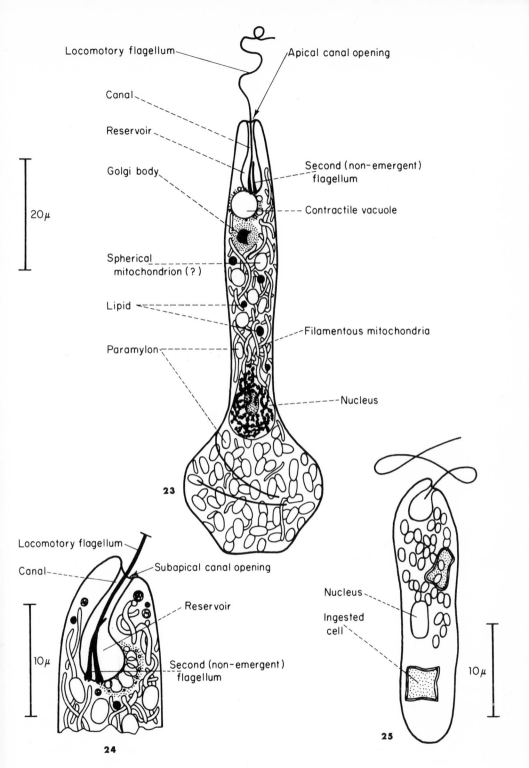

Locomotory flagellum

Apical canal opening

Canal

Reservoir

Golgi body

Second (non-emergent) flagellum

Contractile vacuole

Spherical mitochondrion (?)

Lipid

Filamentous mitochondria

Paramylon

Nucleus

20μ

23

Locomotory flagellum

Canal

Subapical canal opening

Reservoir

Second (non-emergent) flagellum

10μ

24

Nucleus

Ingested cell

10μ

25

Genus 4. Euglenopsis   Klebs 1892

Generic characters:

1. Colourless; phagotrophic, but no special ingestion organelle present.

2. Other generic characters as for genus Astasia subgenus Euglenoidea (q.v.).

Christen (1963) proposes that the generic description for *Euglenopsis* (Klebs, 1892) be adopted for *Astasia* subgenus *Phytophaga*, with *Astasia vacuolata* Skuja 1948 taken as the type species. However, it seems useful to retain the genus *Euglenopsis* until more is known about the cytology of its species. Thus, in the present classification, all phagotrophic "*Astasias*" are regarded as species of *Euglenopsis*.

EUGLENOPSIS EDAX   Christen 1959 nov. comb.

Figure 25. No cultures available. **Notes:** Named *Astasia edax* by Christen (1959); ingests small green algae (*Tetraedron* in Christen's material); no report of cytostome, no ingestion organelle, mode of ingestion not certainly known (see p. 190); flagellum highly mobile during swimming; violent cell contortion on change of direction; euglenoid movement pronounced; species characteristic of eutrophic lakes in regions of low oxygen tension.

Genus 5. Cyclidiopsis   Korschikow 1917

Generic characters:

1. Colourless; osmotrophic.

2. Eyespot and flagellar swelling present.

3. Cell semi-rigid; no euglenoid movement, change of shape restricted to slow bending of the cell.

4. Cell elongated, tapering, unflattened.

5. Canal opening apical.

6. Paramylon granules long and thin, with tapering (but rounded) ends; also small oval granules.

7. Cell free-swimming; solitary; no envelope.

8. Contractile vacuole present, posterior to the reservoir.

9. Nucleus elongated, with a row of endosomes.

10. Only a few species known; fresh-water.

The taxonomic position of this genus is a point of controversy, relationship with *Euglena* or *Astasia* being claimed by different authors (see Pringsheim, 1963). Huber-Pestalozzi (1955) erected a new family (*Cyclidiopsidaceae*) for the three species dealt with in his account.

CYCLIDIOPSIS ACUS   Korschikow 1917

Figures 20, 21, 109, 123, 128, 170. Cultures available. **Notes:** Size varieties exist, ranging from 120 to 210 μ long; swimming quite rapid, with highly mobile emergent flagellum; cell progresses by slow gliding when locomotory flagellum is shed; no euglenoid movement, but cell flexibility allows for formation of loops and S-shapes; canal opening wide and truly apical; limit of pellicular lining to canal very clearly visible; eyespot pale orange, flagellar swelling small, phototactic responses weak; elongated muciferous bodies (not shown in figure) lie along the pellicular striations; no cysts or palmellae, but copious mucilage secretion; cells often stick to a substratum or to one another by a blob of mucilage at their posterior ends to produce stellate clusters of swimming cells (probably cleavage products of one cell); mitochondria packed in peripheral cytoplasm, slowly moving; 10 to 12 Golgi bodies per cell, small, scattered; widespread species of acid habitats; controversy rages as to whether this species is related to *Euglena acus* (q.v.) or whether cytological resemblance is due to parallel evolution (see Pringsheim, 1963).

Genus 6. Trachelomonas   Ehrenberg 1833

Generic characters:

1. Free-swimming *Euglena*-like cell; solitary; enclosed in an envelope, a spherical or ovoid case **with a sharply defined neck or collar** surrounding an apical pore through which the locomotory flagellum emerges; naked cells escape from the envelope during reproduction (and at other times), but immediately secrete a new envelope which is **colourless and smooth at first but soon becomes brown, ornamented and brittle** with ferric hydroxide.

2. Green; phototrophic; chloroplasts of several different types, each type characteristic of a group of species (see below).

3. Eyespot and flagellar swelling present.

4. Naked cells non-rigid; euglenoid movement pronounced; cells can shed the locomotory flagellum and rotate freely within the envelope, even exhibiting restricted euglenoid movement.

5. Cell not flattened; naked cells spindle-shaped, not exactly the same shape as their envelopes.

6. Canal opening sometimes stated to be apical (as the pore of the envelope is), but in naked cells the canal opening is seen to be slightly or markedly subapical.

7. Contractile vacuole always present.

8. Very many species; probably exclusively fresh-water; records from brackish and marine habitats suspect.

The great monograph on *Trachelomonas* by Deflandre (1926) defines many species by the size, shape and ornamentation of their envelopes, elaborating Conrad's (1916) artificial classification of the genus according to envelope shape. This system, followed by Huber-Pestalozzi (1955), must be abandoned if natural relationships are not to be obscured. Pringsheim (1953b) has laid the basis for a "natural" taxonomic treatment by describing chloroplast and pyrenoid structure in a number of *Trachelomonas* spp. and by studying the chemistry and variability in culture of the trachelomonad envelope (see p. 114). Comparative cytological studies reveal groupings which parallel those established as subgenera of *Euglena: Trachelomonas* spp. with (a) numerous, small, discoid chloroplasts without pyrenoids, (b) flat chloroplasts with double-sheathed pyrenoids, (c) flat chloroplasts with inner pyrenoids (p. 171) and (d) flat chloroplasts with naked pyrenoids (p. 171). The concurrence of other cytological features suggests that these are natural groupings of closely related forms, and it is to be hoped that future comparative studies will result in as satisfactory a monograph for the genus *Trachelomonas* as is Pringsheim's (1956) for *Euglena*.

TRACHELOMONAS GRANDIS   Singh 1956

Figures 26, 79, 120, 168, 172. Cultures available. **Notes:** Example of species with flat chloroplasts with inner pyrenoids; envelope thin, yellowish, with minute punctae, never becoming thick enough to obscure cell contents and therefore a good species for study (compare more elaborate envelopes of other species, Figs. 27–29); papilla of mucilage around pore of envelope always colonised by several hundred bacterial cells (except in pure cultures, which are easily established); cells in envelopes 40 to 60 $\mu \times$ 35 to 40 μ, naked cells more narrowly elongated, 60 to 70 $\mu \times$ 25 to 30 μ; swimming slow, with the very long (150 to 200 μ) locomotory flagellum moved in front of cell like a spinning lasso (see footnote, p. 18); euglenoid movement pronounced in stationary naked cells; paramylon caps of pyrenoids show helical organisation clearly when squashed (Fig. 172); chromosomes in interphase nucleus show clearly as relationally-coiled chromatids (see p. 85); chromosome number lies between 40 and 60; species found only once, in a quarry pool; most common species of *Trachelomonas* are much smaller and occur in peaty pools and bodies of water rich in reduced iron and manganese.

TRACHELOMONAS RETICULATA   Klebs 1883

Figures 30, 141. Cultures available. **Notes:** Cell **colourless; osmotrophic;** envelope brown, reticulate; naked cell more elongated than enveloped one; swimming as *Trachelomonas grandis*; euglenoid movement lethargic in naked cells; eyespot of large droplets, pale orange (eyespot in green species usually bright red); flagellar swelling large; contractile vacuole large when full; mitochondria clearly visible as coarse reticulum in peripheral cytoplasmic regions (not shown in drawing; see Fig. 141); cell contains vesicles which appear structureless with anoptral contrast light microscopy; species recorded from pools and puddles.

This latter species, being colourless, does not fit the generic characters listed above for *Trachelomonas*. However, electron microscopy may show that the colourless vesicles in the cell are leucoplasts (plastids without pigments). If not, official establishment of a genus "*Hyalotrachelomonas*" comparable to

---

Fig. 26   *Trachelomonas grandis*: living cell, ventral aspect. Original drawing.

Fig. 27   *Trachelomonas vestita* Palmer 1902: envelope. Redrawn from Palmer, 1902.

Fig. 28   *Trachelomonas lychenensis* Conrad 1952: envelope. Redrawn from Conrad, 1952.

Fig. 29   *Trachelomonas horribilis* Pascher 1927: envelope. Redrawn from Pascher, 1927.

Fig. 30   *Trachelomonas reticulata*: living cell, lateral aspect; anterior organelles as labelled in Fig. 26. Original drawing.

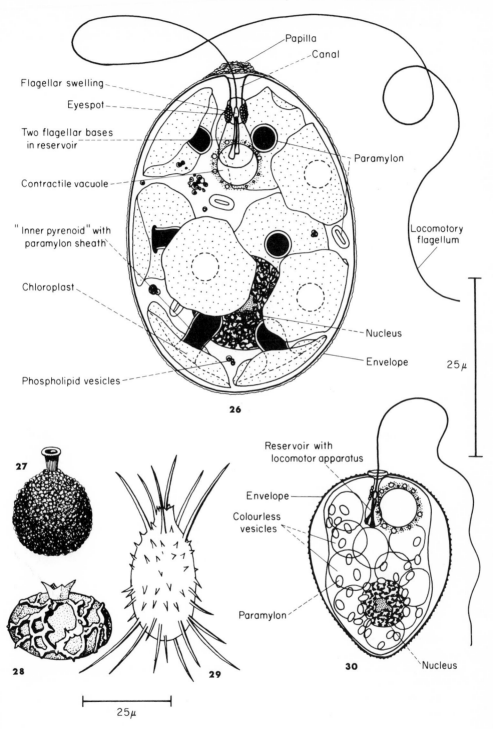

Papilla

Canal

Flagellar swelling

Eyespot

Two flagellar bases
in reservoir

Paramylon

Contractile vacuole

"Inner pyrenoid" with
paramylon sheath

Locomotory
flagellum

Chloroplast

Nucleus

Envelope

25μ

Phospholipid vesicles

26

27

Reservoir with
locomotor apparatus

Envelope

Colourless
vesicles

28   29

Paramylon

30

Nucleus

25μ

Khawkinea and *Hyalophacus* is justifiable. In discussing certain points in the present account (pp. 73 and 145) the name *"Hyalotrachelomonas"* is used for the two known colourless species of *Trachelomonas* (see Pringsheim, 1957, 1963).

Genus 7. Strombomonas   Deflandre 1930

Generic characters:

1. Free-swimming *Euglena*-like cell; solitary; but enclosed **in an envelope which tapers gradually** to the apical pore, **with no sharply defined neck or collar; mature envelope usually remains colourless, non-brittle and without ornamentation,** though deposition of brown particles of manganese peroxide may occur.

2. Other characters as *Trachelomonas* (q.v.); numerous species and forms with (a) discoid chloroplasts or (b) flat chloroplasts with inner pyrenoids (Pringsheim, 1953b); all fresh-water.

Strombomonas has been reviewed by Conrad and van Meel (1952), but before a monograph based on comparative cytology can be written it will be necessary to decide whether the generic separation of *Trachelomonas*, *Strombomonas* and *"Hyalotrachelomonas"* is justified. As described at present, many species of *Trachelomonas* have no necks or collars to their envelopes.

STROMBOMONAS CONSPERSA   Deflandre 1930

Figure 31. Cultures available. **Notes:** Example of species with discoid chloroplasts, no pyrenoids; very variable organism, even in clonal culture; lipid globules (p. 177) show clearly in living chloroplasts; envelope thin and colourless on most cells, occasional cells have yellow envelope covered with brown lumps; envelope of simple shape, other species are slightly more elaborate (Figs. 32, 33); cells in envelope $40 \mu \times 25$ to 30μ, naked cells elongated and tapering posteriorly, 60 to $70 \mu \times 15$ to 20μ; swimming of enveloped cells slow, swimming of naked cells rapid; euglenoid movement violent in naked cells, with the posterior half of cell much more mobile than the anterior half; canal opening markedly subapical; eyespot large, scarlet; contractile vacuolar system large and complex; very little paramylon, copious storage of lipid; muciferous bodies small (not shown in figure), their helical disposition reflected in arrangement of lumps on envelope; nucleus large, chromosomes fine, numerous, minutely granular.

Fig. 31 *Strombomonas conspersa:* living cell, lateral aspect; components of the locomotor apparatus as labelled in Fig. 26. Original drawing.

Fig. 32 *Strombomonas pungens* Conrad 1952: envelope. Redrawn from Conrad, 1952.

Fig. 33 *Strombomonas australica* (Playfair 1915) Deflandre 1930: envelope. Redrawn from Playfair, 1915.

Fig. 34 *Klebsiella alligata:* living cell. Freely redrawn from Pascher, 1931.

Fig. 35 *Ascoglena vaginicola:* living cell. Freely redrawn from Stein, 1878.

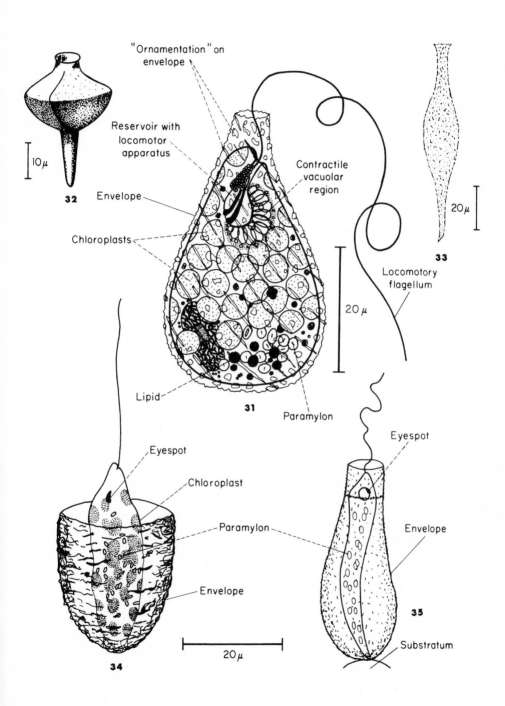

"Ornamentation" on envelope

Reservoir with locomotor apparatus

Contractile vacuolar region

Envelope

Chloroplasts

10μ

32

20μ

33

Locomotory flagellum

Lipid

31

Paramylon

20μ

Eyespot

Chloroplast

Paramylon

Envelope

Eyespot

Paramylon

Envelope

35

Substratum

20μ

34

Genus 8. Klebsiella   Pascher 1931

Generic characters (extracted from Pascher, 1931):

1. Free-swimming *Euglena*-like cell; solitary; but **partially enclosed in a brown, cup-shaped envelope,** the posterior end of the protoplast being attached to the inside of the cup by mucilaginous threads.

2. Green; phototrophic; chloroplasts discoid, pyrenoids absent.

3. Eyespot present; flagellar swelling not recorded but presumably present.

4. Cell non-rigid; lethargic euglenoid movement within the envelope.

5. Cell not flattened.

6. Canal opening subapical.

7. Paramylon deposited as small oval granules.

8. Contractile vacuole absent.

9. Only one species recorded; marine.

KLEBSIELLA ALLIGATA   Pascher 1931

Figure 34. No cultures available. **Notes:** Not recorded again since Pascher's original description (1931); specific characters as listed above; envelope 25 μ × 15 to 18 μ, cell 35 μ long; only the emergent flagellum recorded, but it is reasonable to assume that the second, non-emergent flagellum is present; cell can escape from envelope; species found in samples of *Ulva* and *Chaetomorpha* (green seaweeds) from a very polluted habitat.

Genus 9. Ascoglena   Stein 1878

Generic characters (taken from Huber-Pestalozzi, 1955):

1. Solitary *Euglena*-like cell; enclosed in a flask-shaped envelope, the posterior end of which is attached to a substratum; a naked cell escapes from the envelope during reproduction, but immediately settles on its posterior end and secretes a new envelope which is soft and yellow at first but soon becomes hard and brown.

2. Green; phototrophic; small discoid chloroplasts, with or without pyrenoids.

3. Eyespot present; flagellar swelling not recorded but presumably present.

4. Cell not rigid; pronounced euglenoid movement within the envelope; attachment of cell to envelope not recorded.

5. Cell not flattened.

6. Canal opening subapical.

7. Contractile vacuole present.

8. Two species recorded; fresh-water, epiphytic on filamentous algae.

ASCOGLENA VAGINICOLA   Stein 1878

Figure 35. No cultures available. **Notes:** Apparently not seen again since Stein's account (1878), though another species (*Ascoglena amphoroides*) is recorded by Lemmermann (1913) from Francé (1897); envelope of *A. vaginicola* 40 to 45 μ long, cell shorter; emergent flagellum always present, even in attached cells (but flagellum not recorded for *A. amphoroides*); only the emergent flagellum recorded, but it is a reasonable assumption that the second, non-emergent flagellum is present; pyrenoids present (absent in *A. amphoroides*); both species found growing attached to filamentous algae (*A. amphoroides* on *Tribonema*) in pools and fens.

Genus 10. Colacium   Ehrenberg 1838

Generic characters:

1. *Euglena*-like cell, but normally **attached to a substratum on its anterior end** by means of mucilaginous secretion, the whole cell being enclosed in a thin mucilaginous envelope; **cell division occurs in the settled state, leading to the formation of extensive bunches or sheets of cells, or dendroid colonies** in which the cells are joined to one another by mucilaginous stalks.

2. Settled cells shed the emergent portion of the locomotory flagellum but retain the two flagella within the reservoir; any cell can regrow the locomotory flagellum, escape from its mucilaginous sheath as a free-swimming organism, settle elsewhere on its anterior end and secrete a new stalk and envelope.

3. Green; phototrophic; chloroplasts flat, with inner pyrenoids.

4. Eyespot and flagellar swelling present.

5. Cell non-rigid; lethargic euglenoid movement in colonial state, free cell undergoes pronounced euglenoid movement when not swimming.

6. Cell not flattened.

7. Canal opening subapical.

8. Paramylon present as scattered granules and as spherical or cylindrical pyrenoid caps.

9. Contractile vacuole present.

10. Several species known; mostly fresh-water; epiphytic, or zoophytic on small aquatic animals.

Detailed studies of this genus have been made by Pringsheim (1953c) and Johnson (1934). Some authors (Smith, 1933; Jahn, 1951) place *Colacium* in a separate family (*Colaciaceae*) on account of its colonial habit and on the incorrect information that the flagellum is "without bifurcation" (i.e., the second flagellum is absent; see p. 140). Such separation (maintained by Christen, 1963) hardly seems warranted.

COLACIUM MUCRONATUM   Bourrelly et Chadefaud 1948

Figures 36, 37, 78, 99 [see also Figs. 113, 126, 134, 160, 165, 166, all of *Colacium cyclopicolum* (Gicklhorn 1925) Bourrelly 1947]. Cultures available. **Notes:** Colonies grow more than 1 mm across when undisturbed, each containing hundreds of cells; stalks show longitudinal striations and transverse ridges (Fig. 78); stalk seems to be secreted from canal, some cells show dense rods in reservoir

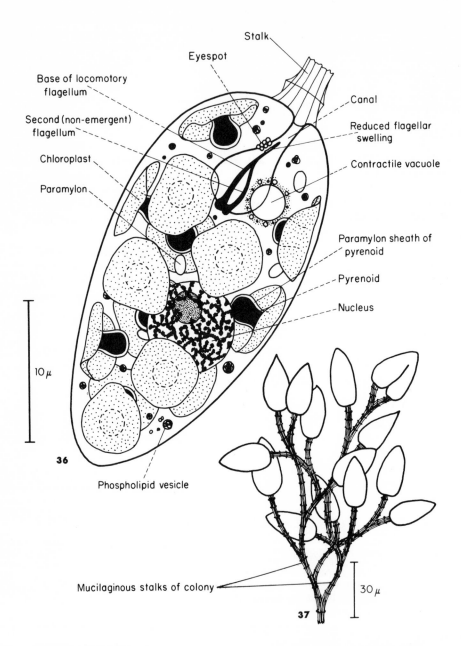

Fig. 36 *Colacium mucronatum:* attached living cell, lateral aspect. Original drawing.

Fig. 37 *Colacium mucronatum:* small portion of a dendroid colony. Original drawing.

(perhaps secretory); two non-emergent flagella clearly seen in attached cells, continually moving inside reservoir but remaining close together; flagellar swelling reduced in size in attached cells (often difficult to see), becoming larger in released, motile cells; released cells develop emergent flagellum (20 to 30 μ long) in approximately 60 minutes (see p. 141); contractile vacuolar activity is same in attached and swimming cells; muciferous bodies minute and numerous, not visible in living cells but presumably producing copious mucilage for sheaths (and stalks?); multinucleate palmellae formed in old cultures; chromosome number approximately 35; species found only once, in mud in a cresspool outlet; other species produce smaller colonies, often attached to *Cyclops*, *Daphnia* and other aquatic animals.

Genus 11. Lepocinclis   Perty 1849

Generic characters:

1. Green; phototrophic; chloroplasts small, discoid, with no pyrenoids.

2. Eyespot and flagellar swelling present.

3. Cell rigid; no euglenoid movement; some pellicular striations very pronounced, running almost longitudinally.

4. Cell not flattened.

5. Canal opening apical in most species.

6. Free-swimming cell; solitary; no envelope; palmelloid stages and cysts unknown.

7. Two large paramylon rings in many species, peripheral, lying opposite one another in the anterior half of the cell.

8. Contractile vacuole present.

9. Numerous species known; typically fresh-water.

There has been no review of the genus since Conrad (1934, 1935), except for that by Huber-Pestalozzi (1955). The name "*Lepocinclis*" has been proposed for priority over "*Crumenula*" Dujardin 1841 (see Lanjouw, 1952), on grounds of common usage.

LEPOCINCLIS OVUM   (Ehrenberg 1840) Lemmermann 1901

Figure 38. Cultures available. **Notes:** Compound species with numerous recorded and named varieties, some merely being forms which can be produced by one strain in clonal culture; locomotory flagellum directed posteriorly during swimming; pellicular striations delicate, with a steep S-helix (see p. 102), some cells have two to eight striae more pronounced than rest (perhaps due to more active muciferous bodies beneath); canal opening apical, but dorso-ventrality of cell shown by positions of eyespot and contractile vacuole (see p. 120); the two paramylon rings lateral in position, some cells have several irregular solid granules; eyespot sometimes very small, most cells have central accumulation of carotenoid droplets (appearing almost as a second eyespot); chromosome number approximately 34; planktonic organism of ponds, lakes, streams and brackish waters.

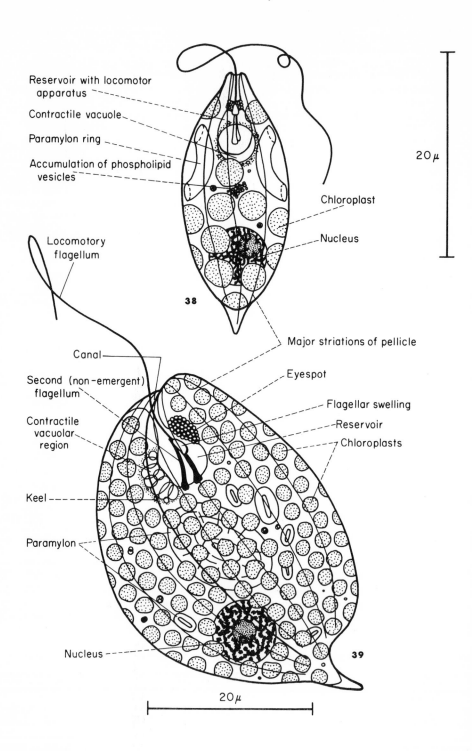

Reservoir with locomotor apparatus

Contractile vacuole

Paramylon ring

Accumulation of phospholipid vesicles

Chloroplast

Nucleus

20μ

Locomotory flagellum

38

Major striations of pellicle

Canal

Second (non-emergent) flagellum

Contractile vacuolar region

Keel

Paramylon

Eyespot

Flagellar swelling

Reservoir

Chloroplasts

Nucleus

39

20μ

Genus 12. Phacus   Dujardin 1841

Generic characters:

1. Green; phototrophic; chloroplasts small, discoid, pyrenoids absent (except in a few species).

2. Eyespot and flagellar swelling present.

3. Cell rigid; no euglenoid movement.

4. Cell slightly or markedly compressed; most species flat and "leaf-shaped"; cell often with ridges, folds or grooves running helically or almost longitudinally, giving an irregular or triradiate cross-section; many species with a long posterior spine.

5. Canal opening slightly or markedly subapical.

6. Free-swimming cell; solitary; no envelope; cysts and palmellae unknown.

7. Paramylon typically deposited as a few large granules together with many small granules.

8. Contractile vacuole present.

9. Very many species known; typically fresh-water, a few marine forms recorded.

Pochmann reviewed all known species in 1942 and established two subgenera, *Chlorophacus* (green species) and *Hyalophacus* (colourless species). These are the genera *Phacus* and *Hyalophacus* in the present account.

Pochmann's (1942) classification is based mainly upon form of pellicle, and a new treatment of the genus based upon all aspects of comparative cytology is desirable. In particular, species having large flat chloroplasts with pyrenoids (such as *Phacus splendens* Pochmann 1942) need to be separated from the majority with discoid chloroplasts (see example below).

PHACUS TRIQUETER   (Ehrenberg 1833) Dujardin 1841

Figures 39, 158 [see also Figs. 76, 118 of *Phacus pyrum* (Ehrenberg 1833) Stein 1878]. Cultures available. **Notes:** Example of a species with numerous discoid chloroplasts, no pyrenoids; cell compressed, with a lateral ridge; pellicular striations in a steep S-helix (p. 102), joined laterally by transverse struts; locomotory flagellum held in front of cell during swimming, with cell gyrating rapidly; cell dorsoventrality indicated by positions of eyespot and contractile vacuole, suggesting that cell is compressed in the lateral sense; subapicality of canal opening indicated by slight overhang of dorsal rim (in a few species, the ventral rim overhangs); muciferous bodies minute (not shown in figure), situated below grooves of helical striations; cosmopolitan species, typically planktonic in clean or polluted ponds and lakes.

Fig. 38 *Lepocinclis ovum:* living cell, ventral aspect; unlabelled organelles as in Fig. 39. Original drawing.

Fig. 39 *Phacus triqueter:* living cell, lateral aspect. Original drawing.

Genus 13. Hyalophacus Pringsheim 1936

Generic characters:

1. Colourless; osmotrophic.

2. Other characters as Phacus (q.v.); except that one known species (see below) has an eyespot and flagellar swelling and another (*H. caecus* Christen 1959) has not.

HYALOPHACUS OCELLATUS Pringsheim 1936

Figures 40, 41, 84. Cultures available. **Notes:** Cell compressed, with single ridge; position of eyespot indicates that cell compression is in lateral sense, with the ridge always on right-hand side of cell [Figs. 41(a)–41(c)]; canal opening sub-apical, dorsal rim of canal overhangs ridge but is itself overhung by ventral rim of body; flagellum held anteriorly during swimming; cell gyrates during rapid swimming, but during slow swimming there is no gyration and cell remains strictly orientated with dorsal edge uppermost; eyespot and flagellar swelling large, cells phototactic (see p. 146); muciferous bodies small (not shown in figure), beneath the prominent pellicular striations; chromosome number 92; possible meiosis recorded (p. 92); species recorded from peaty pools.

Order 3. Rhabdomonadales [= Suborder (3) Rhabdomonadina]

Five genera: *Rhabdomonas, Rhabdospira, Gyropaigne, Menoidium* and *Parmidium*. Characters of the order:

1. One emergent flagellum; a second, non-emergent flagellum not recorded but possibly present (see p. 6); the emergent flagellum **mobile throughout its length during swimming,** usually held straight when the cell is stationary.

2. Colourless; osmotrophic; never phagotrophic.

3. Eyespot and flagellar swelling absent.

4. Cell rigid; no euglenoid movement.

5. Free-swimming; solitary; no envelope.

As indicated below, species at present placed in this order need careful study to determine their exact structure (particularly flagellar arrangement). Revelation of a second flagellum (see p. 73) will affect the status of the order *Rhabdomonadales* with respect to the *Euglenales*, since cell shape would be left as the only distinguishing character. On the other hand, proof that any species does not have a second, non-emergent flagellum will justify inclusion of that species in a separate order.

Genus 1. Rhabdomonas Fresenius 1858

Generic characters:

1. Cell cylindrical, curved, not flattened, with rounded ends.

2. Periplast shallowly fluted, with six to eight steeply helical ridges meeting in a whorl at the posterior end.

46

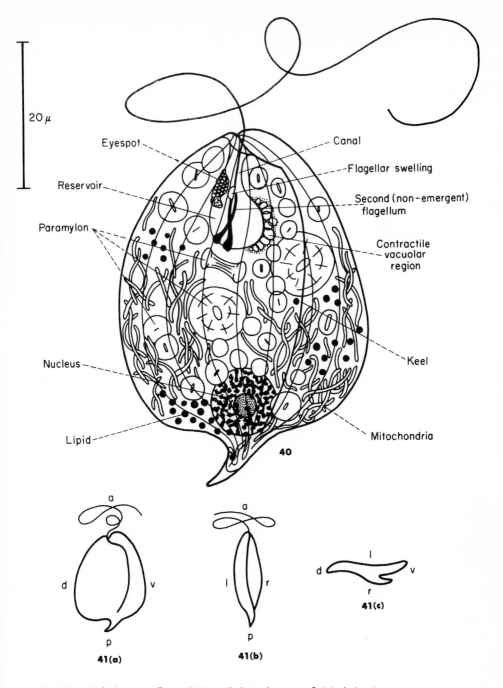

20μ

Eyespot

Reservoir

Paramylon

Nucleus

Lipid

Canal

Flagellar swelling

Second (non-emergent) flagellum

Contractile vacuolar region

Keel

Mitochondria

40

41(a) a d v p

41(b) a l r p

41(c) l d v r

Fig. 40 *Hyalophacus ocellatus:* living cell, lateral aspect. Original drawing.

Figs. 41(a)-41(c) *Hyalophacus ocellatus:* cell shape. 41(a), lateral (right-hand) aspect; 41(b), dorsal aspect; 41(c), transverse section, anterior aspect. *a* anterior, *p* posterior, *d* dorsal, *v* ventral, *l* left-hand side, *r* right-hand side. Original drawings.

47

3. Canal opening subapical.

4. Paramylon abundant, oval links or spherical granules; copious storage of lipid.

5. Muciferous bodies small; sparse slime sheath in some species, but cysts and palmellae unknown.

6. Contractile vacuole present.

7. Several species known; all fresh-water.

The taxonomy of *Rhabdomonas* is discussed by Pringsheim (1942, 1963) and Christen (1963).

RHABDOMONAS COSTATA   (Korschikow 1928) Pringsheim 1936

Figure 42. Cultures available. **Notes:** Cells uniform in size and shape; periplast flutings run in steep S-helix along cell, with the ridges perhaps equivalent to striations (electron microscopy needed for confirmation); short emergent flagellum held like a spinning lasso during swimming (see footnote, p. 18); muciferous bodies not visible in living cell; fairly common species of peaty waters, particularly with decaying leaves.

Genus 2. Rhabdospira   Pringsheim 1963

Generic characters:

1. Cell irregularly spiralled, slightly flattened, tapering posteriorly.
2. Periplast not fluted, without visible striations.
3. Other characters as Rhabdomonas (q.v.).

RHABDOSPIRA SPIRALIS   (Pringsheim 1942) Pringsheim 1963

Figure 43. Cultures available (mostly listed as "*Rhabdomonas spiralis* Pringsheim"). **Notes:** Cell shape peculiar but consistent in different collections and different clones; cell with two major turns, each almost at right angles to long axis and at right angles to each other; pellicle appears smooth in living cells; swimming and other features (distribution of mitochondria, lipid droplets, etc.) as *Rhabdomonas costata*; Golgi bodies not seen; cosmopolitan, relatively rare species of peaty pools and ditches.

Genus 3. Gyropaigne   Skuja 1939

Generic characters:

1. Cell ovoid or cylindrical, not flattened; tapering or rounded posteriorly; **with a number of pronounced, helical keels** running along the body.

2. Canal opening slightly subapical, canal sloping to one side.

3. Paramylon abundant.

4. Muciferous bodies small.

5. Contractile vacuole present.

6. Several species known; all fresh-water.

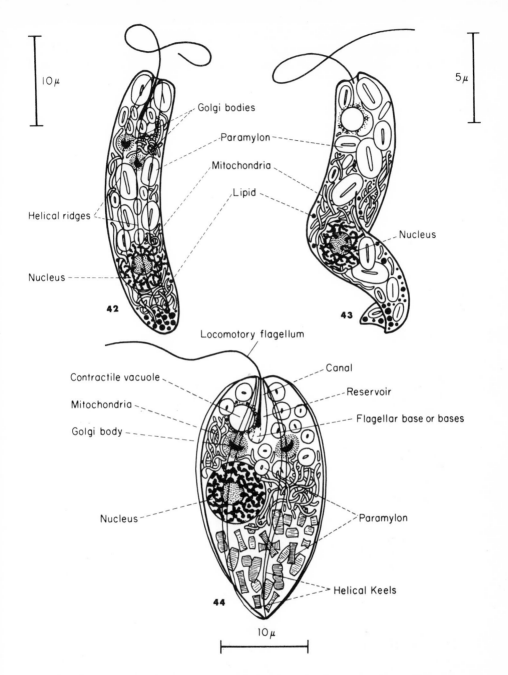

Fig. 42 *Rhabdomonas costata*: living cell, lateral aspect; unlabelled organelles as in Fig. 44. Original drawing.

Fig. 43 *Rhabdospira spiralis*: living cell, lateral aspect; unlabelled organelles as in Fig. 44. Original drawing.

Fig. 44 *Gyropaigne lefevrei*: living cell, lateral aspect. Original drawing.

This genus is discussed by Pringsheim (1942, 1963) and Christen (1960, 1963); Pringsheim regards *Gyropaigne* as possibly a colourless derivative of *Lepocinclis*, but Christen finds this unlikely.

GYROPAIGNE LEFEVREI   Bourrelly et Georges 1951

Figure 44. Cultures available. **Notes:** Cell with six longitudinal keels tracing a steep Z-helix; delicate pellicular striations trace a flatter S-helix (see p. 102), at an angle to keels; swimming rapid, with locomotory flagellum held in front of cell; paramylon of two types, strictly segregated, spheres with a minute central hole at anterior end of cell, ringed rods of various shapes (bobbins, dumb-bells) posteriorly; chondriome reticulate, but mitochondria round off into spheres under certain conditions; as with many other colourless species, two large Golgi bodies are visible anteriorly; species of acidic habitats, especially ponds and ditches with decaying vegetation.

Genus 4. Menoidium   Perty 1852

Generic characters:

1. Cell elongated, curved, strongly flattened; narrowly triangular or elliptical in cross-section; in side view, the dorsal edge appears almost straight, the ventral edge curved; in species with triangular cross-section, it is this curved edge which is the short side of the triangle, the dorsal edge is the most acutely angled.

2. Pellicle with delicate, widely spaced striations; not appearing as ridges or keels.

3. Canal opening apical, but sloping towards the ventral surface; **anterior end of the cell protruded into a narrow neck** around the canal.

4. Paramylon typically includes some large rods or elongated rings, together with numerous small granules.

5. Muciferous bodies small.

6. Contractile vacuole present.

7. Numerous species known; all fresh-water.

The genus *Menoidium* is discussed by Pringsheim (1942, 1963) and Christen (1963).

MENOIDIUM BIBACILLATUM   Pringsheim 1942

Figures 45, 46, 110, 142. Cultures available. **Notes:** Position of contractile vacuole indicates that cell is compressed laterally, with the straight edge dorsal; canal opening can be regarded as fractionally subapical, with slight overhang of dorsal rim; emergent flagellum held in front of cell during swimming, but not like a spinning lasso; cell gyrates during rapid swimming, but slower swimming produces side to side oscillation with either dorsal or ventral edge uppermost; apparently two flagellar bases in reservoir, but confirmation by electron microscopy is desirable (also for other genera of this order); muciferous bodies not visible in living cell; mitochondria show pronounced autonomous movement (p. 163); cytoplasm shows streaming (p. 117); apart from paramylon (with, typically, two

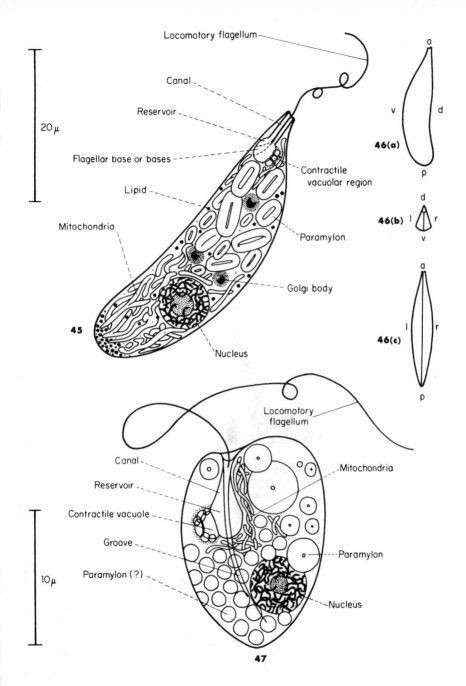

Locomotory flagellum

Canal

Reservoir

Flagellar base or bases

Lipid

Mitochondria

45

Contractile
vacuolar region

Paramylon

Golgi body

Nucleus

a

v   d

46(a)

p

d

46(b) l r

v

a

l   r

46(c)

p

Locomotory
flagellum

Canal

Reservoir

Contractile vacuole

Groove

Paramylon (?)

10μ

Mitochondria

Paramylon

Nucleus

47

20μ

Fig. 45 *Menoidium bibacillatum:* living cell, lateral aspect.

Figs. 46(a)-46(c) *Menoidium bibacillatum:* cell shape. 46(a), lateral (left-hand) aspect; 46(b), anterior aspect; 46(c), dorsal aspect. *a* anterior, *p* posterior, *d* dorsal, *v* ventral, *l* left-hand side, *r* right-hand side. Original drawings.

Fig. 47 *Parmidium scutulum:* living cell, lateral aspect. Original drawing.

51

large rods) and conspicuous lipid droplets, cell also contains vesicles with granular contents which look almost like food vacuoles (investigation of these is highly desirable); recorded once only, from a bog.

Genus 5. Parmidium   Christen 1963

Generic characters:

1. Cell ovoid, greatly compressed; with a single shallow indentation on one flat side, such that the cell is **angularly concavo-convex in cross-section.**

2. Pellicle with delicate, widely spaced striations; not appearing as keels.

3. Canal opening subapical in a slight depression; **no anterior protrusion of the cell.**

4. Muciferous bodies small.

5. Contractile vacuole present.

6. Only two species known; fresh-water.

Parmidium is discussed by Christen (1963) with respect to closely related genera. Christen moves *Petalomonas scutulum* Skuja 1956 into the genus *Parmidium* to join the type species, *Parmidium circulare* Christen 1963, on account of its cell shape and flagellar activity during swimming.

PARMIDIUM SCUTULUM   (Skuja 1956) Christen 1963

Figure 47. Cultures available. **Notes:** Position of contractile vacuole again indicates that cell is compressed laterally; canal opening is overhung by dorsal rim within subapical cell depression; emergent flagellum beats irregularly during swimming, not held straight as in *Petalomonas* and other genera of *Sphenomonadales* (q.v.); cell gyrates when swimming rapidly, during slow locomotion cell moves with dorsal edge held uppermost; paramylon spheres, each with minute hole, accumulate in anterior half of cell, posterior half contains many colourless, solid, unstainable bodies which squash easily, presumably paramylon of different consistency; flagellar base(s), muciferous bodies and Golgi bodies not visible in living cell; characteristic species of acidic habitats, particularly bogs and moorland pools.

Order 4. Sphenomonadales   [= Suborder (4) Sphenomonadina]

Seven genera: *Sphenomonas, Atraktomonas, Calycimonas, Petalomonas, Tropidoscyphus, Notosolenus* and *Anisonema*, combining the following ordinal characters:

1. One or two emergent flagella; **one flagellum always directed anteriorly, straight, not mobile throughout its length during swimming.**

2. Colourless; phagotrophic and/or osmotrophic; no special ingestion organelle.

3. Eyespot and flagellar swelling absent.

4. Cell rigid or almost so; no euglenoid movement; cell **usually with pronounced keels or grooves.**

5. Free-swimming; solitary; no envelope.

Genus 1. Sphenomonas   Stein 1878

Generic characters:

1. Two flagella; both emergent from the canal; unequal in length; heterodynamic; **the longer one directed anteriorly,** the shorter one curving laterally or posteriorly.

2. No confirmed records of phagotrophy.

3. Cell rigid (or possibly capable of some distortion under extreme stimuli); cylindrical (rarely, slightly flattened); usually one or more longitudinal lines or grooves present; pellicular striations delicate.

4. Canal opening apical or subapical; if apical, sloping sharply to one side.

5. Contractile vacuole present, even in marine forms.

6. Colourless body of unknown nature often present in the posterior half of the cell.

7. Several species known; fresh-water and marine.

SPHENOMONAS LAEVIS   Skuja 1948

Figure 48. No cultures available. **Notes** (from wild material): Cell rigid, but squashes easily; anterior end of cell protruded into narrow cylinder around canal, with pronounced overhang of dorsal rim (shape reminiscent of *Menoidium*, but cell not flattened); cell swims with slow gyration, giving appearance of swaying from side to side; longer flagellum held straight in front of cell during swimming, with shallow waves travelling from base to tip; shorter flagellum relatively inactive, with lethargic "cilium-like" beat; muciferous bodies and Golgi bodies not visible in living cell; no evidence of phagotrophy, cell without food vacuoles; hyaline body recorded for other species not seen here, but requires investigation as it might be another instance of leucosin storage (see p. 14).

Genus 2. Atraktomonas   Christen 1962

Generic characters (taken from Christen, 1962):

1. One emergent flagellum; a second, non-emergent flagellum not recorded but possibly present (see p. 6); the emergent flagellum directed anteriorly, straight, during swimming.

2. No confirmed records of phagotrophy.

3. Cell almost completely rigid; no euglenoid movement; **fusiform; not flattened.**

4. Canal opening apical.

5. Contractile vacuole present.

6. One species known; fresh-water.

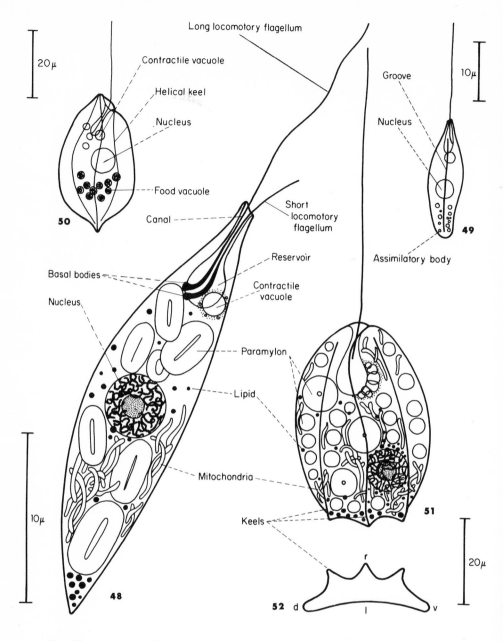

Fig. 48 *Sphenomonas laevis:* living cell, lateral aspect. Original drawing.

Fig. 49 *Atraktomonas laevis:* living cell, lateral aspect. Freely redrawn from Christen, 1962.

Fig. 50 *Calycimonas physaloides:* living cell, lateral aspect. Freely redrawn from Christen, 1959.

Fig. 51 *Petalomonas tricarinata:* living cell, lateral aspect; unlabelled organelles as in Fig. 48. Original drawing.

Fig. 52 *Petalomonas tricarinata:* cell shape, as seen in transverse section, posterior aspect. *d* dorsal, *v* ventral, *l* left-hand side, *r* right-hand side. Original drawing.

54

Regarded by Christen (1962, 1963) as a derivative of *Sphenomonas* by reduction of the latter's shorter flagellum, this genus was postulated by Christen on theoretical grounds before its discovery. *Atraktomonas* is separated from *Rhabdomonadales* by its mode of swimming and flagellar activity.

ATRAKTOMONAS LAEVIS   Christen 1962

Figure 49. No cultures available. **Notes** (taken from Christen, 1962): Cell circular in cross-section (not flattened), except for one groove which runs along body; pellicular striations almost longitudinal, delicate; unidentified assimilatory granules in posterior end of cell; nutrition osmotrophic (phagotrophy possible, but not certain); species recorded once only, from a pond containing rotting leaves.

Genus 3. Calycimonas   Christen 1959

Generic characters (taken from Christen, 1959):

1. One emergent flagellum; a second, non-emergent flagellum not recorded but possibly present (see p. 6); the emergent flagellum directed anteriorly, straight, during swimming.

2. Phagotrophic (perhaps not all species); cells often with many food vacuoles.

3. Cell rigid; ovoid, not flattened, with a number (5 to 8) of pronounced helical keels.

4. Canal opening subapical.

5. Paramylon not recorded for any species.

6. Contractile vacuole present.

7. Several species known; all fresh-water.

The taxomonic position of this genus (near to *Petalomonas* except for the flattened cell of the latter; near to *Tropidoscyphus* except for the latter's two flagella) is discussed by Christen (1959).

CALYCIMONAS PHYSALOIDES   Christen 1959

Figure 50. No cultures available. **Notes** (from Christen, 1959): Cell with eight helical keels; delicate striations between keels; swimming slow, with flagellum stretched out anteriorly; one or more contractile vacuoles present (includes accessory vacuoles? p. 151); absence of paramylon is a peculiarity, but other cytological features leave no doubt that the organism and other species of the genus are euglenoid; food vacuoles always present, but ingestion not observed; a mud-dwelling species in eutrophic ponds.

Genus 4. Petalomonas   Stein 1878

Generic characters:

1. One emergent flagellum; a second, non-emergent flagellum not recorded but possibly present (see p. 6); the emergent flagellum directed anteriorly, straight, during swimming.

2. Phagotrophic (perhaps not all species).

3. Cell rigid; ovoid, flattened, usually very flat and "leaf-shaped"; most species with strong ribs or keels.

4. Canal opening subapical.

5. Paramylon abundant.

6. Contractile vacuole present.

7. Many species; almost exclusively fresh-water.

This genus is reviewed in part by Shawhan and Jahn (1947), mainly with respect to cell shape, and by Christen (1962). Brown (1930) records an ingestion organelle for *Petalomonas;* all other authors deny this. The name *Petalomonas* has been proposed for priority over *Cyclidium* Dujardin 1841 (see Lanjouw, 1952), on grounds of common usage (as with *Lepocinclis;* see p. 43).

PETALOMONAS TRICARINATA   Skuja 1939

Figures 51, 52. No cultures available. **Notes** (from wild material): Cell extremely compressed, with three keels on one face (Fig. 52); position of contractile vacuole and overhang of canal rim indicate that cell is compressed in lateral sense, with keels on right-hand side; slightly subapical canal opening lies at the base of an apical depression; delicate pellicular striations run parallel to keels; cell swims smoothly, with flagellum stretched out anteriorly (see p. 141); as in other genera, cell gyrates during swimming; flagellar base(s) cannot be seen clearly, mainly because cell will not squash; paramylon granules tend to lie in longitudinal rows; muciferous bodies and Golgi bodies not visible in living cell; mud-dwelling species in eutrophic ponds and lakes.

Genus 5. Tropidoscyphus   Stein 1878

Generic characters:

1 Two flagella; both emergent from the canal; unequal in length; heterodynamic; **the longer (usually thicker) flagellum directed anteriorly,** straight, during swimming, the shorter one trailing posteriorly.

2. Phagotrophic.

3. Cell rigid; moderately flattened; with a number (4 to 10) of pronounced helical keels.

4. Canal opening subapical.

5. Contractile vacuole present.

6. Several species known; fresh-water and marine.

TROPIDOSCYPHUS CAUDATUS   Skuja 1948

Figure 53. No cultures available. **Notes** (taken from Skuja, 1948): Cell only slightly compressed, with six longitudinal keels joined transversely by irregular, anastomosing struts; pellicle brownish; anteriorly directed flagellum thicker than shorter, trailing one; canal opening subapical, in ventral depression;

contractile vacuole posterior to reservoir; cell contains globular bodies, not identified as paramylon by Skuja; recorded once only, in lake plankton.

Genus 6. Notosolenus   Stokes 1884

Generic characters:

1. Two flagella; both emergent from the canal; unequal in length; heterodynamic; **the longer flagellum directed anteriorly** during swimming, the shorter one trailing posteriorly.

2. Phagotrophic.

3. Cell rigid; ovoid, flattened, usually very flat; either concavoconvex in cross-section, or with keels.

4. Canal opening subapical.

5. Contractile vacuole present.

6. Several species known; fresh-water.

Reviewed by Skuja (1939), this genus was named *Solenotus* by Stokes (1884a) and renamed *Notosolenus* by the same author one month later (1884b), owing to prior use of the first name.

NOTOSOLENUS APOCAMPTUS   Stokes 1884

Figure 54. No cultures available. **Notes** (from wild material): Cell very compressed; positions of contractile vacuole and canal opening suggest that cell is compressed dorso-ventrally (N.B.), with ventral face markedly concave; longer flagellum outstretched in front of cell during swimming, with minute waves at its tip; shorter flagellum trails passively backwards; food vacuoles present, but ingestion not observed; muciferous bodies and Golgi bodies not visible in living cell; uncommon species, characteristically found in bog-pools and mud.

Genus 7. Anisonema   Dujardin 1841

Generic characters:

1. Two flagella; both emergent from the canal; subequal or unequal in length; heterodynamic; **the shorter flagellum directed anteriorly** during swimming; the longer (and often thicker) one trailing posteriorly, usually two or three times longer than the cell.

2. Phagotrophic.

3. Cell rigid or semi-rigid; some species with considerable euglenoid movement; **ovoid, flattened, usually very flat; cell without keels, but usually with one longitudinal furrow.**

4. Canal opening subapical.

5. Contractile vacuole present.

6. Numerous species known; mostly fresh-water.

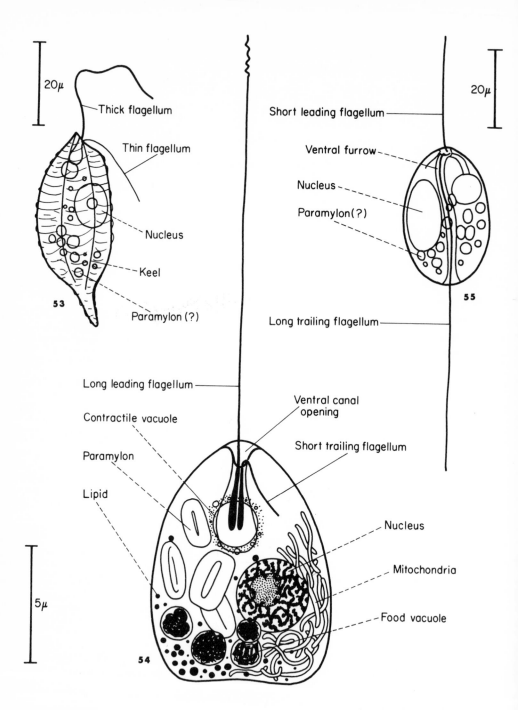

20μ

Thick flagellum

Thin flagellum

Nucleus

Keel

53

Paramylon (?)

Short leading flagellum

Ventral furrow

Nucleus

Paramylon(?)

20μ

55

Long trailing flagellum

Long leading flagellum

Contractile vacuole

Paramylon

Lipid

5μ

Ventral canal
opening

Short trailing flagellum

Nucleus

Mitochondria

Food vacuole

54

Fig. 53 *Tropidoscyphus caudatus:* living cell, lateral aspect. Freely redrawn from Skuja, 1948.

Fig. 54 *Notosolenus apocamptus:* living cell, ventral aspect. Original drawing.

Fig. 55 *Anisonema prosgeobium:* living cell, ventral aspect. Freely redrawn from Skuja, 1939.

An ingestion organelle is recorded for this genus by Brown (1930) and Hollande (1942); other authors deny this.

ANISONEMA PROSGEOBIUM   Skuja 1939

Figure 55. No cultures available. **Notes** (taken from Skuja, 1939): Cell apparently dorso-ventrally flattened (N.B.), with a groove along the concave ventral face; posteriorly directed flagellum lies in the groove and trails behind cell; cell semi-rigid, some euglenoid movement; reserve granules present, not identified as paramylon; phagotrophic (small diatoms, etc.), but ingestion not described; species of brackish pools.

Order 5. Heteronematales   [= Suborder (5) Heteronematina]

Six genera: *Heteronema, Peranema, Peranemopsis, Urceolus, Dinema* and *Entosiphon*. Characters of the order:

1. One or two emergent flagella; **one flagellum outstretched anteriorly during swimming, usually with coiling or flickering movement of the tip only,** giving characteristic gliding locomotion.

2. Colourless; phagotrophic; special ingestion organelle present.

3. Eyespot and flagellar swelling absent.

4. Free-swimming; solitary; no envelope.

Genus 1. Heteronema   Dujardin 1841

Generic characters:

1. Two flagella; both emergent from the canal; unequal in length and thickness; **the longer, thicker flagellum directed anteriorly during swimming; the shorter, thinner one curving posteriorly, lying free from the cell.**

2. Ingestion apparatus composed of separate rods associated with a subapical cytostome independent of the canal and reservoir; poorly developed in some species (which are, perhaps, secondarily non-phagotrophic).

3. Cell non-rigid; euglenoid movement pronounced or moderate in non-swimming cells; **cell not flattened;** pellicular striations coarse.

4. Canal opening subapical.

5. Muciferous bodies large, but cysts and palmellae unknown.

6. Numerous species recorded; mostly fresh-water, some marine.

In common with all genera of this order, *Heteronema* is in need of modern review. Particularly requiring study is the phenomenon of phagotrophy and reports of the absence of an ingestion organelle in a few species (which should, perhaps, be moved to another genus).

HETERONEMA ACUS   (Ehrenberg 1840) Stein 1878

Figure 58. No cultures available. **Notes** (from wild material): Swimming cell fusiform, stationary cells exhibit lethargic change of shape; swimming smooth, with leading flagellum rigid save for the flickering tip; pellicular striations conspicuous, with a steep S-helix (p. 102); paramylon sparse; food vacuoles numerous, containing bacteria and coccoid algae, but ingestion not observed; ingestion organelle of two rods; granular condition of chondriome perhaps typical of gorged cells; muciferous bodies spherical, conspicuous (not shown in figure), sparsely arranged in helical rows beneath the pellicular striations; Golgi bodies not seen; fairly widespread species in fresh-water ponds and brackish pools; studied by Loefer (1931).

Genus 2. Peranema   Dujardin 1841

Generic characters:

1. Two flagella; both emergent from the canal; unequal in length and thickness; heterodynamic; **the longer, thicker flagellum directed anteriorly during swimming; the shorter, thinner one curving posteriorly and pressed closely to the cell.**

2. Ingestion apparatus composed of separate rods associated with a subapical cytostome independent of the canal and reservoir.

3. Cell non-rigid; euglenoid movement violent in non-swimming cells; **cell slightly flattened when swimming;** pellicular striations coarse.

4. Canal opening subapical.

5. Muciferous bodies large, but cysts and palmellae unknown.

6. Probably several species; fresh-water.

Christen (1963) erected a genus "*Pseudoperanema*" to accommodate *Peranema trichophorum* (see below), since this species has been shown to have a second emergent flagellum (tightly pressed to the cell) which was not recorded in the original description. However, the rules of biological nomenclature decree that the description of the type species must be changed, not its name, and "*Peranema trichophorum*" therefore stands. In 1940, Lackey created the genus *Peranemopsis* for a *Peranema*-like species lacking the trailing flagellum. Other species which genuinely have only the one emergent flagellum, as defined by Stein (1878), can conveniently be referred to Lackey's genus (see p. 62).

PERANEMA TRICHOPHORUM   (Ehrenberg 1838) Stein 1878

Figures 56, 57, 75. Cultures available. **Notes:** This species has been studied in detail by Chen (1950), and earlier by Dangeard (1901), Hall and Powell (1928), Lackey (1929, 1933) and Chadefaud (1938); locomotion is discussed on p. 142 of the present account, ingestion apparatus and ingestion on p. 192; swimming cell has shape shown in figure, with very slight lateral flattening; violent euglenoid movement produces gross distortion of stationary cells; pellicular striations very conspicuous, with S-helix (p. 102); anterior flagellum extremely thick (1 μ

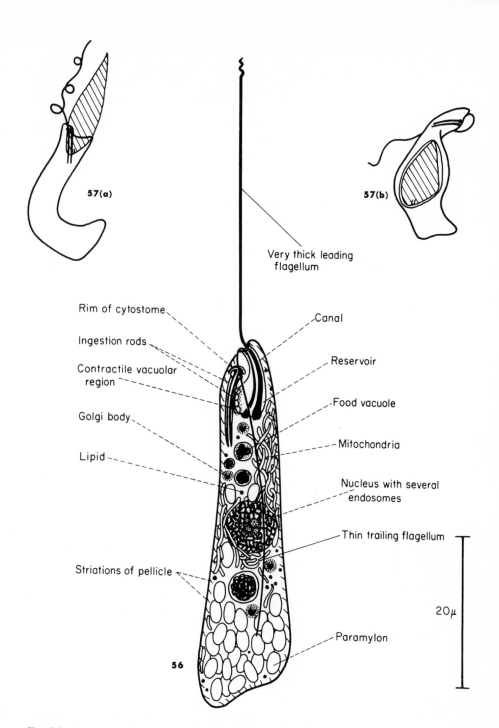

57(a)

57(b)

Very thick leading
flagellum

Rim of cytostome

Ingestion rods

Contractile vacuolar
region

Golgi body

Lipid

Striations of pellicle

56

Canal

Reservoir

Food vacuole

Mitochondria

Nucleus with several
endosomes

Thin trailing flagellum

20μ

Paramylon

Fig. 56 *Peranema trichophorum*: living cell, lateral aspect. Original drawing.

Fig. 57(a), 57(b) *Peranema trichophorum*: living cell; two stages in the ingestion of a cell
of *Euglena*. Original drawings.

or more; see p. 132); trailing flagellum much thinner, lying in a slight groove at anterior end of cell but apparently stuck to cell nearer posterior end; well-fed cells packed with paramylon, obscuring cell structure; batteries of muciferous bodies (not shown in figure) look like trichocysts, but not discharged as such; nucleus typically polyendosomal (see p. 85); chromosome number approximately 175; excellent species for study, but cells need to be starved first to reduce paramylon content; cosmopolitan, common species of ponds, ditches, marshes and other acid-to-neutral habitats.

Genus 3. Peranemopsis   Lackey 1940

Generic characters:

1. One emergent flagellum; a second, non-emergent flagellum not recorded but possibly present (see p. 6); **the emergent flagellum directed anteriorly, straight, during swimming.**

2. Other characters as Peranema (q.v.); several species; mostly fresh-water.

PERANEMOPSIS INFLEXUM   Skuja 1939 nov. comb.

Figure 59. No cultures available. **Notes** (from wild material): Cytology and locomotion similar to *Peranema trichophorum*, except that cell is curved and there is no trailing flagellum; euglenoid movement of stationary cells less violent than *Peranema*; pellicular striations coarse, with an S-helix; muciferous bodies (not shown in figure) smaller, fewer than in *Peranema*; ingestion apparatus, thick leading flagellum, nucleus, paramylon, mitochondria and Golgi bodies all as in *Peranema trichophorum*; fairly common species of small ponds.

Genus 4. Urceolus   Mereschkowsky 1879

Generic characters:

1. One emergent flagellum; a second, non-emergent flagellum not recorded but possibly present (see p. 6); **the emergent flagellum directed anteriorly, straight, during swimming.**

2. Ingestion apparatus composed of separate rods.

3. Cell with an anterior depression in which lie the canal opening and the independent cytostome; the depression **surrounded by a funnel-shaped collar** which gives a level or sloping reflexed rim to the anterior end of the cell.

4. Cell semi-rigid or rigid; euglenoid movement slight or lacking; pellicular striations usually coarse.

5. Several species known; fresh-water and marine.

There is no review of this little-known genus except for that in Huber-Pestalozzi (1955) and the studies of Skuja (1939, 1948, 1956); further investigations of cytology and behaviour are highly desirable. *Urceolus* was redescribed by Stokes (1887) under the name "*Urceolopsis.*"

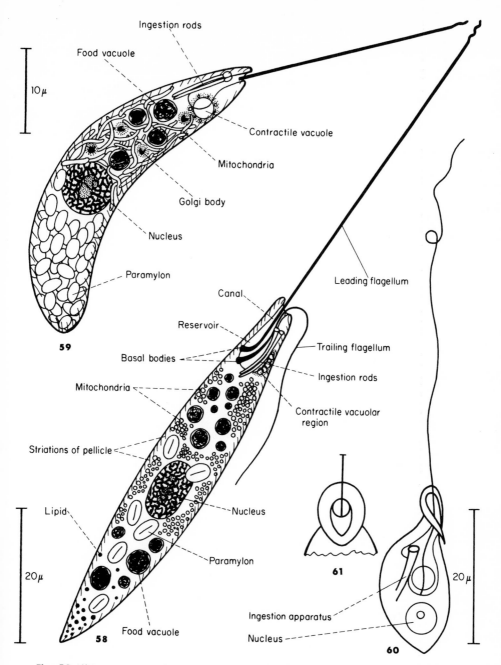

Ingestion rods

Food vacuole

10μ

Contractile vacuole

Mitochondria

Golgi body

Nucleus

Paramylon

Leading flagellum

59

Canal

Reservoir

Trailing flagellum

Basal bodies

Ingestion rods

Mitochondria

Contractile vacuolar region

Striations of pellicle

Nucleus

Lipid

Paramylon

20μ

Nucleus

61

Paramylon

20μ

Food vacuole

58

Ingestion apparatus

Nucleus

60

Fig. 58 *Heteronema acus:* living cell, lateral aspect. Original drawing.

Fig. 59 *Peranemopsis inflexum:* living cell, lateral aspect; unlabelled organelles as in Fig. 58. Original drawing.

Fig. 60 *Urceolus macromastix:* living cell, lateral aspect. Freely redrawn from Skuja, 1948.

Fig. 61 *Urceolus macromastix:* anterior end of cell, ventral aspect. Freely redrawn from Skuja, 1948.

URCEOLUS MACROMASTIX   Skuja 1948

Figures 60, 61. No cultures available. **Notes** (taken from Skuja, 1948): Cell not completely rigid, change of shape possible; pellicular striations moderately coarse, with an S-helix (not shown in figure); flagellum extremely thick and long (more than three times the length of the cell); muciferous bodies not described, but mucilage production copious; ingestion apparatus present, ingestion not described in Skuja's account; recorded once only, from a lake.

Genus 5. Dinema   Perty 1852

Generic characters:

1. Two flagella; both emergent from the canal; unequal in length; heterodynamic; **the shorter flagellum directed anteriorly during swimming; the longer one trailing posteriorly, considerably longer than the cell.**

2. Ingestion apparatus composed of separate rods associated with a subapical cytostome independent of the canal and reservoir.

3. Cell non-rigid; moderate euglenoid movement in non-swimming cells; **cell somewhat flattened;** pellicular striations delicate.

4. Canal opening subapical.

5. Few species known; fresh or brackish water.

The relationships of *Dinema*, another little-studied genus, are uncertain. Shape and motility are reminiscent of *Anisonema* (the flagellation of some species of the two genera is identical), but possession of a fully formed ingestion organelle is a major difference. Brown (1930) and Hollande (1942) record an ingestion apparatus for *Anisonema* but according to Hollande this is an ingestion "gutter," not an organelle composed of rods; all other authors deny possession of an ingestion apparatus by *Anisonema*. On current knowledge, the present position seems best for *Dinema*.

DINEMA SULCATUM   Christen 1963

Figure 62. No cultures available. **Notes** (taken from Christen, 1963): Cell swims rapidly, with long flagellum trailing; pellicular striations not observed; paramylon abundant, obscuring cell details; ingestion not described, but food vacuoles include diatoms; mud-dwelling species in bogs.

Genus 6. Entosiphon   Stein 1878

Generic characters:

1. Two flagella; both emergent from the canal; unequal in length; heterodynamic; **the shorter flagellum directed anteriorly during swimming, the longer one trailing posteriorly, longer than the cell.**

2. Ingestion apparatus a tube ("siphon"), composed of rods fused together; method of ingestion unknown, but the siphon can be protruded from the cell.

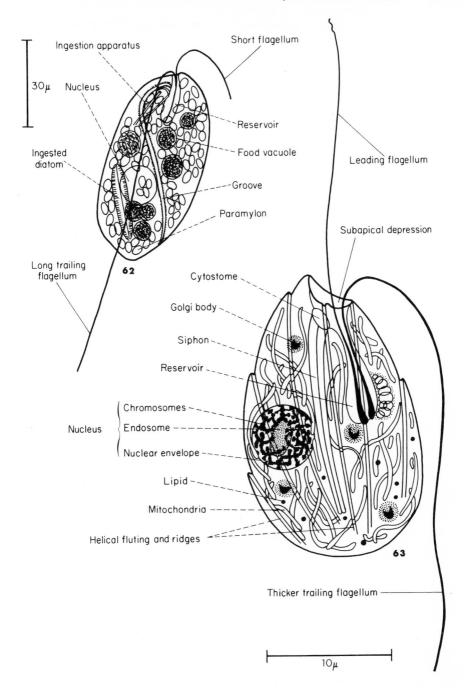

Fig. 62 *Dinema sulcatum:* living cell, lateral aspect. Freely redrawn from Christen, 1963.

Fig. 63 *Entosiphon sulcatum:* living cell, lateral aspect. Original drawing.

3. Cell rigid; slightly flattened; with pronounced helical fluting and ridges.

4. Canal opening subapical.

5. Several species known; fresh-water.

Taxonomic treatment of *Entosiphon* by different authors largely depends upon their interpretation of the ingestion organelle. Christen (1963) places *Entosiphon* in a group with *Anisonema* for convenience [similar flagellation, rigid cell (?)] but does not believe the two genera to be closely related. *Entosiphon*'s position in the present account seems satisfactory until further study can be made.

ENTOSIPHON SULCATUM   (Dujardin 1841) Stein 1878

Figures 63, 122, 173–175. No cultures available. **Notes** (from wild material): Cell with deep apical depression into which both siphon and canal open; positions of canal opening and contractile vacuole indicate that slight cell flattening is in the lateral sense; cell with twelve helical grooves (see Fig. 173); cell swims with slow gyration, the thinner flagellum directed anteriorly, with oscillating tip, but not as rigid as in *Peranema* or *Peranemopsis*; the thicker, longer, trailing flagellum apparently passive; siphon dorsal to canal and reservoir; ingestion not observed, no food vacuoles in cell; no paramylon; small muciferous bodies (not shown in figure) in helical rows beneath the pellicular grooves; chondriome usually visible as a delicate superficial reticulum; Golgi bodies small, scattered; widespread and quite common species, planktonic in ponds and lakes.

Order 6. Euglenamorphales   [= Suborder (6) Euglenamorphina]

Two genera: *Euglenamorpha* and *Hegneria*. Ordinal characters:

1. Three or more flagella; all emergent from the canal; all of the same length, thickness and activity.

2. Green or colourless; not phagotrophic; **endozoic, occurring in the digestive tract of tadpoles.**

3. Cell non-rigid; pronounced euglenoid movement.

4. Cell elongated and unflattened.

5. Cell solitary; no envelope.

Genus 1. Euglenamorpha   Wenrich 1924

Generic characters (extracted from Wenrich, 1924):

1. Three flagella.

2. Green; phototrophic; numerous discoid chloroplasts, no pyrenoids recorded; **colourless form of the only known species also occurs.**

3. Eyespot present; **flagellar swelling present on each flagellum.**

4. Canal opening subapical.

5. Paramylon present, many oval granules.

6. Contractile vacuole not recorded.

7. Only one species known; from rectum of *Rana* tadpoles.

This genus is included in Hollande's (1952) survey of euglenoid flagellates, but omitted by Huber-Pestalozzi (1955).

EUGLENAMORPHA HEGNERI   Wenrich 1924

Figure 64. No cultures available. **Notes** (a) **Green form:** Not recorded again since described by Wenrich (1924); this author found it in 58 per cent of tadpoles examined (Pennsylvania, U.S.A.); endozoic habit proved by Wenrich, organism swims actively in excised tadpole's rectum; pellicular striations said to usually trace a right-handed helix (Z-helix, see p. 104); flagellar swellings on more than one flagellum unique in euglenoids, suggests proliferation of *Euglena*-type locomotory flagellum (see p. 145); phototactic; multiplication rare in host, follows mitosis. **Notes** (b) **Colourless form:** Also seen only by Wenrich (1924), and named "var. *pellucida*"; main characters (in comparison with the green form) are as follows: 1. Four to six flagella. 2. Colourless; osmotrophic. 3. No eyespot; no flagellar swellings. 4. Cell smaller than green form, tapering posteriorly. 5. Reservoir larger than in green form. 6. Nucleus larger than in green form. 7. Multiplication rapid in host, follows mitosis or amitosis (see p. 92). 8. Pellicular striations said usually to trace a left-handed helix (S-helix, see above).

Genus 2. Hegneria   Brumpt et Lavier 1924

Generic characters (extracted from Brumpt and Lavier, 1924):

1. Seven flagella.

2. Colourless; osmotrophic.

3. No eyespot or flagellar swelling.

4. Canal opening subapical.

5. Only one species known; from rectum of *Leptodactylus* tadpoles.

This genus is included in Hollande's (1952) survey but omitted by Huber-Pestalozzi (1955).

HEGNERIA LEPTODACTYLI   Brumpt et Lavier 1924

Figure 65. No cultures available. **Notes:** Not recorded again since described by Brumpt and Lavier (1924) from *Leptodactylus* tadpoles from São Paulo (Brazil); present in vast numbers in tadpole rectum, with a few other flagellates, but not found in caecum or large intestine; most cells with seven flagella, a few with only six; helical striations of pellicle clearly seen, cytoplasm described as "vacuolar," paramylon not recorded; contractile vacuole not recorded; Brumpt and Lavier express the opinion that the "colourless form" of *Euglenamorpha* (see above) is more likely to be this, or another, species of *Hegneria*.

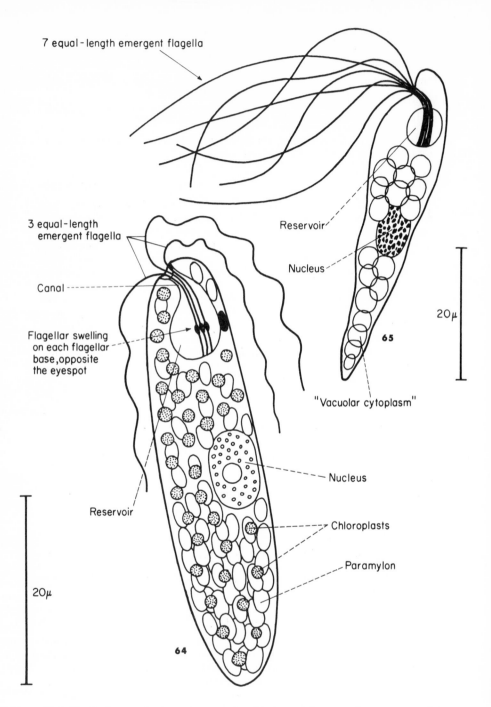

7 equal-length emergent flagella

3 equal-length
emergent flagella

Canal

Flagellar swelling
on each flagellar
base, opposite
the eyespot

Reservoir

20μ

Reservoir

Nucleus

"Vacuolar cytoplasm"

Nucleus

Chloroplasts

Paramylon

20μ

65

64

Fig. 64 *Euglenamorpha hegneri:* composite drawing of the green form, constructed from Wenrich's (1924) figures of living and fixed cells; lateral aspect.

Fig. 65 *Hegneria leptodactyli:* living cell, lateral aspect. Freely redrawn from Brumpt and Lavier, 1924.

Genera of Uncertain Affinity or Validity

The following genera of doubtful affinities or validity have not been included in the foregoing summary but are listed here for completeness. Further investigation of these organisms is desirable, particularly on material isolated into culture. This list does not include invalid synonyms already removed by Huber-Pestalozzi (1955) and earlier authors.*

Green forms

AMPHITROPIS Gicklhorn 1920: of doubtful affinity; monospecific (*aequiciliata*); cell structure and reproduction of this species indicate that it almost certainly belongs to the *Phacotaceae* (order *Volvocales*, phylum *Chlorophyta*).

CHLORACHNE Schiller 1925, *OTTONIA* Schiller 1925, *PROTOEUGLENA* Subrahmanyan 1954: of doubtful affinity; monospecific genera; described as simple marine euglenoids; in fact, their simplicity leaves them with no justifiable claims to euglenoid affinity (and some structures, for example, the eyespot of *Protoeuglena*, are strikingly non-euglenoid in form).

CRYPTOGLENA Ehrenberg 1831: of doubtful affinity; three species described (see Huber-Pestalozzi, 1955); insufficient evidence of euglenoid affinity, especially since paramylon is absent and the eyespot is reported as being part of one of the two chloroplasts.

EUGLENOCAPSA Steinecke 1932: of doubtful validity; monospecific (*ochracea*); described as an encapsuled euglenoid which occasionally produces swarmers; there seems little reason why this should not be regarded as a species of *Euglena* in palmelloid state.

Colourless forms

CALKINSIA Lackey 1960: valid genus; monospecific (*aureus*) [Generic characters: Two flagella; heterodynamic; longer flagellum directed anteriorly, shorter one curving posteriorly; chloroplasts, eyespot and flagellar swelling absent; organism gold-coloured (pellicle or cytoplasm?); osmotrophic; cell elongated, ovoid, slightly flattened, with a long caudal spine; rigid; canal opening subapical, in a ventral groove which continues towards the posterior end of the cell, becoming shallower; paramylon present; contractile vacuole absent; marine; facultatively anaerobic]; seems to be closely related to *Sphenomonas* (p. 53).

CLAUTRIAVIA Massart 1900: of doubtful validity; monospecific (*mobilis*); description and figures inadequate for recognition.

HELIKOTROPIS Pochmann 1955: monospecific (*okteres*); a valid euglenoid species (Characters: Colourless; osmotrophic, but a reddish structure in the anterior of the cell considered by Pochmann to be a reduced ingestion organelle; cell broadly spindle-shaped, not flattened, helicoid, with eight ridges tracing a steep Z-helix along the cell; not completely rigid; canal opening subapical; flagella not seen; paramylon present; fresh-water); probably close to *Gyropaigne* (p. 48), but insufficiently known for this to be certain (see Christen, 1963).

JENNINGSIA Schaeffer 1918: not valid; monospecific (*diatomophaga*; a large species of *Peranema* (p. 60) or *Peranemopsis* (p. 62) which ingests (only?) diatoms.

* Problems of nomenclature are too complex to be considered here, but it may be noted that, strictly speaking, some of the *names* given below and in the main part of this chapter are invalid (genera described since 1935 without a Latin diagnosis, etc.).

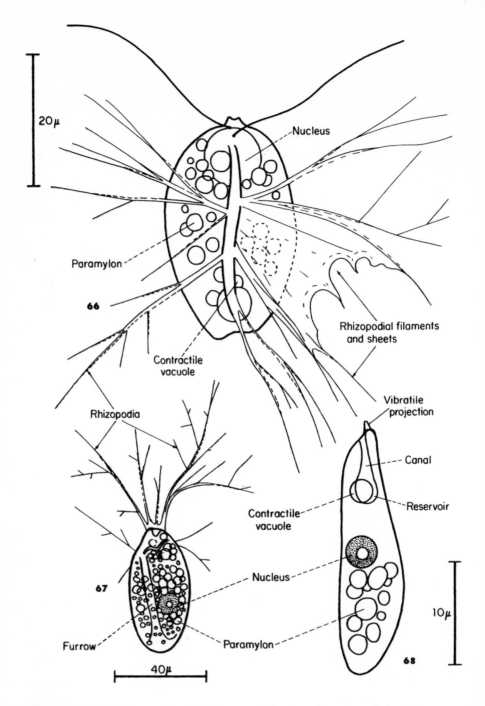

20μ

Nucleus

Paramylon

66

Rhizopodial filaments
and sheets

Contractile
vacuole

Vibratile
projection

Rhizopodia

Canal

Contractile
vacuole

Reservoir

Nucleus

67

10μ

Furrow

Paramylon

68

40μ

Fig. 66 *Protaspis obovata* Skuja 1948: living cell. Freely redrawn from Skuja, 1948.

Fig. 67 *Rhizaspis simplex* Skuja 1948: living cell. Freely redrawn from Skuja, 1948.

Fig. 68 *Rhynchopus amitus*: living cell. Freely redrawn from Skuja, 1948.

MARSUPIOGASTER Schewiakoff 1893: of doubtful validity; two species described (see Huber-Pestalozzi, 1955), but insufficiently for recognition; perhaps species of *Dinema* (p. 64).

PENTAMONAS Lackey 1962: valid genus; monospecific (*spinifera*) [Generic characters: One emergent flagellum; chloroplasts, eyespot and flagellar swelling absent; osmotrophic; ovoid, flattened, with backwardly curving spines produced from the edges of the rigid pellicle; canal opening apical; paramylon present; large posterior vesicle of unknown function (possibly leucosin, see p. 14); no contractile vacuole; nucleus anterior; marine, sand-dwelling]; possibly most closely related to *Petalomonas* (p. 55).

PLOEOTIA Dujardin 1841: of doubtful validity; monospecific (*vitrea*); perhaps a species of *Tropidoscyphus*.

PROTASPIS Skuja 1939: valid genus; several species (see Huber-Pestalozzi, 1955) [Generic characters: Two flagella; flagella unequal in length, heterodynamic, the shorter one directed anteriorly, the longer one directed posteriorly; colourless; osmotrophic and phagotrophic; no ingestion organelle, but rhizopodia are produced from a median furrow; cell rigid or almost so; ovoid, flattened, concavo-convex in cross-section; median furrow down one face; no canal or reservoir; flagella inserted subapically, ventrally; sparse, oval paramylon granules; two contractile vacuoles; nucleus anteriorly placed]; Fig. 66. Skuja (1948) now places this genus in the *Pyrrophyta* (dinoflagellates), but suggests that on some characters it occupies a position intermediate between *Pyrrophyta* and *Euglenophyta*.

PSEUDAMOEBA Behre 1961: of doubtful affinity; monospecific (*planktonica*); colourless, rigid cell, solitary or colonial in gelatinous matrix, no flagella but with fine pseudopodia from two poles of cell; described by Behre as a greatly reduced euglenoid, but with no euglenoid features listed except possession of paramylon.

RHIZASPIS Skuja 1948: valid genus; two species known (see Huber-Pestalozzi, 1955) [Generic characters: Flagella absent; rhizopodia can be extended from the anterior invagination; colourless; osmotrophic and phagotrophic; no ingestion organelle; cell rigid or almost so; ovoid, flattened; canal opening apical, canal and reservoir a shallow invagination only; contractile vacuolar system complex; paramylon present, reserves also stored as "leucosin" (see p. 185); nucleus central; fresh-water]; Fig. 67. The species of this genus are placed in a separate family of the *Euglenophyta* (*Rhizaspidaceae*) by Skuja (1948); affinities are uncertain.

RHYNCHOPUS Skuja 1948: valid genus; monospecific (*amitus*) [Generic characters: Flagella absent; colourless; osmotrophic; cell non-rigid, some euglenoid movement; fusiform or elongated, slightly flattened; apex of cell with short projection which functions in locomotion by vibrating; canal opening subapical; canal long, reservoir typically euglenoid; contractile vacuole present; paramylon present; nucleus central]; Fig. 68. This monospecific genus is placed by Skuja (1948) in a separate euglenoid family (*Rhynchopodaceae*); once again, it is impossible to suggest close affinities.

SCYTOMONAS Stein 1878: of doubtful affinity; several species; all species have a sexual process involving conjugation in pairs; further study is needed to establish whether or not these organisms are euglenoid flagellates; cultures available of one species, *Scytomonas klebsii* Wayland 1963.

TRIANGULOMONAS Lackey 1940: monospecific (*rigida*); a valid euglenoid species, probably a member of *Sphenomonadales* or *Heteronematales*, but insufficiently known for generic relationships to be suggested.

Chapter 5

PHYLOGENY

Despite difficulties of specific and generic demarcation in the *Eugleno-phyta* (*Euglenida*) and the high degree of specialisation attained by present-day forms, studies in comparative cytology permit the inference of relationships at the generic level which, in several cases, are supported by experimental evidence. Furthermore, it becomes possible to suggest what may have been the predominating evolutionary trends within the group. Such considerations have led to the erection of the hypothetical phylogenetic scheme presented at the end of this chapter (p. 75) and to the demarcation of the six orders of *Euglenophyta* discussed in the preceding pages. It remains to consider the reasoning on which this scheme is based and the consequent degree of justification for regarding the taxonomic system as an approach to a natural one.

The key to an understanding of euglenoid phylogeny seems to be flagellar arrangement. On the basis of comparative studies, the non-emergent second flagellum of *Euglena* and other genera is most sensibly explained as a reduction of an originally emergent flagellum which functioned in swimming. It seems logical to suggest that forms with one locomotory flagellum derive from forms with two and that genera with two emergent flagella are "primitive" so far as this feature is concerned. In fact, it appears that flagellar reduction has been a slowly continuing process throughout euglenoid evolution, many grades of the phenomenon being represented in present-day species. A probable sequence is the following: forms with two equal emergent flagella $\longrightarrow$ forms with two unequal emergent flagella $\longrightarrow$ forms with one flagellum emergent from the canal and one flagellum non-emergent, ending within the reservoir $\longrightarrow$ forms with only one flagellum (if such forms exist; see p. 6). The three or more locomotory flagella of the parasitic *Euglenamorpha* and *Hegneria* are probably derived by proliferation of a single emergent flagellum.

If flagellar reduction is accepted as the major structural evolutionary trend in euglenoids, then several other characters emerge as probably "primitive" and changes in these which accompany reduction of flagella may be proposed as further trends of evolutionary significance. The most important such trends are (a) loss of pellicular elasticity (cells with elastic pellicle $\longrightarrow$ semi-rigid cells $\longrightarrow$ rigid cells), (b) imposition of bilateral symmetry on the primary helical symmetry, (c) gradual flattening of cells,*

* The opposite phylogenetic trend is suggested by Pochmann (1953, 1955) for some euglenoid genera. He proposes the hypothesis that radially symmetrical keeled forms (such as *Gyropaigne*) have been produced from two or more flattened keeled individuals (such as *Petalomonas*) by fusion of cell walls during disturbed cell division.

(d) acquisition of more or less permanent envelopes by originally naked cells, and (e) adoption of the colonial habit by originally solitary cells. That most of these changes have probably occurred more than once during euglenoid evolution is indicated in the phylogenetic scheme.

A totally different kind or phenomenon, but one also vitally important in considering euglenoid phylogeny, is loss of chloroplasts. Whereas alteration of the locomotor apparatus is envisaged as a slowly continuing evolutionary process, chloroplast loss appears to have occurred many times in the euglenoid flagellates as an abrupt change. It is difficult to visualise green forms suddenly arising from colourless forms by the appearance of chloroplasts, but the reverse change is both feasible and supported by observational and experimental evidence. Furthermore, colourless species which have an eyespot and flagellar swelling can often be regarded as intermediate between green species and certain colourless ones with no eyespot. One can cite as natural examples the *Euglena/Khawkinea/Astasia* complex (see p. 29), *Phacus* and *Hyalophacus* (p. 46) and *Trachelomonas* and *"Hyalotrachelomonas"* (p. 36), and just such a series has been produced experimentally by Pringsheim and Pringsheim (1952) and others in the "bleaching" of *Euglena gracilis* (see p. 183). This subject has recently been discussed by Pringsheim (1963) in his book on colourless flagellates.

In phylogenetic terms the importance of chloroplast loss is the setting up of a colourless race when the nonphotosynthetic cell has the capacity to survive as a heterotroph. In the present interpretation it is proposed that this has happened during the evolution of all present-day colourless euglenoids. It is also suggested that phagotrophic nutrition has arisen independently more than once, subsequent to or followed by loss of chloroplasts (since no known green species is a phagotroph).

In the light of the above considerations, the "primitive euglenoid flagellate" may be visualised as incorporating the diagnostic euglenoid features (p. 6) into a naked, solitary, green cell, with two equal-length flagella, an elastic pellicle and helical symmetry with no bilaterality or cell flattening. The present-day genus nearest to this is *Eutreptia* and, though obviously specialised, this genus recommends itself as the logical starting point for a scheme of euglenoid phylogeny.

A few points in the phylogenetic scheme presented here (Table 3) call for special comment. If the subgenera of *Euglena* were listed separately, it would be possible to indicate trends of increasing cell rigidity and flattening within this genus and also to relate the subgenera to particular species of *Trachelomonas, Khawkinea, Astasia, Lepocinclis* and *Phacus;* this detailed study in comparative cytology can perhaps be undertaken in the future. *Euglenamorpha* is provisionally considered as a form which has undergone flagellar proliferation but is otherwise close to the primitive condition. The possible flagellar reduction to one only in the *Rhabdomonadales* and certain individual genera is not included in the scheme, since it seems probable that investigation by electron microscopy may reveal a second flagellum (see p. 46). Phagotrophy is indicated as arising independently at three points but the evolution of an ingestion organelle has probably taken place once only. Finally, it should be noted that the cytology of many organisms at present placed in the *Spheno-*

monadales and *Heteronematales* is poorly understood and future studies may well lead to major revisions in these orders. Some of the problems involved are discussed by Christen (1963) and the relevant parts of my scheme owe much to his ideas.

Writing in 1948, Pringsheim commented upon the fact that hypothetical phylogenetic schemes were very much out of fashion. This is even more true today than it was then ("Phylogenetic trees are evil growths" and all that) but, strongly influenced by the teachings of Fritsch and Pringsheim, I present mine without apology. Such a scheme is a visualisation of lines of evolution which *could* have produced present-day genera, shown by linking the genera together in particular sequence. These genera are, of course, the specialised products of evolution, and it is not suggested that they *actually* gave rise to each other in the order shown. The scheme is merely a theoretical exercise with the purpose of assisting in the clarification of relationships and the construction of a rational taxonomic system.

Key to Table 3

All organisms beyond the introduction of a symbol have the character thereby indicated.

Symbols:

● flagellar reduction

✕ loss of chloroplasts

⊗ loss of eyespot and flagellar swelling

Ⓡ loss of pellicular elasticity (non-rigid cell → semi-rigid cell → rigid cell)

Ⓕ flattening of cell

Ⓔ adoption of cell envelope

Ⓢ adoption of sedentary habit

Ⓒ adoption of colonial habit

Ⓟ adoption of phagotrophy

Ⓘ evolution of an ingestion apparatus

⊕ increase in number of flagella

Taxonomy

The scheme is divided into six sections which have been named as the following orders of the Euglenophyta:

① Eutreptiales

② Euglenales

③ Rhabdomonadales

④ Sphenomonadales

⑤ Heteronematales

⑥ Euglenamorphales

The characters delimiting these orders are indicated on the scheme and are discussed in detail elsewhere (pp. 8-10, 72-73).

Table 3

A Scheme of Euglenoid Phylogeny

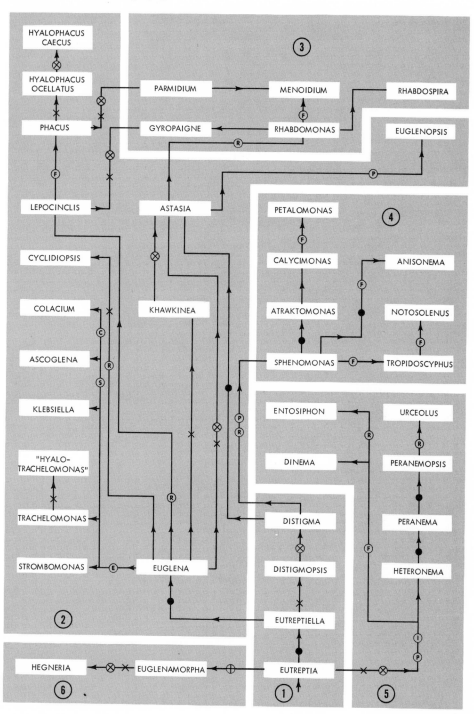

Part II

CELL COMPONENTS AND CELL INCLUSIONS

Chapter 6

INTRODUCTION

A **cell** of any living organism consists of a **protoplast** which may be naked or enclosed within a **cell wall** or **envelope.** The protoplast typically has an external limiting membrane, the **plasmalemma** (or plasma membrane), and may or may not have an internal limiting membrane, the **tonoplast,** separating the living material of the cell from a central aqueous **vacuole**. Within the limiting membranes of a eucaryotic cell (see p. 4) this living material consists of a **nucleus** (p. 81) surrounded by **cytoplasm**. The cytoplasm comprises particulate subunits of cellular function (organelles) such as **chloroplasts** (p. 169) and **mitochondria** (p. 160), together with membranous systems such as **Golgi bodies** (p. 155) and the **endoplasmic reticulum** (p. 115), systems of **fibrils** and **microtubules** (p. 99) and the surrounding **cytoplasmic matrix** with **ribosomes** (p. 115).* Cell inclusions (ergastic materials)include **crystals** of various substances, **carbohydrate reserves** (p. 185), droplets of **lipid, secretory products** and other inert matter.

As the following chapters on euglenoid cell components will illustrate, electron microscopy of sections has led to recognition of the importance of **membranes** in cell ultrastructure. With standard procedures of fixation (p. 203) nearly every transversely cut cytoplasmic membrane appears as two opaque lines separated from one another by a region of low electron density. This triple-layered structure is the **unit membrane** as defined by Robertson (1959). The opaque lines are a minimum of 20 Å in width and are thought to be each a protein layer one molecule thick, while the central region is 40 Å or more in width and is thought to be a bimolecular layer of lipid. This protein/lipid/protein sandwich was originally proposed as the possible composition of any cytoplasmic membrane by Davson and Danielli (1943; see Brown and Danielli, 1964; Robertson, 1964) but recent work (Moor and Mühlethaler, 1963) indicates that some membranes are more complex arrangements of assorted molecules which change in proportion and pattern to allow for changes in membrane permeability and activity. The mobile, fluid, continually changing membranous systems of the living cell provide a large surface area for the orderly array of the enzymes concerned with metabolic processes.

* Frey-Wyssling and Mühlethaler have proposed (1965) that the term "cytoplasm" be redefined to exclude mitochondria and plastids. The term "protoplasm," embodying the old concept of a homogeneous, structureless, colloidal system of living matter surrounding the cell nucleus, has no place in a modern cytological account.

In the pages which follow, the form and function of cell components are considered in general terms* and with particular reference to the euglenoid cell. Although in one sense terminology is quite precise, it will be seen that various structures cannot be dealt with independently; for example, the nuclear envelope is connected with cytoplasmic elements of the endoplasmic reticulum and is sometimes best regarded as part of the latter rather than as part of the nucleus. Even the basic distinction between "nucleus" and "cytoplasm" is more a matter of descriptive convenience than biological structure and function, since there is continuity of cytoplasm and nucleoplasm through the pores of the nuclear envelope and in most cells the delimitation of nucleus from cytoplasm regularly disappears at time of division. The structures and inclusions of the euglenoid cell to be discussed are the nucleus, pellicle, microtubules, muciferous bodies, endoplasmic reticulum, cytoplasmic matrix, ribosomes, canal, reservoir, flagella, photoreceptor, eyespot, contractile vacuole, alveolate vesicles, Golgi bodies, mitochondria, phospholipid vesicles, chloroplasts, pyrenoids, paramylon and the ingestion apparatus.

* Of many books giving a general introduction to cell structure and cell function, those by Loewy and Siekevitz (1963), McElroy (1964), Swanson (1964), Hurry (1965) and Paul (1965) are especially recommended.

Chapter 7

THE NUCLEUS

The distinguishing feature of the eucaryotic cell is possession of a nucleus, the organelle in which all or most of the cell's hereditary material is separated from the surrounding cytoplasm by a membranous envelope (see Table 1, p. 4; also Stanier and van Niel, 1962).

An interphase (non-dividing) nucleus typically consists of expanded chromosomes and a globular nucleolus lying in a matrix of nucleoplasm within a nuclear envelope. Chromosomes consist of deoxyribonucleic acid (DNA), ribonucleic acid (RNA) and proteins and are the repositories of the genetic information of the cell, coded in the DNA molecules. Nucleoli contain RNA and proteins and are thought to be concerned with protein synthesis and the transfer of genetic messages from nucleus to cytoplasm (see p. 115). Recent reviews of interphase nuclear structure and function have been made by Mirsky and Osawa (1961), Tschermak-Woess (1963), Moses (1964) and Frey-Wyssling and Mühlethaler (1965).

Nuclear division occurs mainly by mitosis or meiosis. In mitosis the chromosomes condense and undergo replication, sister chromatids (daughter chromosomes) thus formed segregate to opposite poles of the division figure, and two daughter nuclei are produced which are cytologically and genetically equivalent. In meiosis a complicated process of chromosome pairing, replication, exchange of segments and segregation results in the formation of four genetically different daughter nuclei, each of which has only half the chromosome number of the parent nucleus (fusion of nuclei in pairs restores the original number of chromosomes at a subsequent stage in the life cycle of the organism). In most examples so far studied, these patterns of chromosome behaviour are accompanied by breakdown of the nuclear envelope, dissolution of nucleoli and the formation of a spindle, which latter structure is thought to mediate the process in conjunction with specialised parts of the chromosomes, the centromeres. For detailed reviews of such "classical" mitosis and meiosis, the reader is referred to Mazia (1961), Rhoades (1961) and John and Lewis (1965).

The Interphase Euglenoid Nucleus

The interphase nucleus in euglenoid flagellates (Figs. 69, 70, 81, 97, 110, 131, 132, 137, 143, 144, 161) lies in the centre or posterior half of

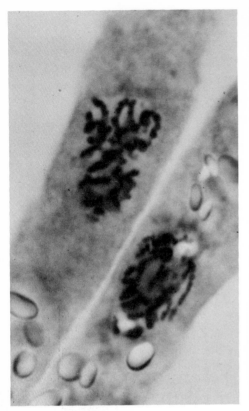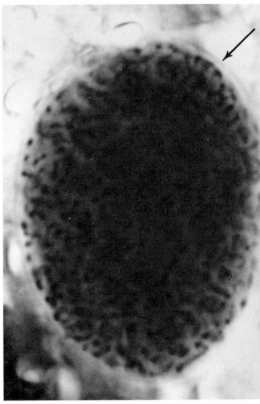

Fig. 69 Interphase nuclei in two cells of *Astasia klebsii,* showing the fully condensed chromosomes. × 3000.

Fig. 70 Interphase nucleus of *Euglena ehrenbergii,* showing the nuclear envelope (arrow), many filamentous chromosomes and numerous endosomes. × 3000.

the cell. It is spherical, ovoid or elongated and contains one or more endosomes ("nucleoli"; see p. 87). The chromosomes remain condensed and stainable throughout the nuclear cycle, appearing single or double, granular or uniformly filamentous in different species.

Electron microscopy shows the nuclear envelope* to consist of two irregularly contoured unit membranes (p. 79) separated by the perinuclear space (Figs. 72, 104) and traversed at intervals by circular pores of uniform size (Fig. 72). Tubular extensions of the outer unit membrane (Fig. 104) proliferate into the cytoplasmic matrix and connect the perinuclear space with other elements of the endoplasmic reticulum (p. 116). Chromosomes, endosomes and nucleoplasm appear as uninformative granular areas of differing electron density.

* To avoid ambiguity, the term "nuclear envelope" is used throughout the present account instead of the more usual light microscopist's term, "nuclear membrane."

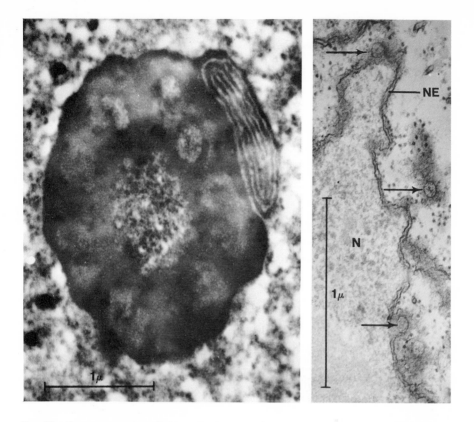

Fig. 71 Transverse section of the endosome of *Euglena gracilis*, with lateral lamellar body of unknown function. Electron micrograph, ×30,000.

Fig. 72 Section of the interphase nucleus (N) in *Euglena spirogyra*, showing the nuclear envelope (*NE*) and nuclear pores (*arrows*). Electron micrograph, ×50,000.

Euglenoid Mitosis

Until very recently, study of euglenoid mitosis has been confined to light microscopy of fixed and living nuclei (see Leedale, 1958b, for a review of the many papers on this subject). Electron microscopy of dividing cells has now added some preliminary information on possible mechanism (see p. 89), but nothing else. We must therefore begin with a survey of nuclear division in terms of classical cytology, based upon light microscopy of all the species so far studied. Such a survey indicates that idiosyncrasies of structure and behaviour exhibited by individual species do not invalidate the concept of a fundamentally similar process of nuclear division common to, and typical of, all euglenoid flagellates. As will be seen, this process has several unique features and, though the terms *prophase*, *metaphase*, *anaphase* and *telophase* have been retained for the stages of euglenoid mitosis as a matter of convenience, they must not be taken to imply the chromosome structure and arrangement found in "classical" mitosis.

The course of euglenoid mitosis

The first sign of approaching mitosis in a euglenoid cell is migration of the nucleus from its interphase position towards the anterior end of the organism. Electron microscopy indicates that some connection is established between the nucleus and the basal bodies of the flagella (p. 89).

During prophase the chromosomes become uniform in thickness and appear as a sphere of threads, tangled around the endosome (Fig. 73). The endosomes of polyendosomal nuclei (Figs. 70, 81) fuse to form a single body which will divide to give the endosomes of the daughter nuclei (see below). Exceptions to this rule are *Euglena acus, Euglena deses, Phacus pyrum* and *Pera-*

Fig. 73 Mitotic prophase in *Euglena gracilis*, with granular chromosomes surrounding the ovoid endosome. ×3000.

Fig. 74 *Euglena gracilis*: cell with the nucleus in mitotic metaphase, showing separated chromatids encircling the elongated endosome; note the delimitation of the nuclear region from the cytoplasm; the division axis runs horizontally in this and subsequent figures. ×3000.

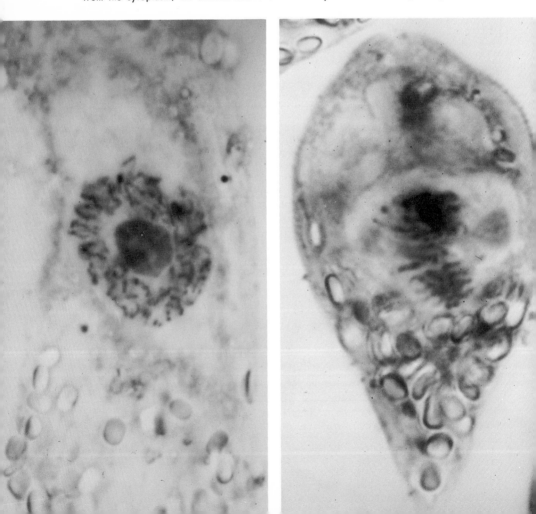

nema trichophorum, in which species the several endosomes often divide separately.

The endosome now elongates along the division axis (perpendicular to the long axis of the cell) while the chromosomes orientate into the metaphase position (Figs. 74, 75). This orientation occurs in one of three ways depending on the species:

(a) In *Astasia klebsii, Colacium mucronatum, Distigma proteus, Euglena acus, Euglena deses, Euglena spirogyra* and *Phacus pyrum,* orientation is of single chromosomes from prophase into a metaphase circlet. These chromosomes lie along the division axis, parallel to one another and to the now rod- or dumb-bell-shaped endosome, and in this position they undergo longitudinal replication to form pairs of chromatids. During anaphase the chromatids separate and segregate into the two daughter nuclei.

(b) In *Euglena gracilis* (Fig. 74), *Lepocinclis ovum* and *Peranema trichophorum* (Fig. 75), orientation is of pairs of chromatids from late prophase into a metaphase circlet of *single* chromatids, separation and segregation having occurred during orientation.

(c) In the third group of species, orientation is of pairs of chromatids (from interphase and prophase) into a metaphase circlet of such pairs, with segregation taking place during late metaphase and anaphase. This sequence occurs in *Euglena viridis, Eutreptia pertyi, Eutreptia viridis* and *Trachelomonas grandis.*

Separation, segregation and anaphase movement of the chromatids are staggered, some chromatids reaching the poles of the division figure while others are still at the equator (Fig. 76). During anaphase movement (Figs. 76-79), chromatids appear as rods, curves or U-shapes, with no constrictions which could be interpreted as centromeres. In species with obviously non-homologous chromosomes, sister chromatids can be seen segregating to opposite poles and into different daughter nuclei. This shows particularly well in species where there is one long chromosome (*Colacium mucronatum, Phacus pyrum;* Fig. 78).

Anaphase of euglenoid mitosis occupies from 47 to 86 minutes in different species (60 to 70 per cent of the total mitotic period) as compared with from one to 26 minutes in all other organisms and tissues for which records exist (2.5 to 22 per cent of the total mitotic period). The absolute velocity of the separating chromatids in anaphase varies between 0.06 and 0.15 μ per minute in different euglenoid species, compared with between 0.3 and 6.0 μ per minute for all other recorded material (Leedale, 1959b). The significance of these figures is discussed below (p. 89).

The end of anaphase is marked by a sudden flowing to the poles of the central region of the greatly elongated endosome (Figs. 77, 79). The two portions of the endosome round off to become daughter endosomes in the telophase nuclei. Adjustment of the nuclear material, in some species involving fragmentation of the endosome or even chromosome duplication into the chromatids of the *next* mitosis (*Eutreptia* spp., *Trachelomonas grandis*), restores the structure of the interphase nucleus typical for the species.

The nuclear envelope apparently persists throughout euglenoid mitosis

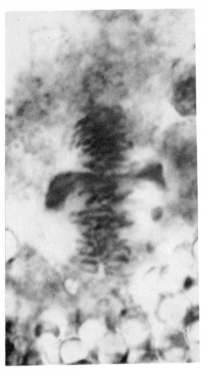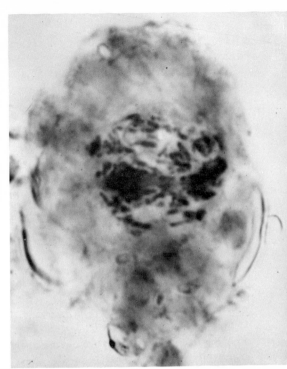

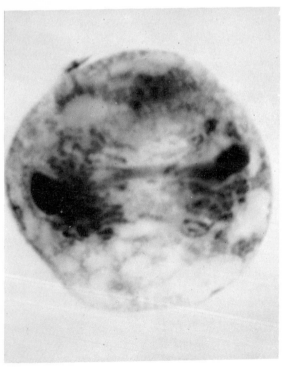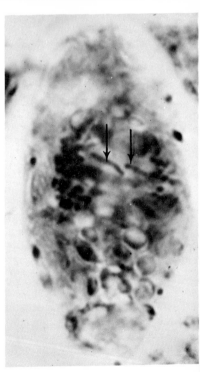

(see Fig. 74, for example) and, at the end of anaphase, the inner surfaces of the envelope presumably meet in the mid-region of the elongated nucleus and seal around the daughter nuclei.

Homology and function of the endosome

Endosomes are similar to nucleoli in their shape and position in the interphase nucleus (Figs. 70, 81, 131, 132, 137), in their ability to fuse and fragment, in their staining affinities, in being Feulgen-negative (thereby showing the absence of DNA) and in containing RNA (as shown by the Unna Pappenheim reaction correlated with nuclease treatment; see Leedale, 1958b). Endosomes differ from nucleoli in persisting and dividing during mitosis (Figs. 73, 74-79), in their retention of (at least some) RNA during mitosis and in apparently not being associated with particular (nucleolar-organising) chromosomes.

Most evidence suggests that the endosome divides passively during mitosis without organising or controlling the process. Colchicine (in any concentration up to saturation) and other recognised spindle inhibitors have no effect upon the euglenoid mitotic process; ionizing radiations at non-lethal (100,000 r)* or lethal (300,000 r) doses do no apparent damage to the endosome or the chromosomes. It remains to be seen whether a spiralled lamellar body which is borne laterally on the endosome of *Euglena gracilis* (Fig. 71) has any function during division.

The nature and mechanism of euglenoid mitosis

It has been shown in the preceding account that euglenoid nuclear division *does* fulfill the essential criteria of mitosis in that individualised chromosomes replicate longitudinally and sister chromatids segregate to opposite poles and into different daughter nuclei. The absence of such attributes of "classical" mitosis as breakdown of the nuclear envelope, dissolution of nucleoli, formation of spindle and possession of centromeres does not prevent recognition of the euglenoid division as a mitotic process.

Euglenoid chromosomes show no cytological or behavioural evidence for the presence of "conventional" centromeres. Evidence for the absence of a

* Fast electrons from a van de Graff generator; Wichterman (1961) reports the LD50 value (dose to kill 50 per cent of a population) with X-irradiation to be 32,000 r for *Euglena gracilis*, with no survival at doses above 55,000 r.

Fig. 75 Metaphase/early anaphase of mitosis in *Peranema trichophorum*, with an equatorial belt of chromatids encircling the dumb-bell-shaped endosome. ×3000.

Fig. 76 *Phacus pyrum*: cell with the nucleus in mitotic anaphase, showing the chromatids spread between the poles as a result of staggered chromatid segregation. ×3000.

Fig. 77 Late mitotic anaphase in *Euglena gracilis*: note the greatly elongated endosome. ×3000.

Fig. 78 *Colacium mucronatum*: cell with the nucleus in late anaphase of mitosis, showing sister chromatids of the long chromosome (arrows) moving to opposite poles. ×3000.

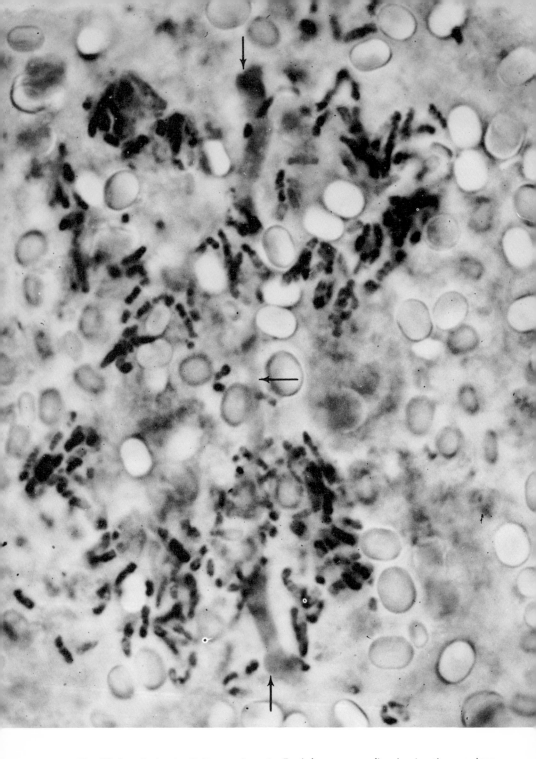

Fig. 79 Squashed out mitotic anaphase in *Trachelomonas grandis*, showing the very long endosome (*arrows*); the division axis runs vertically in this figure. ×3000.

spindle is provided by the lack of inhibition of euglenoid mitosis by colchicine, the staggering of anaphase movement, the long duration of anaphase and the low chromatid velocity during anaphase. However, preliminary results from electron microscopy of dividing cells (Blum, Sommer and Kahn, 1965) provide evidence that spindle elements of some sort *are* present. Mitotic nuclei contain a group or groups of fibrils or microtubules (see p. 99), though the relation between these and "conventional" spindle elements (see, for example, Manton, 1964a) is uncertain. Experimental evidence and light microscopy strongly indicate that a "normal" spindle mechanism is *not* operating in euglenoid mitosis, but electron microscopy introduces the possibility of a related (perhaps primitive) mechanism.

In the apparent absence of centromeres and "conventional" spindle, I originally suggested (Leedale, 1958a; 1958b) that endosome division and chromosome movements are autonomous in euglenoid flagellates, the several forms of chromosome orientation and segregation being due to differences in the timing of initiation of a mutual repulsion between sister chromatids. The extent to which this theory must be modified will not be clear until the detailed fine structure of the various stages of euglenoid mitosis has been investigated by high resolution electron microscopy. It is tempting to cite the anterior migration of the nucleus as evidence that the flagellar basal bodies act as centrioles (see p. 128), especially since the first electron micrographs suggest the necessary structural relation with the "spindle" fibrils or microtubules. Further studies are needed to discover how this is established, and here it must be remembered that mitosis is structurally in progress as the nucleus is moving towards the anterior end of the cell. The easy migration of nuclei from one daughter cell to the other during cleavage (p. 104) argues against there being any permanent connection between the nucleus and basal bodies. Correlation of all the present evidence introduces the intriguing possibility that the euglenoid spindle is doing little other than determining the division axis, with chromosome movement largely autonomous.

The significance of euglenoid mitosis

Peculiar departures from "classical" mitosis are found in various other protista (Grell, 1964) and excursions into the cytology of less common organisms are showing more and more that "classical" mitosis is not necessarily "normal" mitosis. The peculiarities of the euglenoid process are most closely reflected in the division recorded for some dinoflagellates (Dodge, 1963; see p. 3) and for the somatic nuclei of many fungi (Robinow, 1962). The phyletic significance of this must not be overemphasised, but a passing reference to the suggestion that the lower fungi are derived from flagellates (see Martin, 1955) is not out of place.

The possibly primitive nature of euglenoid mitosis may reflect the great relative age of the group, but the most biologically significant feature of the process is perhaps its demonstration of what seems to be a high degree of autonomous chromosome activity. This may well be a more important phenomenon in the mechanism of "classical" mitosis that hitherto supposed.

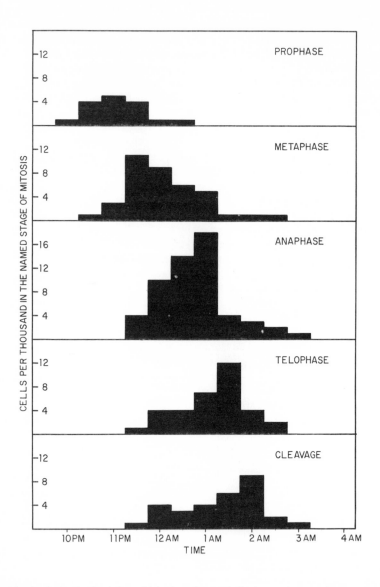

Fig. 80 Analysis of mitosis in a biphasic culture of *Euglena spirogyra* during one night, with onset of darkness at 8 P. M.: note how a wave of prophase is followed by waves of metaphase, anaphase, telophase and cell cleavage, but that some cells are still entering prophase when others are completing division; the maxima recorded for the stages of mitosis reflect their relative duration (see text).

The periodicity of euglenoid mitosis

Green species of euglenoid flagellates growing in biphasic culture with a natural day/night cycle have mitosis confined to the dark period (Leedale, 1959a). Mitosis begins one to two hours after the onset of darkness and successive maxima of the mitotic stages occur (Fig. 80). Unlike the endogenous mitotic rhythms recorded for many higher plants (see Leedale, 1959a), the euglenoid rhythm appears to be exogenous, since growth in continuous light or continuous darkness causes an immediate cessation of mitosis in bi-

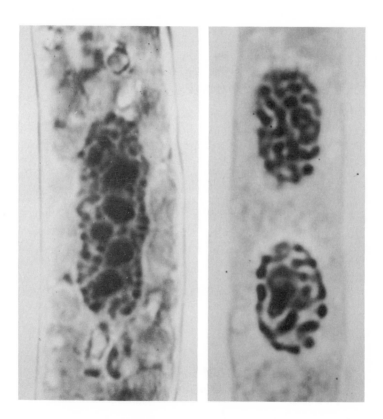

Fig. 81 Interphase nucleus of *Euglena acus*, with granular chromosomes and several large endosomes. × 3000.

Fig. 82 *Euglena acus*: cell with two "half-nuclei" in interphase, the products of amitosis (see text). × 3000.

phasic culture, and growth of *Euglena gracilis* in an organic medium (see p. 201) results in rapid mitosis at a constant rate. Colourless species in biphasic culture under any light regime show non-rhythmic mitotic periodicity.

The rapid mitosis of species growing heterotrophically in liquid media can be synchronised by means of various 24 hour light or temperature cycles (see review by Padilla and James, 1964), a valuable attribute for physiologi-cal studies (Cook, 1961; Wilson and James, 1963; James, 1965). In synchro-nised cultures of *Astasia longa* (Blum and Padilla, 1962) and *Euglena gracilis* Z (Edmunds, 1964) it has been shown that, as in most higher organisms, DNA content per cell doubles stepwise in the few hours prior to mitosis. This indi-cates the actual period of chromosome replication, and such studies are of great interest in relation to the observed cytological events.

Amitosis

Amitosis is the division of a nucleus without the emergence, orientation and division of individualised chromosomes. Such "direct" division of nuclei takes place in many plant and animal tissues (Bucher, 1959) and valid rec-ords of a similar process exist for *Euglenamorpha hegneri* (Wenrich, 1924) and for *Euglena acus*, *Euglena spirogyra* and *Euglena viridis* (Leedale, 1959c).

In the *Euglena* species the process is a nuclear fragmentation not connected with cell division, the usual product being a cell with two "half-nuclei" (Fig. 82; compare with Fig. 81). The fragmentation seems to be a response to unfavourable conditions of growth, and its function is perhaps to increase the ratio of nuclear surface area to nuclear volume.

The binucleate cell is capable of subsequent mitosis in *Euglena acus* and *Euglena spirogyra*, the "half-nuclei" dividing simultaneously (Fig. 83). Cell cleavage produces two binucleate cells, though occasional miscleavage results in a cell with one "half-nucleus" and a cell with three "half-nuclei." These cells are viable, and their progeny retain the characteristics of the species, despite having much less (or much more) than the normal comple-ment of chromosomes. This suggests that these species of *Euglena* have a fairly high degree of polyploidy. The chromosome number in *Euglena spirogyra* is 86; the dividing "half-nuclei" (Fig. 83) contain 40 to 45 chromosomes each.

Euglenoid Meiosis

Meiosis has generally been regarded as lacking in euglenoid flagellates and the absence of sexuality quoted as a euglenoid characteristic. The few ac-counts of conjugation and gamete formation in *Euglena* (reviewed in Leedale, 1962) are unsubstantiated and, although a conjugation of individuals is known for *Scytomonas* (see Mignot, 1962, for a recent account), there are doubts about the affinities of this genus.

In 1937, Krichenbauer described nuclear figures in *Phacus pyrum* which he interpreted as stages in meiosis. He suggested that this followed an auto-gamy (the refusion of two nuclei which are the mitotic products of one cell). Nuclear figures recently found in *Hyalophacus ocellatus* (Leedale, 1962) sup-port the validity of Krichenbauer's observations. The chromatin of these *Hyalophacus* figures (Fig. 84) consists of approximately 90 pairs of minute rods which are very much shorter than the mitotic chromosomes. Since the chromosome number of *Hyalophacus ocellatus* counted at mitosis is 92, it seems that the contents of two nuclei are here combined. Other cells of *Hyalophacus* contain large granular nuclei with much the same appearance as those

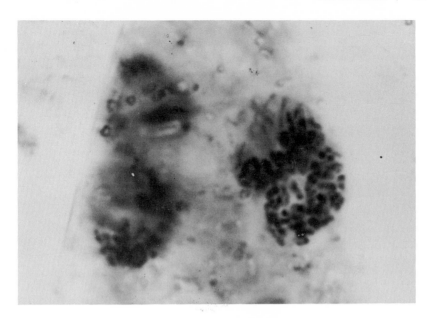

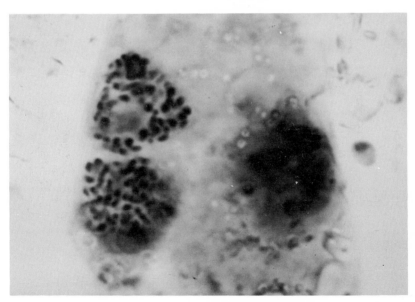

Figs. 83(a), 83(b) Two focal levels of late anaphase of the "double" mitosis in a binucleate cell of *Euglena spirogyra*: note the four groups of chromatids. ×3000.

figured for *Phacus* as "early prophase," and Krichenbauer also saw cells containing two nuclei (one smaller and denser than the other), possible first and second anaphases of the supposed meiotic process and cleavage into four daughter cells.

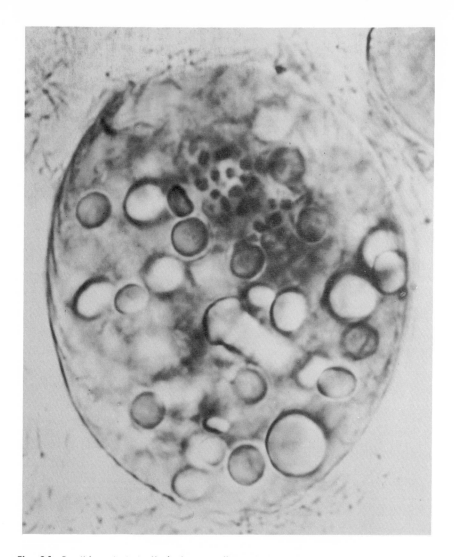

Fig. 84 Possible meiosis in *Hyalophacus ocellatus*, showing pairs of minute chromatinic rods in the anterior half of the cell (see text). ×3000.

If the nucleus containing short, paired, chromatinic rods is a stage in euglenoid meiosis, then the chromosome counts in *Hyalophacus* suggest that it is following autogamy or sexual fusion of gamete nuclei rather than preceding the formation of gametes. That is, as Krichenbauer maintained for *Phacus*, the reduction division is occurring immediately after fusion in the zygote nucleus, and the vegetative cell is thus haploid. Despite the high chromosome number, the absence of multivalents in the division figure (Fig. 84) argues against a polyploid condition such as has been suggested for certain species of

Euglena. It is therefore relevant to note here that the *single* long chromosome (p. 85) in the nuclei of *Phacus pyrum* and *Colacium mucronatum* (both with approximately 35 chromosomes) is good evidence for a haploid condition in these species also.

It is clear that if meiosis does occur in the euglenoid flagellates it does so as a rare phenomenon, possibly in response to poor growth conditions. Cell behaviour associated with cyst formation and "germination" (p. 114) should perhaps be investigated in search of further evidence. It may be anticipated that euglenoid meiosis will be as peculiar in form and as specific to this group of flagellates as is the mitosis.

Chapter 8

THE PELLICLE

The nature of the euglenoid pellicle has been a topic of interest among cytologists for many years, particularly in relation to the characteristic flowing activity of the cell known as euglenoid movement (Figs. 2, 22; see p. 99). Stein (1878) first suggested that the helical striations of the pellicle (periplast) act as muscle fibres, but, in fact, some of the most violently contorting species have the most delicate pellicular striations. This apparent contradiction has had to await electron microscopy for explanation. Modern studies on the structure and chemistry of the euglenoid pellicle have recently been collated (Leedale, 1964) and are outlined in possible relation to function in the following pages.

Organisation of the Pellicle: Associated Organelles

The longitudinal helices of the pellicular striations are readily visible on living cells of most euglenoid flagellates, though they are more easily studied in cells from which the contents have been burst (Fig. 85). Total disruption of the cell causes the pellicle to dissociate along the striations into flat strips of material which have a thickened edge and a thinner flange (Fig. 86).

Electron microscopy of sectioned cells confirms that the pellicle consists of flat interlocking strips which pass helically along the cell. The strips are intracellular structures lying immediately beneath the plasmalemma, a continuous tripartite membrane 80 to 100 Å thick (Figs. 87, 165). Thus the pellicle is *not* equivalent to a cell wall, since the latter is always laid down outside the plasmalemma.

In *Euglena spirogyra* each pellicular strip has an elaborate cross-sectional shape (Fig. 87), the significant feature of which is a continuous ridge which faces outwards and articulates in a groove running along the overlapping edge of the next strip. Surface replicas of entire pellicles show that the troughs between adjacent strips start as a whorl at the posterior end of the cell (Fig. 89), bifurcate a few times before passing helically along the length of the cell and then meet again as they reach the canal opening (Fig. 88). The strips of pellicle curve over and continue into the canal, and sections of the canal and posterior spine suggest that the strips fuse into one another at both ends of the cell. In different genera, pellicular strips vary considerably in thickness, shape and, probably, details of articulation (compare Figs.

96

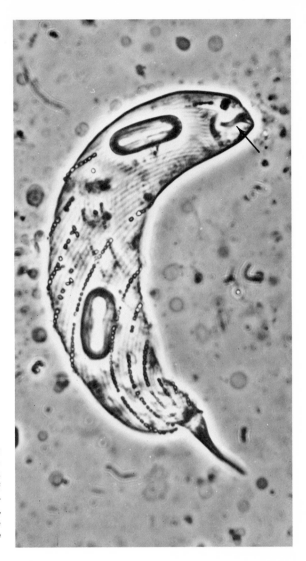

Fig. 85 Pellicle of *Euglena spirogyra*, showing the striations, a few rows of warts and the pellicular lining of the canal (*arrow*); cell contents have been removed, except for the two large paramylon granules. Phase contrast, ×1500.

87, 165 and 173), but the form of construction described above is found in all euglenoids so far examined.

Correlated electron and light microscopy reveals that certain structures occur in regular association with the pellicle. Parallel with each pellicular strip is a row of muciferous (mucilage-producing) bodies (Figs. 87, 98, 111, 165, 173) from which narrow canals pass to the groove and thence to the exterior (Figs. 87, 98). Microtubules, 200 to 250 Å in diameter, are also arranged parallel to each pellicular strip (Figs. 87, 165, 173), numbers and distribution varying in different species. The possible significance of these structures in relation to euglenoid movement is considered below.

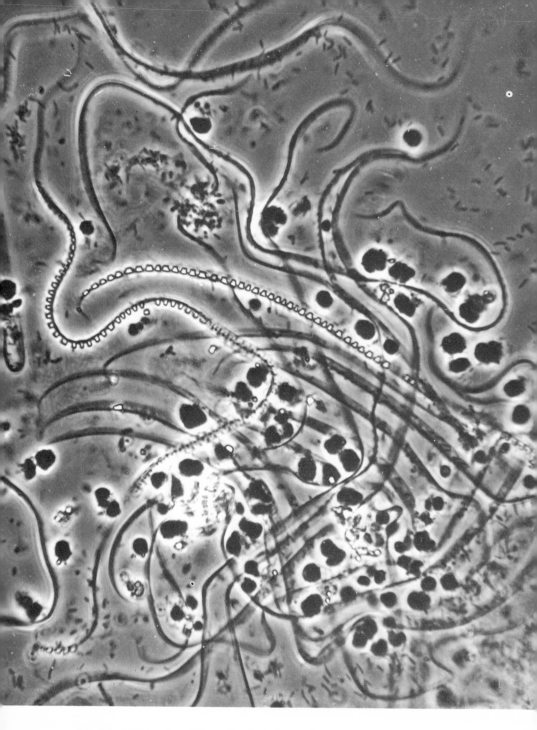

Fig. 86 Pellicle of a living cell of *Euglena spirogyra* var. *fusca*, dissociated into its component strips by sudden pressure; the pellicular warts are seen to be attached to just two of the strips; the large dense bodies are chloroplasts. Phase contrast, ×1750.

Some euglenoid flagellates have a rigid pellicle, whereas others have pellicular flexibility which allows the cell to undergo flowing movements when not swimming. This flowing activity (Figs. 2, 22) is known as euglenoid movement* and is especially violent in the genera *Eutreptia*, *Distigma* and *Peranema*. Semi-rigid cells, such as *Euglena spirogyra*, exhibit sluggish euglenoid movement when stationary but return to a fixed shape for swimming, thus indicating that the pellicular strips are both flexible and elastic.

Barras and Stone (1965) have determined the chemical composition of isolated pellicle of *Euglena gracilis* var. *bacillaris*: 80 per cent protein, 11.6 per cent lipid and 6.4 or 17 per cent carbohydrate (according to the method of analysis). Since the material presumably consists of pellicular strips and associated cytoplasmic structures, this result agrees with earlier observations (Klebs, 1883; Hamburger, 1911; Chadefaud, 1937; Pigon, 1947) that the euglenoid pellicle is largely protein with no cellulose and it seems reasonable to suggest that the strips may contain a protein of the fibrous elastic group, something akin to keratin. When more is known about the detailed chemistry of the pellicle, the surface architecture of individual strips (Fig. 90) may become interpretable in relation to elasticity and flexibility.

Observations on living cells of *Euglena spirogyra* show that a certain amount of relative sideways movement is possible between one pellicular strip and the next. This is presumably accomplished by the ridge sliding in the groove, together with some compression and stretching of the pellicular material. One possible function of the muciferous bodies, considering their position and the path of their canals, may, therefore, be to supply mucilage to the articulations as a lubricant. If this is so, it should be noted that it is an intracellular release of mucilage, since the whole of the pellicular system lies *within* the plasma membrane. Presumably in rigid cells the interlocking strips have no flexibility and are firmly cemented together (by modified mucilage?); some difference in the chemistry or ultrastructure of the pellicular material is indicated, but no information is available on this at present.

Sliding of pellicular strips against one another operates in cell bending but is insufficient, of course, to explain more violent euglenoid movement. Pringsheim has suggested (1956) that the latter may be an expression of cytoplasmic flow restricted within the confines of an elastic pellicle of definite shape (see Jahn and Bovee, 1964). One would then expect species which show the most intense euglenoid movement to have the thinner pellicular strips, and this is so in species of *Astasia*, *Euglena*, *Eutreptia* and *Peranema*.

There is no evidence that the microtubules associated with the pellicle are concerned in euglenoid movement. Indeed, their abundance in rigid cells (for example, *Entosiphon*, Fig. 173) and their relation to the microtubules of the canal and reservoir (p. 121) suggest a skeletal or transporting function more readily than a contractile one. Microtubules with a diameter of 200 to 300 Å are proving to be components of many cell types and organisms

* The phenomenon is often referred to as "metaboly" (*Metabolie*, Klebs, 1883) but, as suggested elsewhere (Leedale, Meeuse and Pringsheim, 1965), this ambiguous term is best avoided.

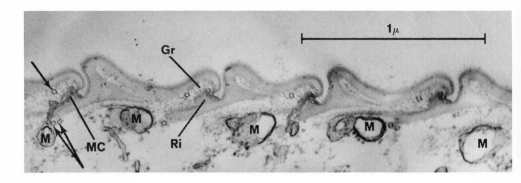

Fig. 87 Pellicle of *Euglena spirogyra*, sectioned transversely to several pellicular strips: note the ridge (Ri) of one strip articulating in the groove (Gr) of the next; note also the associated structures, the muciferous bodies (M) with canals (MC) passing to the grooves, and microtubules (arrows); the tripartite plasmalemma lies externally to the entire pellicular complex. Electron micrograph, × 50,000.

(see Slautterback, 1963, for references), occurring in positions in the cell where they can be related to cytoplasmic or cell movement, or to a possible requirement for intracellular support or transport.

Ornamentation

Pellicular ornamentation occurs in a number of euglenoids, notably in species of *Phacus* and of the *Euglena spirogyra* complex. The process is related to envelope formation in *Trachelomonas* and stalk formation in *Colacium*, phenomena which are dealt with elsewhere (p. 110).

In *Euglena spirogyra* ornamentation takes the form of warts or lumps arranged in rows along some of the pellicular strips (Figs. 85, 86, 91). The warts contain a large proportion of ferric hydroxide (Klebs, 1883; Lefèvre, 1932), and the degree of pellicular ornamentation depends upon the availability of ferric iron and manganese in the habitat (Leedale, Meeuse and Pringsheim, 1965). Electron microscopy shows that the warts lie outside the plasmalemma (Fig. 92), approximately the same distance apart as the canals from the muciferous bodies (Fig. 98). The form of ornamentation may, therefore, be due to inorganic deposition on gradually accumulating areas of mucilage near the muciferous pores. Why this should occur in *Euglena spirogyra* and not in other species of *Euglena* is yet one more euglenoid mystery.

Figs. 88 and **89**   Carbon/platinum replicas of the anterior (Fig. 88) and posterior (Fig. 89) ends of a cell of *Euglena pisciformis*: at the anterior, some pellicular striations show a bifurcation where they curve over into the canal; at the posterior end, the striations arise in a whorl and bifurcate several times before passing helically along the cell; the replicas show an S-helix, hence the true direction is a Z-helix; note accumulations of mucilage along the striations. Electron micrographs, × 15,000.

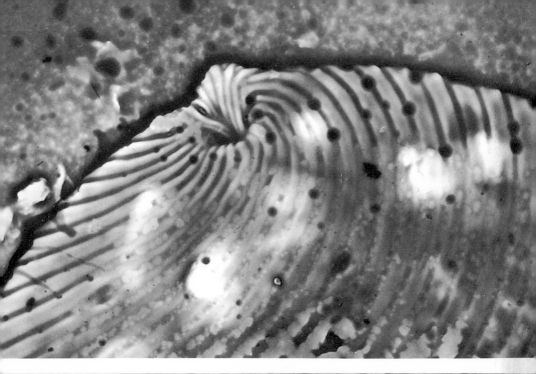

1μ

101

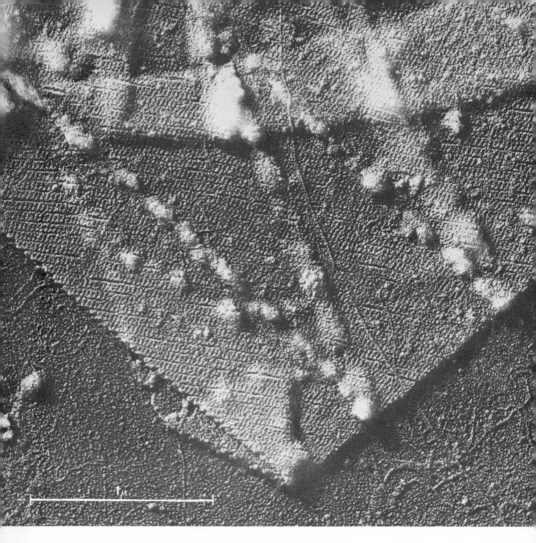

Fig. 90 Pellicle of *Distigma gracile* Pringsheim 1942: shadowcast preparation of a minute portion of pellicle, showing the surface architecture. Electron micrograph, ×50,000.

Cell Symmetry

The helical (screw) symmetry characteristic of the euglenoid cell is most clearly exhibited by the pellicle and the immediately underlying cyto-plasmic structures (muciferous bodies, microtubules and the chloroplasts in some species). In nearly all euglenoid flagellates the pellicle has a left-handed (S) helix (counter-clockwise as seen from the posterior end of the cell), but *Euglena oxyuris* Schmarda 1846 provides a rare example of a species

Fig. 91 Pellicle of an ornamented cell of *Euglena spirogyra* var. *fusca*: the two large paramylon granules are still inside the cell; liberated chloroplasts are swelling in the surrounding water. Phase contrast, ×1500.

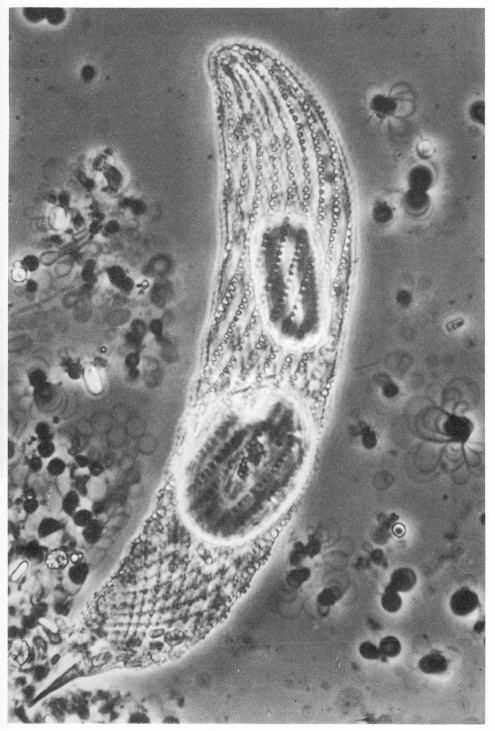

which always has a right-handed (Z) helix. *Euglena spirogyra* is peculiar (uniquely so in my experience) in showing a non-random variability of this feature; 70 to 95 per cent of the cells in a culture have striations tracing a left-handed (S) helix, and 5 to 30 per cent of the cells show a right-handed (Z) helix. Experiments with clonal cultures prove that this typically proportioned mixture arises from a single cell and the helical pitch must, therefore, be adjustable, probably at cell cleavage. Occasionally an adjustment must be sufficient to produce a change in helical direction, but why more cells are "left-handed" than "right-handed" and why the variability is confined to one species of *Euglena* remain unsolved mysteries.

In addition to their helical symmetry, many euglenoid species also show bilateral symmetry. This is often apparent in a flattening of the cell, in the subapical opening of the canal (on the side termed "ventral" by some authors) and in the position of the contractile vacuole, flagellar bases, eyespot and ingestion apparatus. Pochmann (1953) believes that the euglenoid cell is fundamentally bilateral and that the helical symmetry is secondarily imposed. Alternative views are that bilaterality is imposed on a primary helical symmetry (p. 72) or that the orders of symmetry have a more complex interrelation than one merely transforming the other (Picken, 1960). Replicas of entire pellicles do not settle the issue, some showing a posterior whorl of striations which can be interpreted as originating from a short bilateral axis (Leedale, 1964), others clearly showing a single whorl of striations arising from a point (Fig. 89).

Cell Cleavage and Pellicular Growth

Following mitosis and replication of the organelles associated with the locomotor apparatus (pp. 84, 140, 143), cell cleavage begins with an inpushing of the periplast at the anterior end of the cell between the openings of the two daughter canals. The cleavage line progresses helically backwards between the daughter reservoirs and nuclei (Fig. 93), following the helix of the pellicle until two cells are formed with a narrow connection at their posterior ends. This part of the cleavage process takes from five minutes to more than an hour, according to the species (Leedale, 1959b), but the breaking of the posterior connection may take very much longer.

In genera with an elastic pellicle, the cleavage process is accompanied by intense euglenoid movement, and there is a continuous pouring back and forth of cytoplasm across the connection from one cell to the other. This involves movement of mitochondria, chloroplasts, paramylon and even the daughter nuclei. When the walls of the posterior connection finally meet, partition of the organelles is usually equal, such that the two cells formed are identical in size and content. Occasionally, unequal distribution results in one cell receiving nearly all the mitochondria, chloroplasts and paramylon. Very rarely, one cell receives all the chloroplasts (see p. 000) or both daughter nuclei (Leedale, 1959d).

This account, based upon light microscopy of living cells, tells us little about the behaviour of the pellicle during cell division. Pochmann's analysis (1953) of cleavage in *Phacus* depends upon his contention that the pellicle

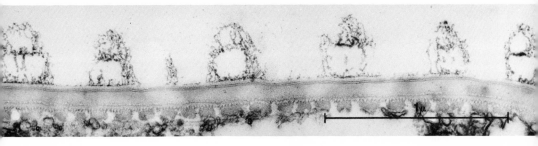

Fig. 92 Wart-bearing pellicular strip of *Euglena spirogyra* in median longitudinal section, showing the warts on a layer outside the plasmalemma; most of the material composing the warts has been dissolved away during processing. Electron micrograph, ×50,000.

Fig. 93 Cell cleavage in *Euglena deses:* note the daughter eyespots (*arrows*) at the anterior ends. ×1000.

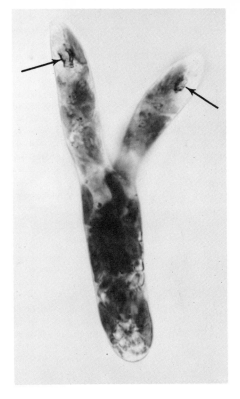

consists of independent co-axial closed loops (*"Intergyren"*), cemented or grooved together by other loops (*"Gyren"*) which are the striations visible in the light microscope. However, electron microscopy shows that the striations are lines of junction and articulation between pellicular strips and not interposed structures. Furthermore, the reduction in number of strips to a few at both ends of the cell disproves Pochmann's idea of independent closed loops of pellicle.

The main period of pellicular growth is probably immediately after cell cleavage. If a living cell is burst open along one striation, the empty pellicle can be flattened out to show that wide strips are separated from one another by narrower ones in regular sequence (Fig. 94), suggesting that the pellicle has grown by the laying down of new strips between older ones. Thus light

105

Fig. 94 Pellicle of *Euglena spirogyra*, opened along one striation and flattened out to show the internal surface; the striations are arranged in pairs of pairs (see text). Anoptral contrast, ×1000.

Fig. 95 Cleavage monster of *Euglena deses*, with sixteen "heads." ×600.

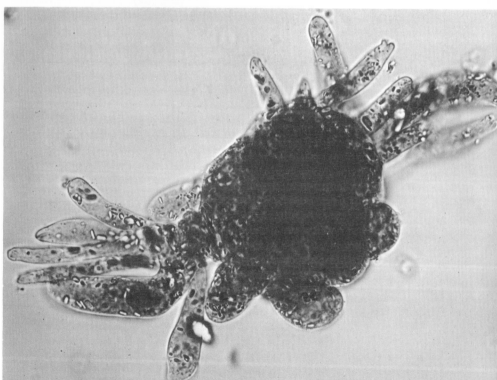

microscopy supports the older idea of pellicular growth by intussusception, whereas electron microscopy of sectioned cells suggests that the pellicular strips actually divide. The appearance of surface replicas can be explained by either interpretation, and the resolution of this apparent conflict must await further observations on growing cells. Another problem requiring elucidation by modern methods is the frequent departures from normal patterns of growth and cleavage which produce many types of monster cell and complex examples of multiple fission (Fig. 95).

Chapter 9

MUCIFEROUS BODIES

Subpellicular bodies containing mucilage occur in all species of euglenoid flagellates and can be demonstrated in living cells by application of dilute vital stains such as neutral red, cresyl blue or ruthenium red. Where the bodies are large and of characteristic shape, they are readily seen in untreated living cells as helical rows parallel to the pellicular striations (Fig. 96). Staining reactions show the mucilage to be a water-soluble mucopolysaccharide, but its exact chemical nature has not been investigated.

The muciferous (mucigenic) bodies have been variously interpreted (see Gojdics, 1953; Pringsheim, 1956) as part of a vacuolar system or as being homologous with the trichocysts of ciliates. Although it is true that lumps of mucilage can be ejected from the muciferous bodies (Fig. 97), electron micro-

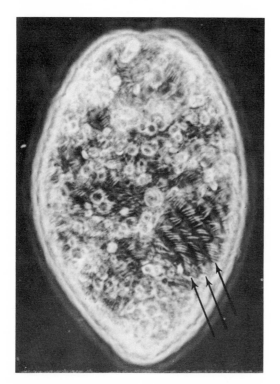

Fig. 96 Helical rows of fusiform muciferous bodies (*arrows*, etc.) in a living cell of *Euglena magnifica*. Anoptral contrast, ×1000.

scopy shows that they do not have the complex organisation of trichocysts (for a discussion of which see Pitelka, 1963). Mignot (1963) has shown batteries of organelles in *Entosiphon sulcatum* which do have fine structure reminiscent of trichocysts (Fig. 174), and it is significant that these are present *in addition to* normal small muciferous bodies. Electron microscopy of species of *Astasia*, *Colacium*, *Euglena*, *Eutreptia* and *Trachelomonas* has shown the muciferous bodies to be the peripheral elements of the endoplasmic reticulum (see pp. 7, 116 and Figs. 87, 98, 111, 165), opening to the outside of the cell through pores of regular disposition (Fig. 98).

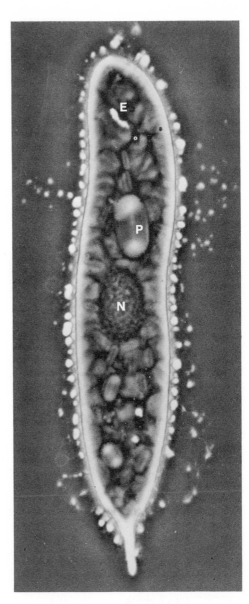

Fig. 97 *Euglena spirogyra:* living cell showing discharge of muciferous bodies; the cell is surrounded by large lumps of mucilage; other cell components visible are the eyespot (E), the nucleus (N), a large paramylon granule (P), and numerous chloroplasts and small paramylon granules. Anoptral contrast, ×1500.

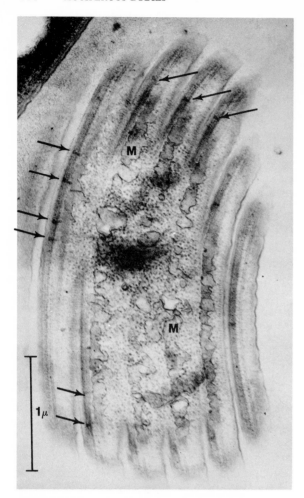

Fig. 98 Glancing section of *Euglena gracilis*, showing the helical rows of closely packed muciferous bodies (M) immediately beneath the pellicle; muciferous canals which pass through the pellicular strips are cut in longitudinal section (*arrows*). Electron micrograph, × 30,000.

Mucilage secretion occurs in all euglenoid flagellates, and living cells are permanently coated with a thin slime layer. This sometimes accumulates at the posterior end of the cell as a trailer of slime, and some species have the habit of sticking to a substratum by their "tails." Species with large muciferous bodies eject the contents on irritation and produce a copious slime sheath around the cell; species previously described as lacking muciferous bodies are now being shown to have small ones which cannot form conspicuous amounts of slime.

The envelopes and stalks of *Colacium* (Figs. 36, 37, 99, 165) are organised products of mucilage secretion. The envelopes of species of *Trachelomonas* (Figs. 26-30, 100) and, presumably, *Strombomonas*, *Klebsiella* and *Ascoglena* (Figs. 31-35) are built up by inorganic deposition on a foundation of mucilaginous threads (Figs. 101, 102). In all these cases there has presumably been some alteration in the solubility characteristics of the mucilage. Pringsheim

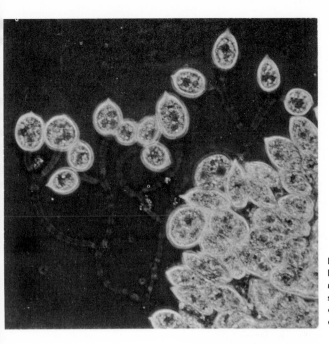

Fig. 99 The edge of a living colony of *Colacium mucronatum*, showing the striated mucilaginous stalks of attached cells. Anoptral contrast, × 500.

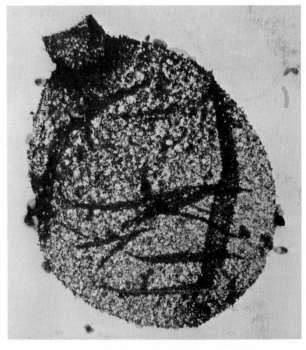

Fig. 100 Envelope of *Trachelomonas bulla* (Stein 1878) Deflandre 1926. Electron micrograph, × 3000.

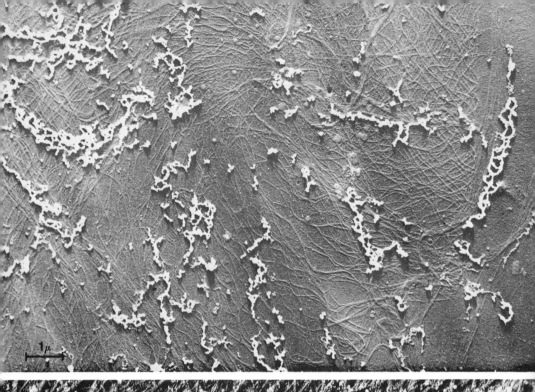

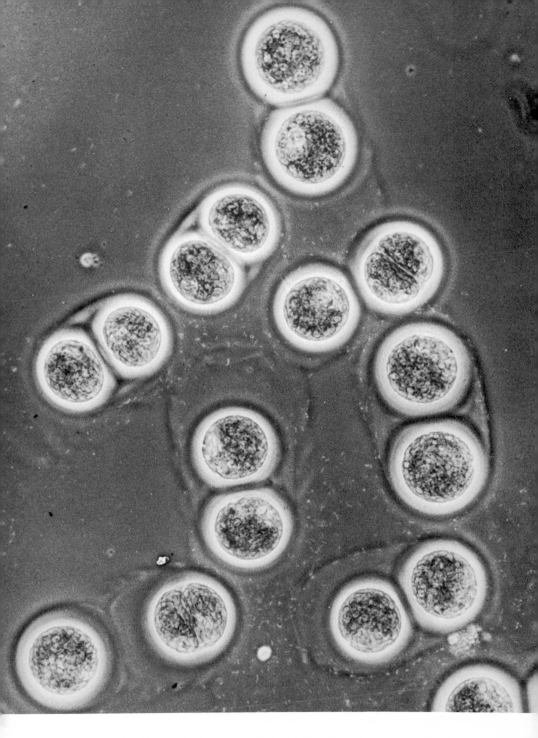

Figs. 101 and **102** (Opposite) Highly magnified details of envelope construction in *Trachelomonas bulla*: Fig. 101 shows the foundation of mucilage threads, with inorganic deposition just beginning; Fig. 102 shows the orientated threads of mucilage and heavier deposition in an older envelope. Electron micrographs, ×10,000 (Fig. 101) and ×30,000 (Fig. 102).

Fig. 103 (Above) Palmella of *Euglena proxima*. Anoptral contrast, ×400.

(1953b) has shown that the thickness and degree of ornamentation of the envelope in species of *Trachelomonas* depend upon the availability of reduced iron and manganese (as do the warts of *Euglena spirogyra*, p. 100). The taxonomy of the genus must therefore be based upon all features of cell organisation (particularly chloroplasts and pyrenoids, p. 36) and not on the envelope alone.

Another function of mucilage secretion is the formation of cysts and palmelloid colonies. Cysts are formed by species of various genera (notably *Distigma* and *Euglena*), presumably as a means of surviving unfavourable periods. The cell rounds off and secretes a thick sheath of mucilage, often with successively added concentric layers which harden after formation. This may survive for months until the cell emerges by cracking the cyst. In conditions of partial desiccation or excessive light the slime sheath sometimes acts as a temporary cyst, cells emerging from the sheath as soon as conditions revert to normal. In certain species (especially of *Eutreptia* and *Euglena*) cell division within the slime sheath leads to the formation of palmellae (Fig. 103), which may become extensive sheets of cells covering many square feet of mud surface.

Chapter 10

ENDOPLASMIC RETICULUM, RIBOSOMES

AND CYTOPLASMIC MATRIX

The endoplasmic reticulum (ER) is an intricate system of membrane-limited cavities extending throughout the cytoplasmic matrix of most eucary-otic cells. Electron microscopy indicates that the cavities are in continuity with one another and with the nuclear envelope, which is, therefore, properly regarded as part of the system. Elements of the ER are termed "rough" (granular) if their membranes carry ribosomes on the outer surfaces and "smooth" (agranular) if ribosomes are absent. Ribosomes are angular particles of ribonucleoprotein, 100 to 200 Å in diameter.

Functions of the endoplasmic reticulum are for the most part poorly understood. Cytochemical studies (mainly on mammalian cells) support suggestions that the system provides channels for intracellular transport of metabolites while the extensive membrane surfaces provide sites for orderly enzyme localisation. There is good evidence that rough ER is involved in protein synthesis, since ribosomes are considered to be the primary sites of this activity in the cell. It is thought that ribosomes are the cytoplasmic recipients of "messenger RNA," which carries genetic information from the nucleus. The ribosomes thereby become "coded" to act as templates for the synthesis of specific proteins from amino acid residues brought to the ribosomes by "transfer RNA" (see Barry, 1964; Hartman and Suskind, 1965; Frey-Wyssling and Mühlethaler, 1965; for concise accounts of this theory). There is also circumstantial evidence for the involvement of smooth ER in glycogen storage and release, steroid synthesis, lipid metabolism and the concentration and secretion of specific ions. For reviews of ER structure and function the reader is referred to Porter (1961a, 1961b, 1963) and Sjöstrand (1964). The latter author is in disagreement with the integrated interpretation outlined above.

Endoplasmic Reticulum and Ribosomes in the Euglenoid Cell

Three elements of the euglenoid endoplasmic reticulum have already been mentioned, the muciferous bodies (p. 109), the nuclear envelope (p. 82) and irregularly tubular extensions of the perinuclear space (p. 82).

This tubular ER is confined mainly to the region around the nucleus (Fig. 104), although occasional elements are found elsewhere in the cell.

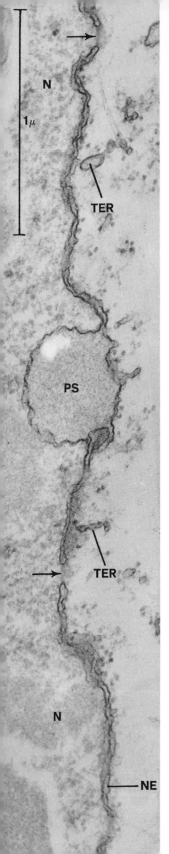

The membrane is free from ribosomes, and the system can be tentatively equated with the smooth ER of higher organisms. The tubular ER connects with an extensive vesiculate system, numerous elements of which appear in sections throughout the cell (Figs. 105, 111, 139, 140). The membrane of the vesiculate ER is studded with ribosomes, and this system is presumably equivalent to the rough ER of other organisms. The vesiculate ER frequently contains amorphous material (Figs. 105, 139, 140), and the peripheral elements of the system become orientated to form the muciferous bodies, retaining their ribosomal coating to a greater or lesser degree (Figs. 87, 111, 165). This part of the euglenoid ER is thus concerned with the production (or at least the accumulation and release) of mucilage and is potentially open to the articulations of the pellicle (within the plasmalemma) and to the outside of the cell. Amorphous material of unknown nature is also located in occasional distended regions of the perinuclear space (Fig. 104).

An intimate association between elements of the ER and the Golgi bodies is also evident (Fig. 106), but it is difficult to determine whether or not the Golgi bodies are an integral part of the ER system (see p. 159). However, one other special localisation of undoubted ER in the euglenoid cell is the cylindrical sheath which surrounds the canal (p. 120) and delimits an area of microtubules from the general cytoplasmic matrix. The relation of this sheath to the vesiculate ER is clearly seen in Figs. 105 and 111. Its function may be merely skeletal, but it is noticeable that the region within the sheath is almost free from ribosomes; the presumed lack of protein synthesis may be significant.

In electron micrographs, the euglenoid cytoplasmic matrix has the typical appearance (for osmic-fixed cells, see p. 203) of a dispersion of fine fibrous elements and granules in a low-density phase (Figs. 105, 111, 140, 166, etc.). Cell fractionation studies on *Euglena gracilis* by Brawerman and co-workers have shown the angular cytoplasmic granules to be ribosomes. The isolated ribosomes are highly active in incorporating leucine into protein (Eisenstadt and Brawerman, 1964a) and differ in sedimentation coefficient and nucleotide ratios from the ribosomes of the chloroplast matrix (Brawerman, 1963; Brawerman and Eisenstadt, 1964a;

Fig. 104 Nuclear envelope of *Euglena spirogyra*: the edge of a nucleus (*N*), showing the nuclear envelope (*NE*) with a distended region of the perinuclear space (*PS*), nuclear pores (*arrows*) and elements of the tubular endoplasmic reticulum (*TER*). Electron micrograph, ×60,000.

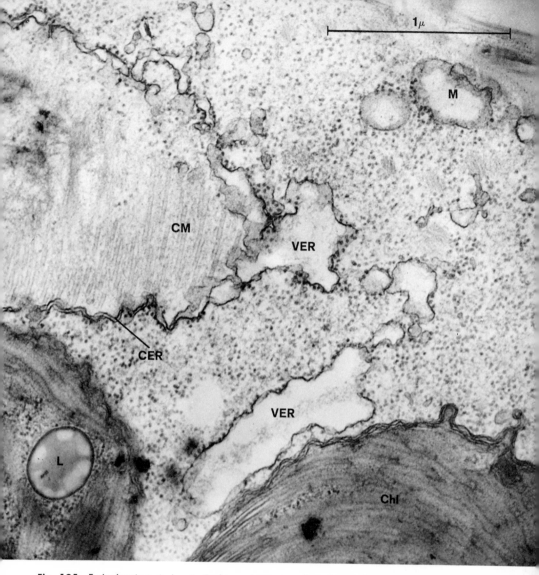

Fig. 105 Endoplasmic reticulum in *Euglena spirogyra*: region of cytoplasm near the canal, showing elements of the vesiculate endoplasmic reticulum (*VER*) with amorphous contents and ribosome-studded membranes; other components shown include many ribosomes in the cytoplasmic matrix, microtubules of the canal region (*CM*) and the canal sheath of endoplasmic reticulum (*CER*); see later text for explanation. *Chl* chloroplast, *L* lipid globule, *M* muciferous body. Electron micrograph, ×50,000.

Eisenstadt and Brawerman, 1964b). The significance of the "special" RNA of the chloroplast ribosomes is discussed later (p. 183).

Cytoplasmic flow occurs when cells exhibit euglenoid movement (p. 99) but cause and effect have not yet been elucidated. Autonomous cytoplasmic streaming (cyclosis) is found in the larger species of *Euglena* (p. 21) and in some species of semi-rigid and rigid genera. Species of *Menoidium*, for example, have a cytoplasmic streaming which is powerful enough

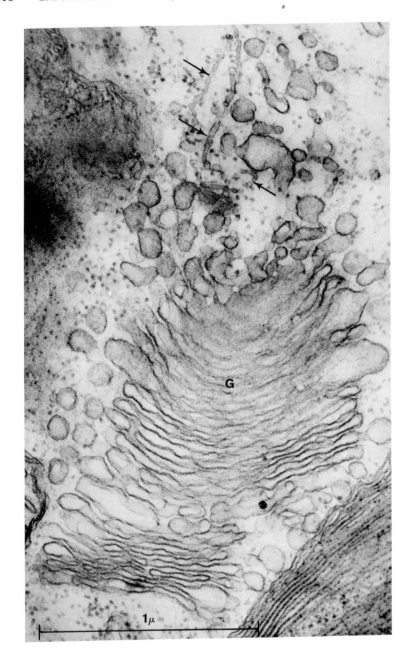

Fig. 106 Tubular endoplasmic reticulum (arrows) in *Euglena spirogyra*, showing intimate association with a Golgi body (G); see text. Electron micrograph, ×60,000.

to carry along large paramylon granules and even to move the nucleus (Fig. 142), but mitochondria immediately beneath the pellicle have autonomous movement independent of any cytoplasmic streaming (see p. 163). In fact, the peripheral cytoplasm in euglenoid cells is fairly solid and displays helical symmetry in the disposition of its components (p. 102). The fluidity of the cell resides in the inner cytoplasmic regions and, when a cell is punctured, this liquid phase flows out in a stream which only subsequently carries paramylon granules, chloroplasts, mitochondria and the nucleus (Fig. 163). Cytoplasmic streaming is a generally unexplained phenomenon, and no structural interpretation of cyclosis in euglenoid cells can yet be offered.

Chapter 11

CANAL AND RESERVOIR

All euglenoid flagellates have an anterior invagination from which emerges the locomotory flagellum or flagella. This invagination (Figs. 107-110, 114, 115, 123, 124, 128, 132, 137, 142, 158) consists of a narrow tubular portion, the canal, and a spherical or pyriform chamber, the reservoir. Associated with the invagination are the eyespot (p. 143) and the contractile vacuole (p. 149).

Structure

Light microscopy of living cells shows the funnel-shaped opening of the canal to be subapical in most species (Figs. 107, 108), on the side of the cell away from the eyespot when present (Fig. 107). This is one indication of bilaterality in the euglenoid cell (see p. 000), and the surface on which the canal opens is sometimes termed "ventral." In other species, particularly of the genera *Cyclidiopsis*, *Lepocinclis* and *Menoidium*, the canal opening is apical (Figs. 109, 142), though even here the slope of the canal or the shape of the cell may reveal bilateral symmetry (for details, examine the sequence of drawings, Figs. 1-68). The canal may be straight (Figs. 109, 110, 142) or curved (Figs. 85, 107, 108, 143), sometimes doubling back on itself or forming an S-shape. Anomalies include the system in *Euglena obtusa* (Fig. 13), in which there is a gradual transition from reservoir to canal, a marked constriction of the canal opening, and occasionally a second canal as an offshoot of the first.

In all species the canal is rigid, whereas the reservoir easily changes shape and is regularly distorted by the contractile vacuole (p. 151; Fig. 131). A pellicular lining of the canal can be seen in living cells (Figs. 107, 110, 128, 142) and whole pellicles (Fig. 85), and electron microscopy shows that the pellicular strips which line the anterior part of the canal (Figs. 88, 111, 112, 125; p. 96) thin out and end as the reservoir is approached. Hence, the reservoir is bounded by the plasmalemma only (Figs. 113, 125, 129, 134).

In *Euglena spirogyra* (and, to a lesser extent, in all other species so far examined) several layers of microtubules, 200 to 250 Å in diameter, form a flat helix around the canal (Figs. 111, 112). The region of cytoplasm in which the microtubules lie is delimited from the rest of the cell by a cylin-

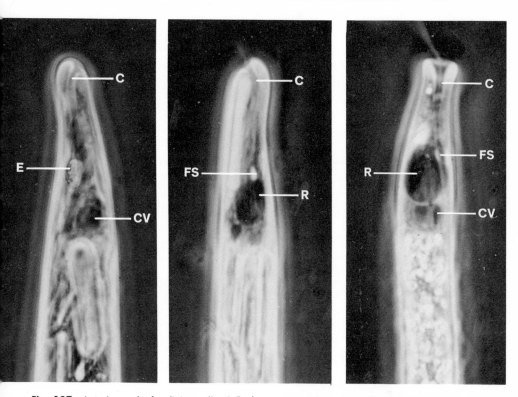

Fig. 107 Anterior end of a living cell of *Euglena acus*: note subapical canal opening, pellicular lining of the canal (C), eyespot (E) and contractile vacuole (CV). Anoptral contrast, ×2000

Fig. 108 Anterior end of a living cell of *Euglena acus* var. *hyalina*: note subapical canal opening, canal (C), flagellar swelling (FS) and reservoir (R) with flagellar bases. Anoptral contrast, ×2000.

Fig. 109 Anterior end of a living cell of *Cyclidiopsis acus*: note apical canal opening, canal (C), flagellar swelling (FS), reservoir (R) with flagellar bases and contractile vacuole (CV). Anoptral contrast, ×2000.

drical sheath of endoplasmic reticulum and is almost free from ribosomes. Occasional groups of microtubules pass from the canal collar through gaps in the sheath (Fig. 111), individual tubules appearing to reach the muciferous bodies and pellicular strips. Towards the posterior end of the canal the broad collar of microtubules narrows and the helical pitch increases so that the reservoir has a single layer of microtubules beneath the plasmalemma (Figs. 113, 129).

Function

Despite reports to the contrary, it is certain that the anterior invagination is *not* concerned with food ingestion in most species (see p. 190), and terms implying such a function ("gullet," "cytopharynx") should be avoided.

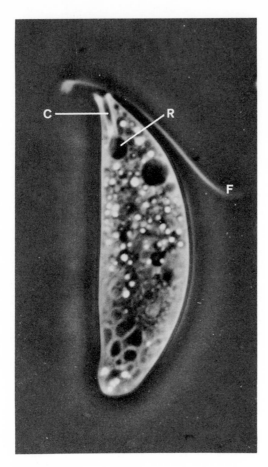

Fig. 110 Living cell of *Menoidium bibacillatum*, especially to show the canal (C) and reservoir (R); the emergent portion of the locomotory flagellum (F) has been shed. Anoptral contrast, × 2000.

The reservoir provides the only region of the cell surface which is limited by plasmalemma alone (without underlying pellicle), and it is here that discharge of the contractile vacuole takes place (see p. 151). Whether or not the reservoir is also a region of pinocytosis (intake of liquid and macro-molecules by means of small vesicles) is a controversial point (p. 153), though this could be the "mechanism" of possible chemoreception. In phototac-

Fig. 111 Canal region of *Euglena spirogyra*: transverse section of the canal (C), showing the encircling microtubules (CM) cut in oblique longitudinal section; occasional groups of microtubules (*arrow*) pass through the sheath of endoplasmic reticulum (CER) which delimits the collar of microtubules from the general cytoplasmic matrix; the relation of this sheath to the ribosome-studded vesiculate endoplasmic reticulum (VER) is clearly seen; the canal at this level still shows pellicular striations. *Chl* chloroplast, F^1 locomotory flagellum, *L* lipid globule, *M* muciferous bodies, *Mit* mitochondrion, *Pel* pellicle. Electron micrograph, × 50,000.

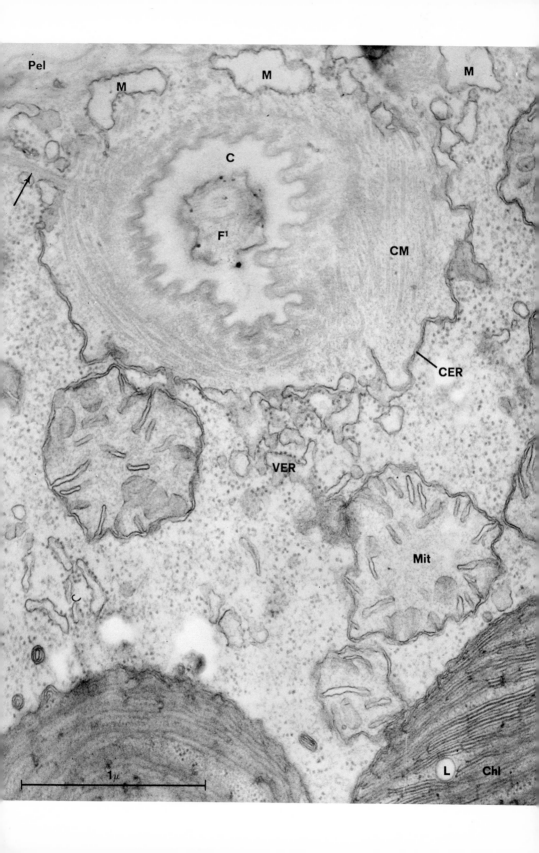

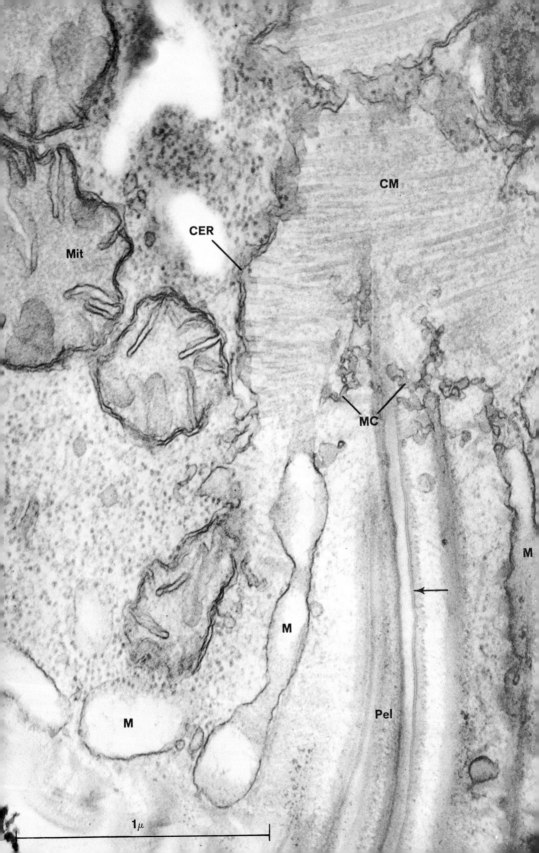

CM

CER

Mit

MC

M

M

M

Pel

1μ

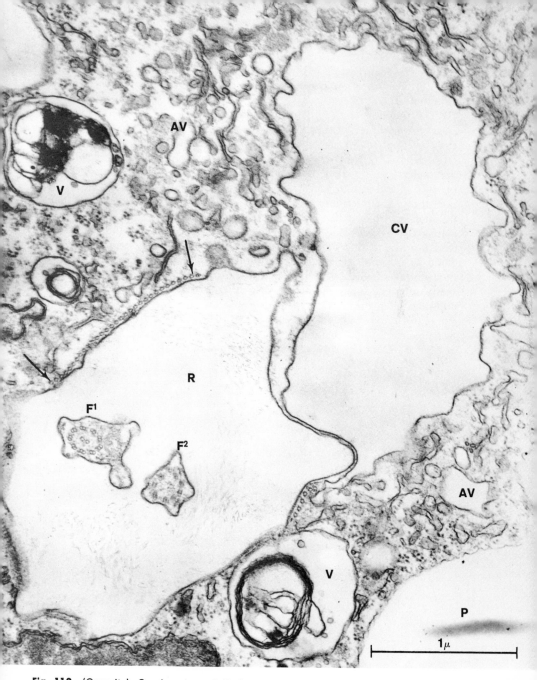

Fig. 112 (Opposite) Canal region of *Euglena spirogyra:* glancing longitudinal section, showing the relation of the canal microtubules (CM) to the muciferous bodies (M), muciferous canals (MC) and the canal sheath of endoplasmic reticulum (CER). *Mit* mitochondrion, *Pel* pellicle, *arrow* plasmalemma. Electron micrograph, ×70,000.

Fig. 113 (Above) Reservoir region of *Colacium cyclopicolum,* cut in transverse section: within the reservoir (R) lie transverse sections of the two flagella (F¹, F²), the potentially locomotory one (F¹) with a paraflagellar rod (see p. 132); to one side of the reservoir lies the contractile vacuole (CV), surrounded by a zone of accessory vacuoles and alveolate vesicles (AV, see p. 151); immediately beneath the reservoir membrane are groups of a single layer of microtubules (*arrows*); the hairs in the reservoir emanate from the membrane (not from the flagella) and are of unknown significance (see p. 153, also Fig. 134). *P* paramylon, *V* unidentified vesicles. Electron micrograph, ×40,000.

tic species, the apparatus of photoreception comprising the flagellar swelling and the eyespot is organised with respect to the canal and reservoir (see Chapter 13).

The function of the microtubules is unknown. If those encircling the canal are contractile, they could have the function of closing the canal in the way implied by earlier authors who named this region the "sphincter" (e.g., Klebs, 1892). However, it seems more likely that the microtubules are skeletal in function, adding to the rigidity already given to the canal by its pellicular lining. A skeletal function also suggests itself for the microtubules underlying the reservoir membrane: if flexible, they could function in pulling the reservoir back into shape after discharge of the contractile vacuole. As for the microtubules which pass from the canal sheath to the pellicle (Fig. 111), though these may merely be anchoring the canal in position, there are some indications that they connect with the microtubules beneath the pellicular strips. Similar microtubules found in many other cell types and organisms (Slautterback, 1963) are thought to be contractile (in protistan myonemes and axostyles, for example; see Grimstone, 1961), skeletal, or concerned with intracellular transport. All three functions commend themselves as possible explanations of the distribution and relations of microtubules in the euglenoid cell.

Chapter 12

FLAGELLA

Flagella and cilia are mobile threads which extend from the eucaryotic cell surface and which are usually concerned with locomotion or the generation of water currents. In common parlance, cilia are short, grouped elements with co-ordinated beat, whereas flagella are long, independently mobile structures, usually only one or two per cell. In terms of morphology, physiology, ultrastructure and function, no clear-cut distinction can be drawn between the two (except "bacterial flagella"; see below).

General Considerations of Function and Structure

Among the functions of flagella and cilia are *locomotion of single cells*, as in flagellates, ciliates, zoospores and gametes of algae and aquatic fungi, spermatozoids of bryophytes, pteridophytes and some gymnosperms, and spermatozoa of most metazoans; *locomotion of whole metazoans*, such as turbellarians, nemertines, annelids, molluscs and many larval forms; *creating currents for food collection* in protozoans, sponges and molluscs; *creating currents for food transport* through alimentary tracts as in molluscs, echinoderms and higher animals; *circulation of body fluids* in various animals from sipunculoids to vertebrates; *creating currents in connection with respiration and excretion* in animals of many phyla; *protection and cleaning* of many tissue surfaces, such as the respiratory tracts of mammals; *gamete transport* in the reproductive ducts in most animal phyla; *fertilisation* by flagellar fusion with the egg, as in some species of algae; and *transformation into non-motile sensory structures*, such as cnidocils and the photosensitive elements in the retina of the molluscan, amphibian and mammalian eye.

The amazing thing is that the basic organisation of the flagellum and cilium, though complex, is the same in all these situations. Each is enclosed within a unit membrane which is continuous with the cell plasmalemma, and each has an axis of eleven fibrils or microtubules, arranged as two single central strands of circular cross-section, 200 Å in diameter and 300 Å apart, surrounded by a cylinder of nine double peripheral strands with a "figure-of-eight" cross-section, 200 × 300 to 350 Å in dimensions (see Figs. 113, 116). This construction (often referred to as the "9 + 2 pattern") is common to all cilia and flagella of eucaryotic cells,* whereas a bacterial flagellum consists of a helical coil of several protein fibres with no bounding membrane, the total structure being only 120 to 250 Å in diameter (see Fig. 121) and a few microns long. The flagella of eucaryotic cells, by comparison, are at least 2000 Å wide and may reach more than 200 μ in length.

Every flagellum and cilium of a eucaryotic cell arises from an intracellular basal body, the construction of which is similar in widely different organisms (Gibbons and Grimstone, 1960; Manton, 1964b). Ultrastructural details of flagellar replication have not yet been established but the available evidence suggests that one basal body acts as a template for the construction of another, from which a daughter flagellum subsequently arises. It is unlikely that basal bodies actually divide, and "*de novo*" origin (see footnote, p. 160), though apparently occurring in flagellated cells which develop from certain non-motile plant and animal cells, is a concept difficult to accept (see Mazia, 1961, and Pitelka and Child, 1964, for discussion of this point). Migration of basal bodies into the cell to act as centrioles (division centres) during mitosis has been traced in various organisms, and, conversely, the centrioles move to act as basal bodies when flagella are about to be formed in a range of animal, algal and fungal cells. Thus the homology between basal bodies and centrioles of non-motile cells is now established.

Despite such detailed knowledge of structure, the mechanism of flagellar movement is not understood. Theories have been formulated in terms of the energy supply for, and the mechanics of, flagellar activity, and the conversion of this activity into directional cell movement (for details, see Fawcett, 1961; Sleigh, 1962; Pitelka and Child, 1964; Satir, 1965), but suggestions of a functional reason for the constancy of the 9 + 2 pattern are very rare (see Manton, 1964b).*

Much information on the structure and function of cilia and flagella has been conveniently assembled in reviews by Fawcett (1961), Sleigh (1962) and Satir (1965). Readers are referred to these works for discussion of the features outlined above.

Flagella in Euglenoid Cells

The flagella of euglenoid flagellates are inserted in the anterior invagination of the cell, on the lateral or posterior wall of the reservoir (Figs. 114, 115; see p. 120). On the basis of comparative studies it has been suggested (p. 72) that the various types of flagellar arrangement found in different euglenoid genera (pp. 11–71, 141) are derived from an ancestral condition of two flagella of equal length, both emerging from the canal as organelles of locomotion.

---

* The few recorded exceptions to this rule ("9 + 1," "9 + 0" and "8 + 1") are listed in Satir (1965). Most 9 + 0 patterns are non-mobile ciliary derivatives, but the rare instance of functional flagella which lack the two central fibrils or microtubules throughout their length is known for the sperm of *Myzostomum* (Afzelius, 1963) and for the uniflagellate spermatozoids of *Lithodesmium*, a centric diatom (Manton and von Stosch, 1966). This must mean that the central microtubules are not absolutely essential for flagellar activity.

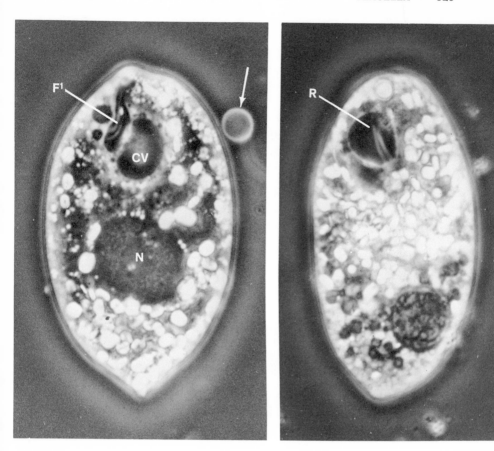

Figs. 114 and **115** Flagellar bases in squashed living cells.

Fig. 114 *Euglena gracilis* var. *hyalina*, showing the bases of the two flagella within the reservoir; the emergent portion of the locomotory flagellum (arrow) has been shed (see p. 140), but its base (F¹) still bears the flagellar swelling; immediately adjacent is the (unlabelled) base of the non-emergent flagellum. CV contractile vacuole, N nucleus. Anoptral contrast, × 2000.

Fig. 115 *Khawkinea quartana*: emergent portion of the locomotory flagellum shed, but the bases of the two flagella are clearly seen as independent units within the reservoir (R). Anoptral contrast, × 2000.

Construction of the flagellar axis

Euglenoid flagella are of relatively wide diameter in comparison with cilia and flagella of many other organisms. In particular, the leading flagellum of many members of the *Sphenomonadales* and *Heteronematales* is remarkable for its great thickness, more than one micron in the larger species. Electron microscopy of all genera so far examined (*Eutreptia*, *Distigma*, *Euglena*, *Astasia*, *Trachelomonas*, *Colacium*, *Peranema* and *Entosiphon*) shows

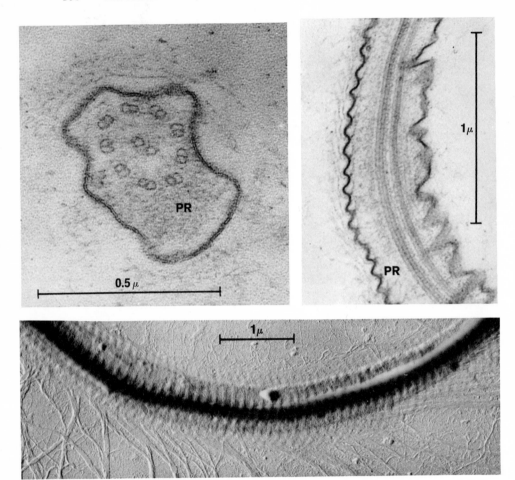

Figs. 116-118 Flagellar structure.

Fig. 116 Transverse section of the locomotory flagellum of *Euglena gracilis*: note the "9+2 pattern" of microtubules in the axis, the lateral amorphous material of the paraflagellar rod (*PR*), the tripartite flagellar membrane and the sections of external appendages (see text for details). Electron micrograph, ×100,000.

Fig. 117 Longitudinal section of the locomotory flagellum of *Euglena gracilis*: note the fibrils or microtubules of the axis, the flagellar membrane regularly folded on the side next to the paraflagellar rod (*PR*) and the sections of external appendages (see text). Electron micrograph, ×50,000.

Fig. 118 Locomotory flagellum of *Phacus pyrum*, shadowcast preparation: this small portion shows a banded or helical arrangement of material beneath the flagellar sheath (see text). Electron micrograph, ×20,000.

Fig. 119 (Opposite) Long flagellum of *Distigma gracile*: shadowcast preparation of a small portion of the flagellum, dismembered to show its constituent parts: *1* the two central microtubules, *2* the nine double peripheral microtubules, *3* the flagellar sheath (?), *4* the paraflagellar rod, *5* lumps of accessory material, *6* long hairs (appendages), *7* short hairs or fibrous material; see text for discussion. Electron micrograph, ×18,000.

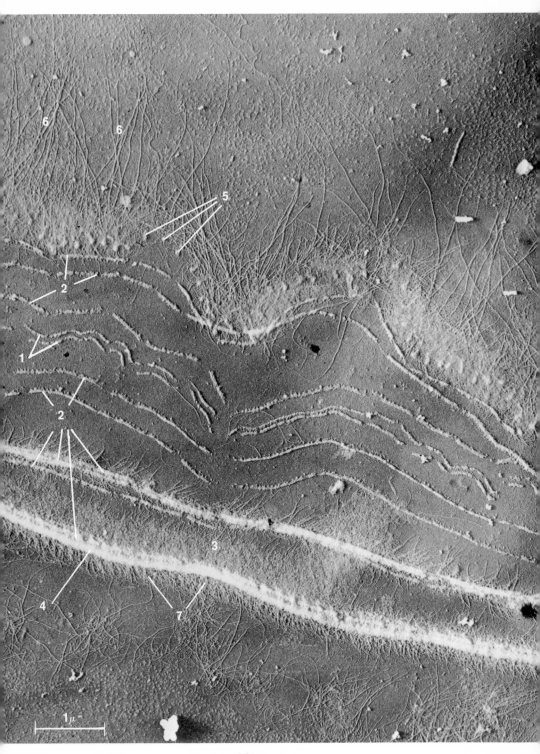

that the flagellar thickness is increased by a rod of paraflagellar material running almost the full length of the flagellum, to one side of the 9 + 2 axis (Figs. 113, 116, 117, 121, 122, 134), and most species have additional accessory material within the flagellar membrane.

Some of the thickness of the leading flagellum of *Peranema trichophorum* is due to two striated bands which Roth (1959) showed to be fluted ribbons flanking the flagellar axis, one curved around the 9 + 2 core and the other around the paraflagellar rod. According to Roth, these ribbons lie outside the flagellar membrane, and this would mean that they are non-living structures (as are the scales on the flagella of some chrysophycean and chlorophycean flagellates; see p. 156). However, shadowcast preparations of whole flagella of *Peranema* do not show *external* ribbons, and it is probable that the bands described by Roth lie within the flagellar membrane. Whether they are represented in other genera is not certain, but dismembered euglenoid flagella often show two long ribbons in addition to the 9 + 2 fibrils, the flagellar membrane and various other accessory material (Fig. 119). Furthermore, strips of material often detach themselves from the axis when flagella disintegrate after being shed from living cells (Fig. 120). Pitelka (1963) assumes the striated appearance of the flagellar axis in shadowcast preparations (Figs. 118, 121) to be due to such bands, but many flagella

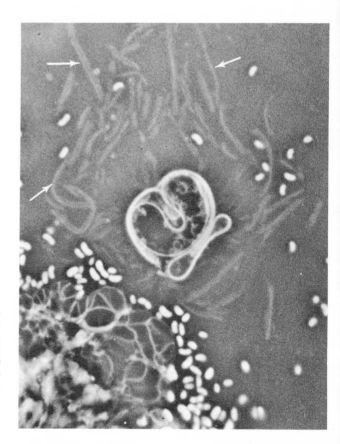

Fig. 120 Cast off locomotory flagellum of *Trachelomonas grandis*, showing accessory material (arrows) being shed from the (coiled) axis; the small dense bodies are bacteria. Anoptral contrast, × 2000.

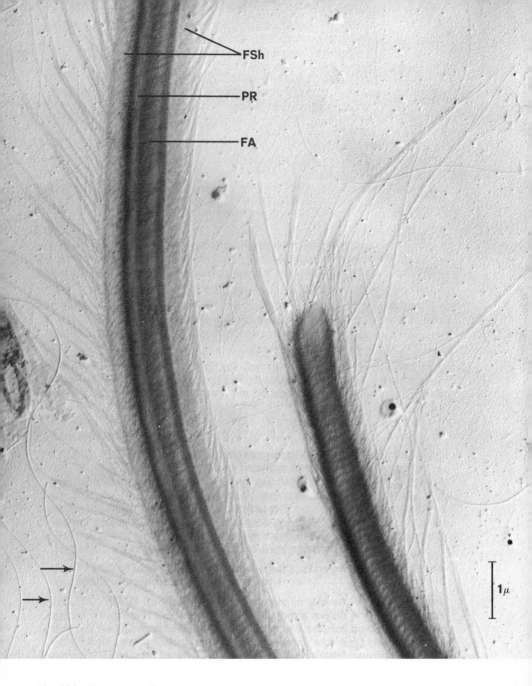

Fig. 121 The two flagella of *Distigma proteus*: shadowcast preparation, showing the tip of the shorter flagellum and the mid-region of the longer one; each flagellum bears several ranks and lengths of fine hairs [compare their thickness with the bacterial flagella (*arrows*) at bottom left]. *FA* flagellar axis, *FSh* flagellar sheath, *PR* paraflagellar rod (see text). Electron micrograph, ×15,000.

which have similar striations show little accessory material in sections, apart from hairs (see below) and the paraflagellar rod (Fig. 116). The impression from shadowcast flagella is of a flat helix of sheathing material, probably immediately within the flagellar membrane. Mignot (1964) has shown that the thickness of the trailing flagellum in *Entosiphon* is increased by an elaborate paraflagellar rod (Fig. 122). This has well-defined regular structure, in contrast to the amorphous appearance of the rod in the leading flagellum (Fig. 122) and in the main flagellum of *Euglena* (Fig. 116) and other genera. The universality of the single paraflagellar rod in euglenoid flagella extends

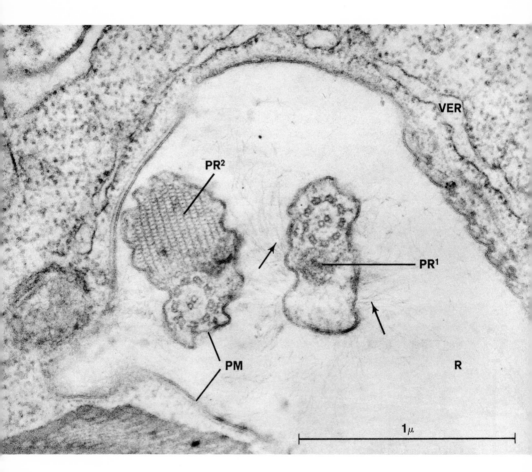

Fig. 122 *Entosiphon sulcatum*: transverse sections of the two flagella seen in an oblique section of the transitional zone between canal and reservoir (R); note the "9 + 2 pattern" of microtubules in the axis of each, with amorphous paraflagellar material (PR¹) in one and structured material (PR²) in the other. PM tripartite plasma membrane of reservoir/canal and flagellum, VER vesiculate endoplasmic reticulum (becoming the canal sheath), arrows flagellar hairs. Electron micrograph by Dr. J.-P. Mignot, ×60,000.

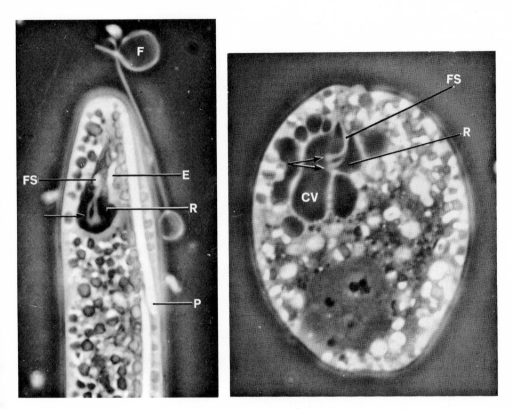

Figs. 123 and **124**   Flagellar basal bodies in squashed living cells. Anoptral contrast, ×2000.

Fig. 123 *Cyclidiopsis acus:* two basal bodies (*arrow*) side by side on the wall of the reservoir (R). E eyespot, FS flagellar swelling, F shed locomotory flagellum, P paramylon.

Fig. 124 *Euglena gracilis* var. *hyalina:* two basal bodies (*arrows*) one behind the other on the wall between the reservoir (R) and contractile vacuole (CV). FS flagellar swelling on the more anteriorly-placed flagellar base.

to the non-emergent flagellum of the *Euglenales*, though it may be so poorly developed that this second flagellum appears slightly or markedly thinner than the locomotory flagellum (Figs. 113, 123).

The remaining feature of the euglenoid flagellar axis, the swelling on the locomotory flagellum of all green and a few colourless species, is considered in the next chapter in relation to the eyespot.

Basal bodies

The basal bodies of euglenoid flagella can be clearly seen in living cells at the points of flagellar insertion into the reservoir wall (Figs. 123, 124). They are usually 0.5 to 1μ in diameter and in some species are no wider than the swollen bases of the flagellar axes (Fig. 124; swelling of the basal

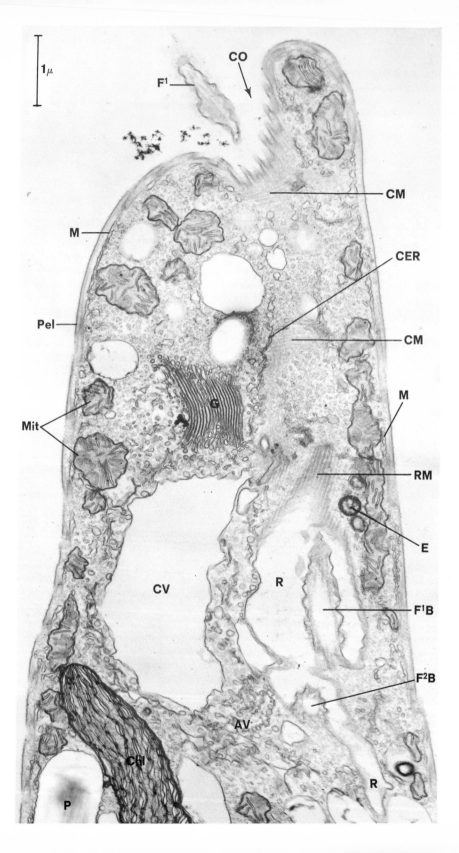

Fig. 125 Longitudinal section of the anterior end of a cell of *Euglena gracilis*, showing the distribution of various organelles: the locomotory flagellum (F^1) is seen emerging from the subapical canal opening (CO), which latter shows closely placed pellicular ridges; the canal itself is not sectioned, but parts of the canal sheath of endoplasmic reticulum (CER) are, together with two areas of canal microtubules (CM); at the level of transition from canal to reservoir, the helical pitch of some of the microtubules steepens so that the microtubules (RM) lining the reservoir (R) lie almost parallel to the long axis of the cell; the eyespot (E) lies "dorsal" to the reservoir at this point; within the reservoir, the bases of the two flagella (F^1B, F^2B) are sectioned; "ventral" to the reservoir lies the contractile vacuole (CV), surrounded by a zone of accessory vacuoles and alveolate vesicles (AV); anterior to the contractile vacuole is a Golgi body (G); numerous profiles of mitochondria (Mit) and muciferous bodies (M) lie in the peripheral regions of the cell, just internal to the pellicle (Pel). *Chl* chloroplast, *P* paramylon. Electron micrograph, ×18,000.

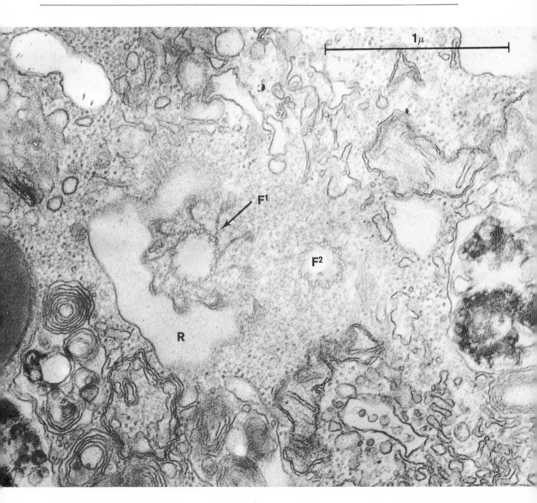

Fig. 126 Flagellar basal bodies in *Colacium cyclopicolum*, sectioned transversely, one (F^1) at the level of origin of curved bands from each doublet of the axis, the other (F^2) at the lower level of triplets (see text). *R* reservoir. Electron micrograph, ×50,000.

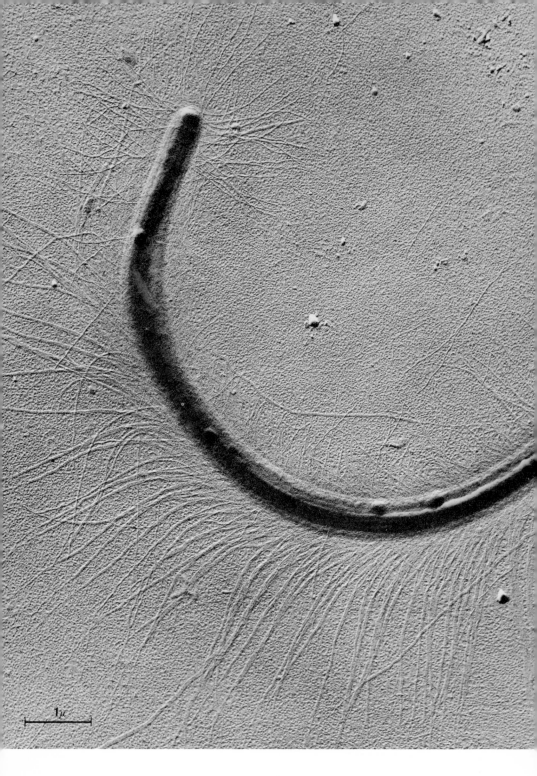

1 μ

portions of the flagella is common to all euglenoids, and there is no justification for the taxonomic use that has been made of the "presence" and
"absence" of this character).

The ultrastructure of euglenoid basal bodies has not been worked out
with the clarity and elegance of detail found in the studies of Gibbons and
Grimstone (1960) on *Trichonympha* and other flagellates, or of Manton
(1964b) on various algae. From the sparse observations that have been made,
it can be said that euglenoid basal bodies conform to the general plan (see
Pitelka, 1963). The two central microtubules of the flagellar axis end within
the free flagellum, leaving the swollen basal region of the flagellum hollow
(Fig. 125). The microtubules of the peripheral ring enter the body of the
cell, and a blunt-ended root radiates from each of the nine doublets (Fig.
126). The roots pass to the wall of the reservoir and apparently anchor
the flagellum in the cell. At a lower level the nine doublets give way to the
pattern of nine skewed triplets (Fig. 126) typical of basal bodies and also
of centrioles (see Fawcett, 1961; Sleigh, 1962; Pitelka, 1963). At a lower
level still, a heavy striated band joins the two basal bodies to one another
while one or more roots, each consisting of a single row of at least seven
microtubules, pass from the basal body towards the microtubules lining the
reservoir. The function of these various elements is at present unknown.

Appendages

The flagella of many motile algal cells carry appendages in the form of
"hairs," "bristles," spines or scales (see Manton, 1965).

The characteristic appendages of euglenoid flagella are long, fine hairs
inserted in a single row along the emergent portions only. These hairs, 2
to 3 μ long in *Euglena* (Fig. 127) and other genera, are extremely fine compared with the stiff bristles (mastigonemes) of many algal flagella. Pitelka
and Schooley (1955) have suggested that in life the hairs are wrapped
compactly around the flagellum, but anoptral contrast microscopy of living
cells reveals the hairs fully extended (Leedale, Meeuse and Pringsheim,
1965), apparently waved about in a passive way by the beating flagellum.
Jahn, Landman and Fonseca (1964) have suggested a locomotory function
for the stiff hairs of the flagellum in *Ochromonas*, but it is difficult to visualise
anything similar for the lax hairs of euglenoid flagella.

Refined techniques are now demonstrating further appendages on euglenoid flagella, including a felt of fibrous material which coats the entire
length of both locomotory and non-locomotory flagella in all species so far
examined (Figs. 113, 116, 122, 127). The coating is particularly dense on
the leading flagellum of *Peranema*, accounting for at least some of this organelle's extra thickness. More specifically, the locomotory flagellum of *Euglena*

Fig. 127   Distal end of the locomotory flagellum of *Euglena spirogyra:* shadowcast preparation, showing the unilateral array of long, fine, lax hairs, the weft of short hairs and an
assemblage of medium-length, stiffer (?) hairs at the tip. Electron micrograph, $\times$18,000.

spirogyra bears a tuft of stiffer hairs at its tip (Fig. 127), and both flagella of *Distigma proteus* (Fig. 121) bear serried ranks of short hairs in addition to the unilateral row of long ones.

The function of these appendages is unknown, and their mode of attachment has not been fully elucidated. They perhaps pass through the flagellar membrane, since in dismembered flagella (Fig. 119) the hairs are often associated with lumps or strips of accessory material. What is certain is that the simple picture of a euglenoid flagellum bearing only a unilateral row of long hairs will need revising when further observations have been made, and it remains to be seen whether possession of this single row will survive as a unique and diagnostic euglenoid character.

Replication of the locomotor apparatus

Details of the formation of daughter flagella vary in different euglenoid species. In dividing cells of many members of the *Euglenales*, the locomotory flagellum is often shed and daughter basal bodies appear on the reservoir wall next to the parent ones. New flagella then grow out so that the widened reservoir has four flagellar stumps projecting from its wall. These undergo rapid flickering movements, and at this time the complete independence of the flagella of *Euglena* is self-evident (oft-repeated descriptions of a single flagellum in *Euglena*, "bifurcate at the base," are incorrect). A ridge arises from the floor of the reservoir to cut the invagination in two, and one flagellum grows out of each daughter canal and moves actively during cell cleavage. In other species of *Euglena* and many other genera, the flagella retain their normal lengths, and daughter flagella arise and grow beside them. It can then be seen that one daughter cell takes the old set of flagella and the other receives the new pair. During division in *Peranema trichophorum*, however, the leading flagellum shortens and disappears at the same time as *two* new flagella grow out for the daughter cells (Tamm, 1965; 1966), possibly suggesting that the old basal body is not used again.

The casting off of locomotory flagella, a standard euglenoid response to irritation, raises the problem of how subsequent regrowth occurs. In *Euglena* the flagellum is usually shed distally to the flagellar swelling and if, as is generally supposed, regrowth occurs from the basal body, then the flagellar swelling must either contract and form again later or else slide down the growing flagellum; otherwise it would be carried out of the canal! Redevelopment of the swelling after flagellar regrowth is the more likely process, since this must occur in species which lose the whole of the flagellar axis during cell division. On the other hand, observation of the persistance of the swelling at a fixed level during flagellar regrowth could be taken as indirect evidence that flagellar growth occurs at the tip.*

Flagellar growth will be a difficult process to study with the electron microscope, but much remains to be done with living cells. The time taken

* Note added in proof: Similar indirect evidence for tip growth *has* been obtained for the leading flagellum of *Peranema trichophorum* (Tamm, 1966) by fraying the flagellar sheath after partial amputation and noting that the distance between the damaged region and the cell body remains the same during flagellar regeneration. Labelling experiments with leucine-H[3] on *Ochromonas* (Rosenbaum and Child, 1966) indicate tip addition during flagellar growth.

for flagellar regrowth after shedding or amputation is recorded as 2 hours for the leading flagellum of *Peranema trichophorum* (Chen, 1950), 8 hours for the emergent flagellum of *Astasia longa* (Rosenbaum and Child, 1964) and $4\frac{1}{2}$ hours for the emergent flagellum of *Euglena gracilis* Z (Rosenbaum, 1965). Growth of *Astasia* in tritiated acetate (Rosenbaum and Child, 1964) and of *Euglena gracilis* Z with cycloheximide inhibition (Rosenbaum, 1965) shows that at least some of the flagellar components are synthesised *de novo* (that is, from compounds of low molecular weight) during regeneration and that flagellar proteins, once formed, are relatively stable. Further observations of this kind could add interesting information to our knowledge of flagella, both in euglenoid flagellates and in other organisms.

Flagellar activity in euglenoid flagellates

The euglenoid flagellates show many different types of flagellar movement. One group of genera has the locomotory flagellum or flagella continually mobile from base to tip (usually resulting in cell gyration with the anterior end of the cell tracing a wide circle). Within this group are the *Eutreptiales* with two flagella emerging from the canal, equal in thickness but with different activity (heterodynamic); the *Euglenales* with one long flagellum emerging from the canal and a second one so short as to be non-emergent from the reservoir; the *Rhabdomonadales* with one emergent flagellum and possibly a short second one (p. 46); and the *Euglenamorphales* with several emergent flagella of equal length, thickness and activity (homodynamic).

A second group of euglenoids has the locomotory flagellum usually held out straight in front of the cell, with just the tip mobile or with a "cilium-like" beat of part of its length (resulting in smooth swimming or gliding locomotion in contact with a substratum or water-air interface). Some genera in this group have a long leading flagellum and a (usually) shorter, thinner, trailing one (*Sphenomonas, Tropidoscyphus, Notosolenus, Heteronema, Peranema, Protaspis, Calkinsia*). Others have a short leading flagellum and a longer trailing one (*Anisonema, Dinema, Entosiphon*). Yet others are said to have only the leading flagellum (*Atraktomonas, Calycimonas, Petalomonas, Peranemopsis, Urceolus, Pentamonas*), although further investigation may reveal a short second one within the reservoir.

Finally, the genera *Rhynchopus* and *Rhizaspis* are recorded as having no flagella.

The many variations of euglenoid flagellar movement are at present being studied by Jahn and co-workers with high-speed cinemicrography (see Jahn and Bovee, 1964, for a review and references). Organisms are filmed swimming in a medium containing 1μ-diameter polystyrene spheres, so that subtle changes in flagellar path can be recorded and water currents generated by flagellar movement can be analysed by plotting the displacement of the spheres.

Preliminary work on *Peranema trichophorum* and *Petalomonas* indicates that during gliding on a substratum the leading flagellum has a snapping action of the anterior 30 per cent of the flagellar length, whereas *Entosiphon* uses a similar "cilium-like" action of the anteriorly directed flagellum, 80 to 90 per cent of its length bending laterally in a power stroke with an overlapping, relaxed recovery stroke. The trailing flagellum of *Entosiphon* acts as a non-propulsive skid during such gliding locomotion. This activity of the leading flagellum was not recorded in a study of *Peranema trichophorum* by Chen (1950). He found that the leading flagellum was held straight, with a beating tip, during gliding and described a funnel shape during free swimming. The lack of agreement is, no doubt, partly due to the lesser effectiveness of visual observation as compared with analysis by high-speed filming. However, the gliding locomotion recorded by Chen (1950) was seen *and filmed* by Lowndes (1936), and one cannot escape the conclusion that this flagellate has several different modes of flagellar activity. Flagellar movement in *Euglena* and other genera with highly mobile flagella is too rapid and complicated to allow for analysis merely by microscopic observation, but it is clear that activity varies from species to species within a genus, and it is undesirable to refer to a "*Euglena* type of flagellar movement."

As outlined above and elsewhere (pp. 12, 21, etc.), owing to the wave form and path of the flagellum (at least partially lateral to the cell axis), many euglenoid species exhibit cell rotation during rapid swimming with the anterior end tracing a wider circle than the posterior. It has therefore been suggested (Lowndes, 1941) that the whole cell acts as a rotating inclined plane and screws itself forwards through the water. Indeed, Lowndes claims that the flagellar beat in some euglenoids has no forward component at all, serving only to cause cell rotation and gyration which are translated into locomotion. This neat idea is unfortunately not supported by modern hydrodynamic theory, since Holwill (1967) has calculated that the gyration of euglenoid cells is far too slow to be causing the observed rate of swimming, whereas flagellar thrust is more than sufficient.

Subjective impressions of flagellar activity and cell gyration are recorded in the notes on euglenoid species given in the present account (pp. 12–71), but detailed comparative studies must await the results of the high-speed filming by Jahn and his co-workers. Earlier observations on flagellar activity in euglenoids, particularly the classic papers by Lowndes, are summarised by Sleigh (1962) and Jahn and Bovee (1964). One point worthy of special mention is the report (Chen, 1950) that the leading flagellum of *Peranema* is apparently sensitive to mechanical and chemical stimuli (see p. 194).

Chapter 13

EYESPOT AND FLAGELLAR SWELLING

Most flagellates and swarmers of the *Chlorophyta, Phaeophyta, Xanthophyta* and *Chrysophyta* possess an eyespot (stigma). This consists of lipid droplets lying in a specialised region of a plastid and containing orange-red pigments which are usually β-carotene derivatives. The eyespot is believed to be a primary light receptor, inducing phototactic responses which take the organism to the zone of light intensity optimal for photosynthesis, zoospore germination or some other cell function.

The Euglenoid Eyespot

The eyespot in euglenoid flagellates, though also a collection of orange-red lipid droplets, is unique in being independent of the chloroplasts. It lies in the anterior end of the cell, curving to ensheathe the neck of the reservoir on the dorsal side (Figs. 107, 128). In most green euglenoids the eyespot is 3 to 10μ in diameter, a compact group of 20 to 50 droplets. In *Eutreptia* and *Khawkinea* it may consist of just one or two large droplets.

The pigment, on dubious evidence, is often stated to be astaxanthin. Recent studies (Krinsky and Goldsmith, 1960) have failed to detect this substance in *Euglena gracilis*, although Green (1963) records it for *Trachelomonas volvocina* Ehrenberg 1833. The work of Krinsky and Goldsmith (1960) suggests the β-carotene derivitave, echinenone, as the main eyespot pigment, together with two keto carotenoids, euglenanone and hydroxyechinenone; Batra and Tollin (1964) have recorded β-carotene, cryptoxanthin, lutein and an unidentified compound in isolated eyespots of *Euglena gracilis*.

Electron microscopy confirms that the eyespot is fundamentally different from that of all other algae in being independent of the plastids. Each eyespot droplet is separately enclosed within a membranous envelope (Fig. 129) and there is no indication of any special matrix or common membrane uniting the droplets into an integral organelle. The independence of the euglenoid eyespot from the chloroplasts is emphasised by the existence of colourless species with an eyespot but no plastids (*Khawkinea, Cyclidiopsis, Hyalophacus*, etc.).

Though there is no structural evidence that the eyespot is a permanently defined organelle, it often divides during cell division (Fig. 93) and always appears in a fixed position in the vegetative cell. Pringsheim (1956) has

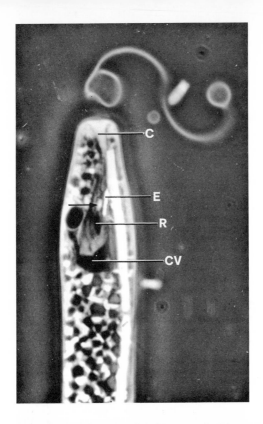

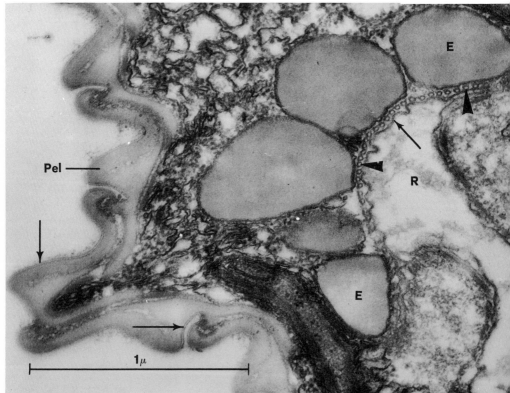

Fig. 128 *Cyclidiopsis acus*: anterior end of living cell to show the flagellar swelling (*arrow*) opposite the eyespot (*E*), the two flagellar bases in the reservoir (*R*), the pellicular lining of the canal (*C*) and the posteriorly placed contractile vacuolar region (*CV*). Anoptral contrast, ×2000.

Fig. 129 Eyespot in *Euglena spirogyra*: transverse section of a cell in the mid-reservoir region, showing several of the independently membraned droplets which compose the eyespot (*E*). *Pel* pellicle, *R* reservoir, *arrows* tripartite plasmalemma, *arrowheads* reservoir microtubules. Electron micrograph, ×60,000.

related these facts to dependence upon the flagellar swelling (see below), suggesting that the latter induces deposition of oil droplets in the adjacent cytoplasm. This helps to explain the frequent cases of eyespot dispersion in dividing cells, with re-aggregation during cell cleavage.

The Flagellar Swelling

One flagellum of all green euglenoid cells bears a lateral swelling near the transition region from canal to reservoir, opposite the eyespot (Figs. 108, 109, 114, 123, 128, 132). In *Euglena, Trachelomonas, Strombomonas, Ascoglena* (?), *Klebsiella* (?), *Colacium, Lepocinclis* and *Phacus* the swelling is on the longer flagellum, and this is also true of those colourless cells which have the swelling, species of *Khawkinea, Cyclidiopsis*, "*Hyalotrachelomonas*" and *Hyalophacus*. In cells of *Eutreptia* and *Eutreptiella* only one of the pair of emergent flagella bears a swelling (Fig. 1), but *Euglenamorpha hegneri* is described as having a swelling on each of its several locomotory flagella (Fig. 64).

Electron microscopy of the flagellar swelling shows it to be a dense body within the flagellar membrane (Fig. 130). Some sections reveal delicate striations in the matrix and regularly patterned (possibly crystalline) structure at the point of junction with the fibrillar core of the flagellar axis.* There is,

* If, as appears possible, the flagellar swelling is a specialised region of the paraflagellar rod (p. 132), its "disappearance" and "reappearance" during replication of the locomotor apparatus in some species (p. 140) may merely be a re-orientation of the paraflagellar material.

Fig. 130 Flagellar swelling in *Euglena gracilis* : transverse section of the two flagellar bases (F¹, F²) inside the reservoir, showing the flagellar swelling (FS) within the membrane of the locomotory flagellum (F¹). Electron micrograph, ×70,000.

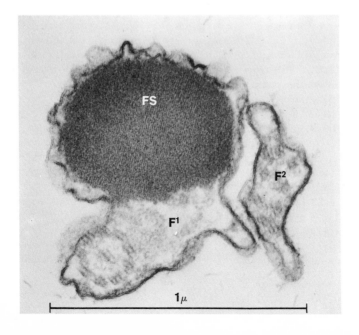

however, no evidence of the lateral connection between eyespot and swelling recorded by some authors (in the belief that the swelling is a *structural* part of the eyespot; see Gojdics, 1953).

Photoreception

All euglenoid species with an eyespot and flagellar swelling exhibit phototaxis, usually swimming away from bright light (negative phototaxis) and away from darkness towards subdued light (positive phototaxis) to accumulate in a region of low light intensity. Similar responses are shown by many pigmented algae, both with and without eyespots (see reviews by Bendix, 1960; Halldal, 1964), and by certain colourless motile cells. The phototactic response in *Euglena* is controlled by a "biological clock" (see Harker, 1963), the sensitivity of the response showing a diurnal rhythm even when the day/night stimulus is removed (Pohl, 1948; Bruce and Pittendrigh, 1956). Colourless euglenoid flagellates with no eyespot are not phototactic, though they seem to have some method of light perception resulting in a general irritable response to very bright light. The phototaxis of colourless species which have an eyespot and flagellar swelling is presumably a useless relict of their green ancestry (p. 73).

The argument concerning photoreception in the euglenoids is whether the eyespot is a primary light receptor or whether it acts merely as a light-absorbing screen which intermittently shades the flagellar swelling as the swimming cell rotates through the medium. On the latter interpretation the flagellar swelling is considered to be the true photoreceptor, directly controlling the activity of the locomotory flagellum to produce the observed phototactic responses of the cell (see reviews by Mast, 1941; Halldal, 1964).

Following Engelman (1882) and Mast (1917), Pringsheim (1937a) has pointed out that the distribution of phototactic sensitivity in the spectrum (with a peak at 485 μ) coincides with the absorption of wavelengths in the eyespot of *Euglena* (with the major peak at 480 to 500 μ), while the flagellar swelling does not appear to be pigmented. More recent correlation of the "action spectrum" of phototaxis and the absorption spectrum of the eyespot is made by Wolken and Shin (1958), Strother and Wolken (1961), Wolken (1961), Cobb (1963) and Halldal (1964). This correlation seems to favour the eyespot as the primary light receptor, but cytological factors which support the alternative theory have beeen summarised by Pringsheim (1956) as follows: (a) species with an eyespot always have a flagellar swelling as well, (b) the flagellar swelling always lies at the level of the eyespot, in exactly the right position for intermittent shading, (c) colourless species with no eyespot never have a flagellar swelling, (d) in heat- and streptomycin-treated *Euglena gracilis* the eyespot and flagellar swelling usually disappear together (p. 183), (e) once lost, the eyespot and flagellar swelling are never formed "*de novo.*" In fact, according to Gössel (1957), "bleached" *Euglena gracilis* can retain its eyespot and flagellar swelling (and show both positive and negative phototaxis) or just the flagellar swelling (and show only negative phototaxis), but never just the eyespot. Ultrastructural considerations (lack of eyespot integrity, degree of organisation of the flagellar swelling) favour the idea that the swelling is the photoreceptor. Pringsheim (1956) suggests that the swelling may perhaps contain lactoflavin which is known as a sensitiser in phototropic reactions. Chemical investigation of this hypothesis is highly desirable.

As association between flagellum and eyespot has been found in other organisms besides the euglenoid flagellates. The recurrent flagellum of brown algal zoospores and spermatozoids (e.g., *Fucus, Scytosiphon*) is swollen and adherent to the cell in the locality of the peripheral eyespot (Manton and Clark, 1955); *Ochromonas* has a flagellar swelling opposite the eyespot (Gibbs, 1962a); *Chromulina psammobia*, another chrysomonad, has a non-locomotory, non-emergent flagellum lying within an interior invagination of the cell in the curve of the eyespot (Rouiller and Fauré-Fremiet, 1958). Fauré-Fremiet (1958) draws a parallel between this last example and the cilium-derived retinal receptor cells of the vertebrate eye. Unfortunately, in the one comparison made between these metazoan sensory structures and the photoreceptive apparatus in *Euglena*, Wolken (1956, 1961) considers only the eyespot and flagellum, without reference to the flagellar swelling. It is to be hoped that future investigation will decide whether or not the swelling is photoreceptive and, if so, the structure and material on which the photosensitivity is based.

Chapter 14

THE CONTRACTILE VACUOLE

A major biological problem for organisms living in fresh water is that there exists a permanent osmotic potential for water to enter their cells from the surrounding medium. Cells of many aquatic plants are prevented from swelling continuously by their rigid walls, and equilibrium of pressures becoming established when the protoplast presses in turgid state against the confining wall. Naked cells of fresh-water protista and algae (including zoospores and gametes released from walled cells) are subject to continuous osmotic uptake of water and, in the absence of a confining layer outside the plasmalemma, there must be some other mechanism which prevents the cells from bursting and enables them to maintain their normal size and shape. The presence of contractile vacuoles in most of these cells and the absence of such structures from most marine and parasitic related forms (which live in an isotonic medium), together with the available experimental evidence (Kitching, 1956), suggest that the contractile vacuole is an organelle of osmoregulation, a means of actively pumping water from the cell against an osmotic gradient.

Some contractile vacuoles have been shown by electron microscopy to possess complex organisation (see Pitelka, 1963; Trager, 1964). In ciliates there is a permanent vacuole, which is regularly filled with fluid from a surrounding zone of canaliculi and vesicles, and a permanent canal which is closed or very narrow during the period of vacuolar filling (diastole) and open during discharge (systole). Contractile vacuoles of amoebae, in contrast, have no fixed site in the cell and no permanent discharge pore, though a zone of circumvacuolar canaliculi has been demonstrated. In most flagellates the contractile vacuole appears as a unit-membrane-limited sac surrounded by collapsed vesicles which are interpreted as the accessory vacuoles seen in living cells; there is no canalicular system.

The cytoplasmic region around the contractile vacuole is believed to be a zone of phase segregation, involving a retention of solutes by the cytoplasm and the secretion of water (and possibly waste materials) into the vacuole. Both the segregation and secretion will require energy, and mitochondria often accumulate around contractile vacuolar regions. The essence of contractile vacuolar function is that the cell must retain essential solutes even though it is continually pumping out large quantities of fluid (equivalent to the cell's total water content every few minutes).

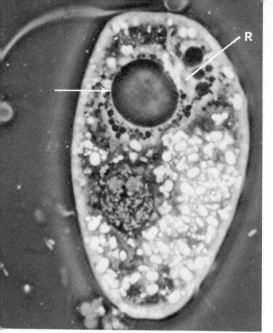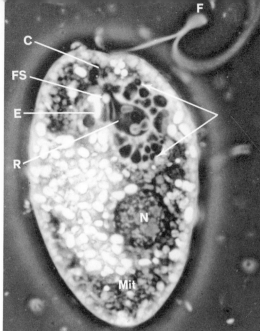

Figs. 131 and **132** Contractile vacuolar activity in squashed living cells. Anoptral contrast, ×1300.

Fig. 131 *Khawkinea quartana*: cell with full contractile vacuole (arrow), surrounded by small accessory vacuoles; the reservoir (R) is very much flattened; other organelles as in Fig. 132.

Fig. 132 *Khawkinea quartana*: cell showing the contractile vacuolar region immediately after systole (arrows); the volume of the reservoir (R) is increased by inclusion of the contractile vacuole; the two flagellar bases can now be seen more clearly, one bearing the large flagellar swelling (FS) opposite the eyespot (E). C canal, F locomotory flagellum, *Mit* mitochondria, N nucleus, P paramylon.

The Contractile Vacuole in Euglenoid Flagellates

All euglenoids, with the possible exception of a few marine and parasitic species, have a contractile vacuolar region in the anterior part of the cell, either to one side of (ventral to) the reservoir (Figs. 114, 132) or immediately behind it (Fig. 109).

Contractile vacuolar activity in living cells—observation and interpretation

Observations on living euglenoid flagellates show that a single vacuole enlarges in the contractile vacuolar region and empties at regular intervals (once every 15 to 60 seconds under normal conditions, depending on the species). The full contractile vacuole is almost spherical and is surrounded by accessory vacuoles in a region of dense cytoplasm (Fig. 131). At systole, the fluid from the vacuole is discharged into the reservoir (Figs. 132, 143)

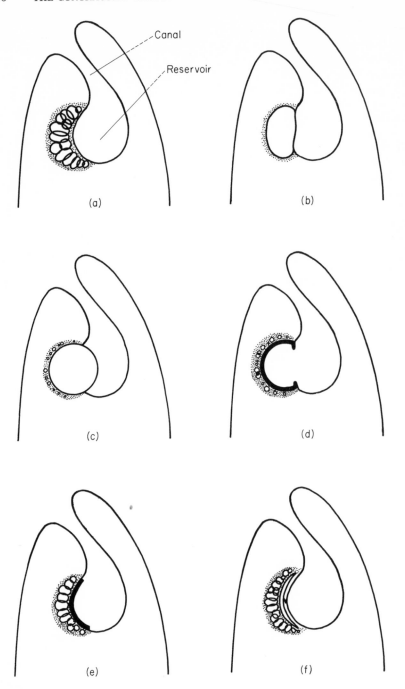

Fig. 133 Diagrammatic representation of theories of contractile vacuolar function in the euglenoid cell; see text for explanation.

and then expelled through the canal as the reservoir quickly returns to its normal shape (Figs. 115, 123). A "new" vacuole appears at once in the same region of cytoplasm, the continuously swelling accessory vacuoles coalescing with one another and, apparently, with the contractile vacuole.

The generally accepted interpretation of these observations (see Hollande, 1952; Gojdics, 1953) is summarised diagrammatically in Figs. 133(a)-(e). Accessory vacuoles in a region of dense cytoplasm [Fig. 133(a)] coalesce to form a single contractile vacuole (b); this steadily enlarges by fluid additions from further accessory vacuoles until it is spherical and maximally distorting the reservoir (c); systole occurs when the wall between vacuole and reservoir breaks down (d) and the contractile vacuole collapses into the reservoir (e), becoming part of the latter and forcing water out through the canal; accessory vacuoles which have formed behind the collapsing contractile vacuole [(d) and(e)] begin to coalesce (a) to form a new vacuole (b), and the cycle continues.

This interpretation raises particular problems of membrane dynamics. The "loss" of the contractile vacuole at each systole will involve incorporation into the plasmalemma of new membrane from the vacuole [shown as a heavier line in Figs. 133(b)-(e)], whereas the rapid return of the reservoir to its normal shape will involve the reverse, a sudden diminution in membrane area. Such changes are, of course, possible, but a new, alternative, explanation (supported by electron microscopy, see below) is that there exists a permanent contractile vacuole which collapses after systole, lying flattened between the restored reservoir and the accessory vacuoles [Fig. 133(f)]. The reservoir's return to shape will then involve a closing of the gap made in its wall under pressure from the full vacuole but will not involve any incorporation of vacuolar membrane. The apparent coalescence of accessory vacuoles will, in fact, be their emptying into one another *and* into the collapsed vacuole during diastole. Figures 133(a), (b), (c), (d) and (f) [that is, omitting(e)] illustrate such a cycle, except that the collapsed flattened contractile vacuole should now be present in (a). Immediately after systole and the recovery of the reservoir, this flattened vacuole would not be detectable in living cells.

Ultrastructure of the contractile vacuolar region

A full or filling contractile vacuole appears in sections as a unit-membrane-limited cavity (Figs. 113, 125), partially collapsed by processing techniques. Other cells which do not contain this cavity sometimes show the profile of a flattened vesicle lying immediately beneath the reservoir membrane, on the side opposite the eyespot (Fig. 134). In either case, the surrounding cytoplasmic matrix contains profiles of collapsed accessory vacuoles and numerous alveolate vesicles, 1000 Å in diameter. These latter are distinctive structures (Figs. 135, 136), their walls carrying a well-defined alveolate patterning which in sectioned vesicles appears as hairs radiating from the surface.

The large flattened vesicle (Fig. 134) is possibly the (permanent) contractile vacuole just after systole, as suggested above [see Fig. 133(f)].

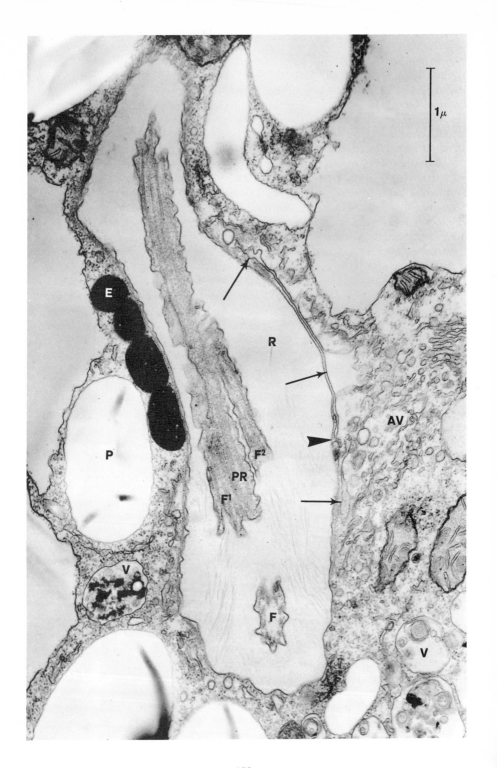

There is also indication of a pore or canal (Fig. 134) which can be interpreted as a special region where the reservoir wall opens under pressure from the full vacuole. Subsequent recovery of the reservoir to its normal shape is perhaps brought about by means of its lining of microtubules (p. 126). The significance of the fibrous material in the reservoir, emanating from the plasmalemma (Figs. 113, 134) and not to be confused with hairs from the flagella (Fig. 122), is unknown.

Alveolate vesicles are proving to be a component of all euglenoid cells, occurring only in the contractile vacuolar region and being particularly numerous after systole (Fig. 135). It has therefore been suggested (Leedale, Meeuse and Pringsheim, 1965) that the alveolate vesicles are specifically concerned with osmoregulation, a proposal supported by the association of identical vesicles with contractile vacuoles in other algal flagellates and zoospores, for example in the green alga *Stigeoclonium* (Manton, 1964c). In these cells the vesicles originate from the nearby Golgi complex, and it is pertinent to note that a Golgi body is regularly found adjacent to the euglenoid contractile vacuole (Figs. 125, 135). This is of interest in relation to the suggestion that the Golgi apparatus controls the water balance in some animal cells (Dalton, 1961). Whether the euglenoid alveolate vesicles act in osmoregulation by passing water to the contractile and accessory vacuoles, or whether they are the euglenoid means of phase segregation, being engaged in the retention and recapture of solutes valuable to the cell, remains to be investigated experimentally.

The latter function would most closely relate to the observation that in cells of certain animal tissues (see Roth and Porter, 1964) similar alveolate vesicles take up protein from the cell surface. This introduces the possibility that the euglenoid alveolate vesicles are engaged in pinocytosis from the *reservoir*, though their restriction to the immediate contractile vacuolar region argues against this. Pinocytosis, the engulfing of droplets of liquid into the cytoplasm (see Wittekind, 1963; Trager, 1964; Frey-Wyssling and Mühlethaler, 1965), is an attractive explanation of how a cell absorbs molecules which are too large to pass across the plasma membrane. In euglenoids it could possibly be the basis of chemoreception (p. 122). Experimental demonstration of protein uptake from the reservoir would be an important contribution towards understanding the biology of these flagellates.

Fig. 134 Oblique longitudinal section of the reservoir region in an attached cell of *Colacium cyclopicolum*, especially to show details of the contractile vacuolar region after systole: an elongated profile of a flattened vesicle (*arrows*) lies immediately beneath the reservoir membrane, separating the zone of accessory vacuoles and alveolate vesicles (AV) from the reservoir (R); it is suggested (see text) that this flattened vesicle might represent a collapsed, permanent contractile vacuole with, possibly, a permanent discharge "pore" (*arrowhead*); in the reservoir, the two flagellar bases (F^1, F^2) are sectioned longitudinally for part of their lengths, the base of the locomotory flagellum (F^1) showing the paraflagellar rod (PR) lateral to the microtubular axis; the tip of the second flagellum (F^2) is in close proximity with the first, but serial sections indicate that the two remain independently-membraned structures. E eyespot, F one flagellar base in transverse section, P paramylon, V unidentified vesicles (lysosomes?); other cytoplasmic components as labelled in Fig. 113. Electron micrograph, $\times 25,000$.

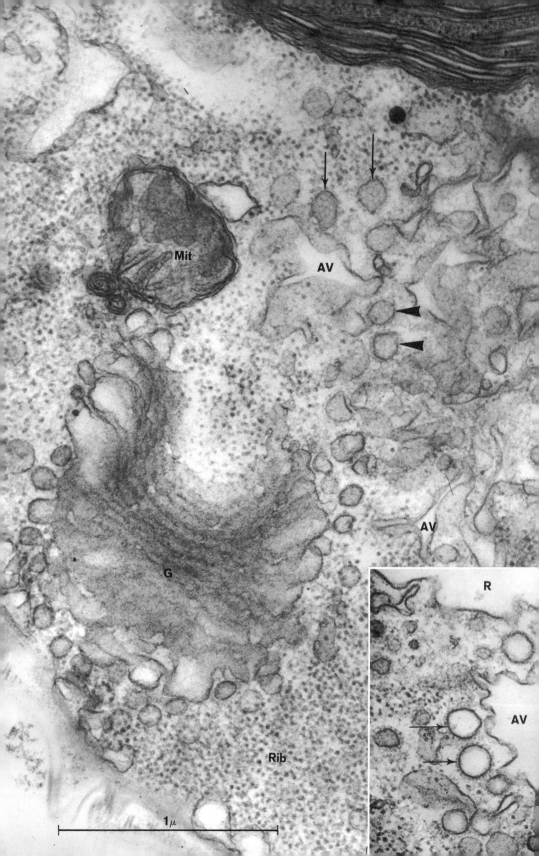

Mit

AV

G

Rib

AV

R

AV

1μ

Chapter 15

GOLGI BODIES

Golgi bodies occur in almost all eucaryotic cells, with certain fungi apparently the only exceptions. The bodies can be demonstrated light microscopically by silver or osmium impregnation of fixed material and are sometimes recognisable in the living cell by their characteristic shape and situation.

Electron microscopy shows that a Golgi body typically consists of a stack of flattened, unit-membrane-limited cisternae which exhibit proliferation of small vesicles from their fenestrated edges. Intermittent continuity between Golgi bodies and the endoplasmic reticulum has been demonstrated but it is clear that mature Golgi bodies are permanent structures which divide periodically. "*De novo*" formation (see footnote, p. 160) and origin from the nuclear envelope (see p. 183) have been postulated for Golgi bodies in some cells (Moore and McAlear, 1963), but direct division of this organelle can easily be followed in various living cells; for example, in flagellates with a single Golgi body (such as *Paraphysomonas*, Manton and Leedale, 1961).

There is good evidence that Golgi bodies are involved in the collection, possible modification and subsequent export of metabolic products, and they may also be concerned with the control of water balance in the cell (see review by Dalton, 1961). Accumulations of certain substances (plant cell wall material, zymogen granules, milk protein, lipid granules) dilate the edges of Golgi cisternae in various types of cell, and these secretory products are subsequently transported through the cytoplasmic matrix in Golgi-derived vesicles. Whether all such substances are synthesised by the rough endoplasmic reticulum (p. 000) and then passed to the Golgi bodies or whether Golgi bodies can function directly in forming secretory products remains uncertain (the absence of ribosomes from Golgi membranes argues against protein synthesis). The intricately patterned scales which cover the

---

Fig. 135 Contractile vacuolar region of *Euglena spirogyra*, immediately after systole: the area contains collapsed accessory vacuoles (AV) and numerous alveolate vesicles in surface view (*arrows*) and section (*arrowheads*); a Golgi body (G) is nearby. *Mit* mitochondrion, *Rib* ribosomes. Electron micrograph, ×60,000.

Fig. 136 (Inset) Alveolate vesicles of *Euglena spirogyra*, in section (*arrows*). AV accessory vacuole, R reservoir. Electron micrograph, ×60,000.

cell (and in some species the flagella) of certain chrysophycean and chloro-phycean flagellates are constructed within the cisternae of the Golgi apparatus and transported to the cell surface in vesicles (see Manton, 1965, for references), and this remains the only case so far demonstrated of the formation of a finished, recognisable cell *structure* within the Golgi complex.

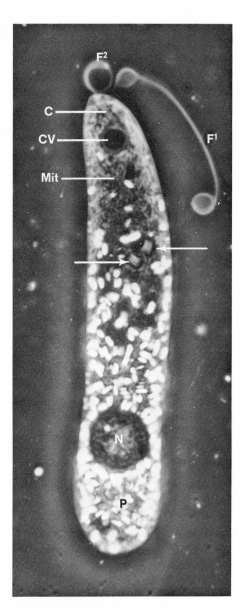

Fig. 137 Living cell of *Distigma proteus*, showing two large Golgi bodies (*arrows*) and other organelles. C canal, CV contractile vacuole, F^1 long flagellum, F^2 short flagellum (both flagella looped in this squashed cell), *Mit* mitochondria, *N* nucleus, *P* paramylon. Anoptral contrast, ×2000.

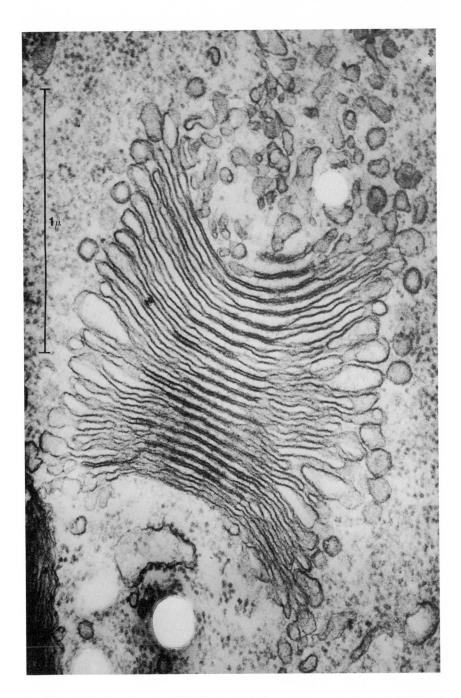

Fig. 138 Vertical section of a Golgi body of *Euglena spirogyra*, showing the full stack of 24 to 25 curved and flattened cisternae. Electron micrograph, ×70,000.

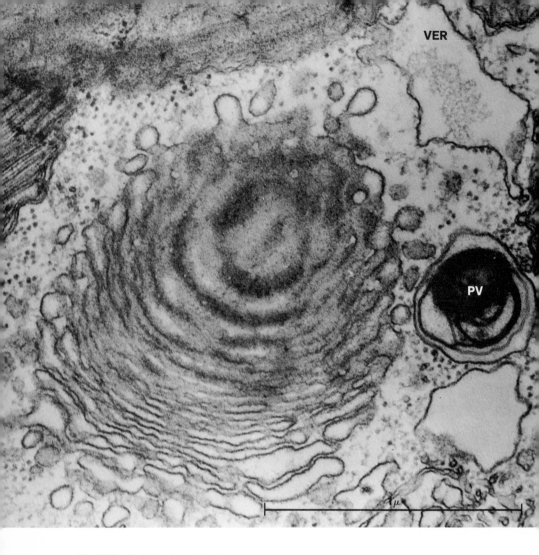

VER

PV

1 μ

Fig. 139 Golgi body of *Euglena spirogyra*, sectioned parallel to some of the cisternae and showing proliferation of vesicles from the fenestrated cisternal margins. *PV* phospholipid vesicle, *VER* vesiculate endoplasmic reticulum. Electron micrograph, ×70,000.

Golgi Bodies in the Euglenoid Cell

Euglenoid flagellates have several to many Golgi bodies distributed throughout the cell. The Golgi bodies are difficult to distinguish in living cells of green species, but colourless euglenoids often have two or three very large Golgi bodies anterior to the nucleus (Figs. 5, 23, 44, 137), apparently constituting the total Golgi complement of the cell. The fission of these large organelles can be followed during cell division, and Mignot (1965) has recently published electron micrographs of Golgi fission in *Distigma proteus*. Colourless species which might be more closely related to green forms, such

158

as *Cyclidiopsis acus* (Fig. 20), have numerous small Golgi bodies scattered through the cell.

Electron microscopy of species of *Eutreptia, Distigma, Euglena, Trachelomonas, Peranema* and *Entosiphon* reveals that each euglenoid Golgi body (Figs. 106, 125, 138) has the exceptionally high number of twenty to thirty curved, flattened, discoid cisternae. Compression of the central portion of each cisterna is seen in sections perpendicular to the stack (Fig. 138), while the origin of vesicles from the fenestrated cisternal margins is most clearly seen where the cisternae are almost parallel to the plane of section (Fig. 139).

Golgi bodies are presumably concerned with the collection and redistribution of metabolites in euglenoid cells. Elements of the endoplasmic reticulum often appear in intimate association with the Golgi bodies (Fig. 106), though interconnection has not been demonstrated and recognisable cell products are not seen in the cisternae. The regular positioning of a Golgi body adjacent to the contractile vacuole (Figs. 125, 135) suggests a possible function in the water relations of the cell (see p. 153).

Chapter 16

MITOCHONDRIA

Mitochondria occur in all aerobic eucaryotic cells as the organelles concerned with the oxidative processes of respiration, whereby much of the energy stored in food and reserve products is made available for use in cell function and metabolism.

Contrast microscopy or vital staining of living cells reveals the mitochondrial complex (chondriome) as a reticulum or as discrete rods with marked plasticity and powers of autonomous movement. In plant cells mitochondrial movement is often rapid, but in certain animal cells assemblies of immobile mitochondria seem to be related to a constant high demand for energy at specialised sites (in cells of the renal tubule, in muscle cells and in spermatids, for example).

It has been variously maintained that mitochondria either arise "*de novo*," develop from other cell organelles or originate only from pre-existing mitochondria (see Frey-Wyssling and Mühlethaler, 1965). Theories of "*de novo*" origin* are supported by studies in which mitochondria reappear after apparent destruction by X-rays and other agents, but descriptions of mitochondria arising in daughter cells which apparently had none at the time of division owing to centrifugation are now discredited (see Novikoff, 1961a). Reduction of mitochondria to a simpler form ("promitochondria") is recorded for cells of some higher plants and animals prior to mitosis and, especially, meiosis, with sharing of promitochondria at cell cleavage and subsequent redevelopment into mature organelles. Alternatively, Bell and Mühlethaler (1962, 1964) describe a periodic degeneration of the chondriome with formation of new mitochondria from the nuclear envelope in the fern egg cell. This has led to advancement of the theory that all mitochondria draw their genetic information from the nucleoplasm and the chondriome cannot be considered an autonomous, self-determining system (Frey-Wyssling and Mühlethaler, 1965). Even so, direct division of mature mitochondria (by constriction, septation or budding) is now known for

* To make any sense at all, "*de novo*" origin must be taken as meaning formation from submicroscopic cellular materials, as opposed to the division or conversion of an existing organelle. Replication of a structure by "copying" rather than division (as may be the case with flagellar basal bodies; see p. 128) could perhaps be regarded as *de novo* under a broad definition, but the older accounts of "*de novo*" origin implied the appearance of an organelle without *any* relation to existing homologous structures in the cell. Such strictly "new" formation has not been proven for any major cytoplasmic organelle.

numerous organisms. Indeed, the plasticity of mitochondria allows for their *constant* fragmentation (and fusion) and the concept of a *definite process* of mitochondrial division is meaningful only in certain cases, such as the minute green flagellate, *Micromonas pusilla*, which has a nucleus, one chloroplast, one Golgi body and one mitochondrion, all of which divide during cell division (Manton, 1959).

Electron microscopy of thin sections shows remarkable uniformity of mitochondrial structure throughout the whole range of eucaryotic cells. Any mitochondrion (e.g., Fig. 140) has a limiting layer of two unit membranes separated from one another by a region of low electron density. The surface area of the inner membrane is greatly increased by invaginations into the mitochondrial matrix, either as microvilli or as flattened vesicles (cristae). The matrix appears structureless with some fixatives but may show granules, density variations or filamentous inclusions with others.

Mitochondria are the chief repositories of the electron transport ap-

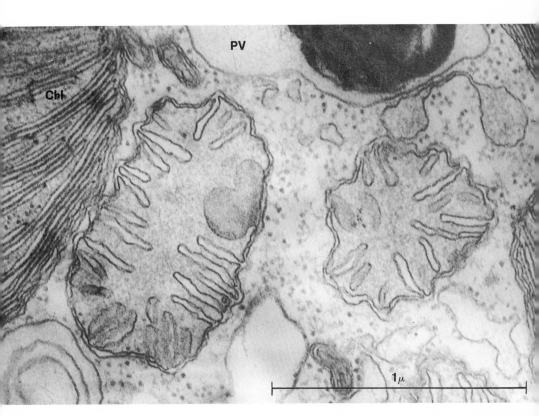

Fig. 140 Sections of two mitochondria of *Euglena spirogyra*, showing the characteristic form of the cristae (see text). *Chl* chloroplast, *PV* phospholipid vesicle. Electron micrograph, ×70,000.

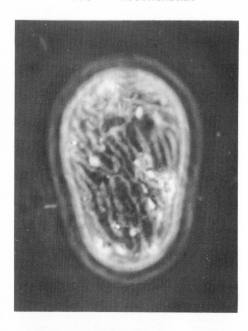

Fig. 141 Coarse mitochondrial reticulum in a living cell of *Trachelomonas reticulata*. Anoptral contrast, × 2000.

Figs. 142(a), 142(b) and **142(c)** *Menoidium bibacillatum*: three shots of the same living cell, taken at intervals of one minute and ten minutes; note changes in the pattern of the reticulate chondriome in the posterior half of the cell and changes in position of the nucleus (N), Golgi bodies (G) and lipid droplets (*arrows*, etc.) caused by cytoplasmic streaming. C canal, CV contractile vacuole, P paramylon, R reservoir. Anoptral contrast, × 2000.

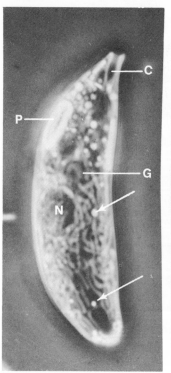

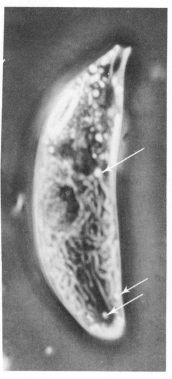

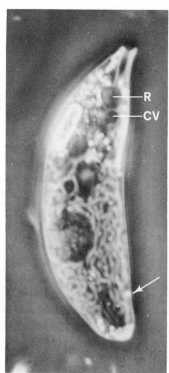

paratus involved in generation of ATP (adenosine triphosphate) by oxidative phosphorylation, and also of the enzymes responsible for oxidation of organic, fatty and amino acids. Flavoprotein, cytochrome oxidase and the enzymes of the tricarboxylic acid cycle are thought to be located exclusively on the inner (matrical) surfaces of cristae and microvilli, arranged in evenly spaced repetitive arrays of multi-enzyme units. Secondarily, mitochondria are believed to be capable of active ion absorption and transport of water.

For detailed reviews of mitochondrial structure, chemistry and function see Novikoff (1961a), Bourne and Tewari (1964), Lehninger (1964) and Frey-Wyssling and Mühlethaler (1965).

Mitochondria in Euglenoid Cells

The mitochondrial complex of a living euglenoid cell appears in the light microscope as a reticulum (Fig. 141), as discrete ovoid or elongated bodies, 0.5μ in breadth and up to 10μ long (Figs. 143, 144) or as a combination of the two states (Fig. 142). A reticulate state is typical for green cells in the light, the chondriome consisting of delicate interconnecting threads confined to the superficial region of cytoplasm between the pellicle and chloroplasts. During the dark period of a day/night culture cycle, these same green cells typically contain discrete mitochondria more widely dispersed in the cytoplasmic matrix. In either state the complex is labile, its pattern changing as mitochondria slowly branch, fragment and then flow back into one another. The particulate state of the chondriome is also characteristic for cells of most colourless species (Figs. 137, 143), but some display a rather coarse reticulum (Fig. 141).

Mitochondria are always more numerous in equivalent-sized cells of a colourless euglenoid species than a green one, and this is spectacularly demonstrated when green cells are decolourised by heat or streptomycin (see p. 183). Cells of the aplastidic race show a several-fold increase in the volume of the chondriome, becoming packed with filamentous mitochondria (Fig. 144). This may reasonably be interpreted as a reflection of the change from phototrophic to heterotrophic nutrition.

Electron microscopy of sectioned mitochondria reveals the expected basic architecture together with features which are characteristically euglenoid (Figs. 111, 140). The outer membrane is strongly undulated; the cristae are ovoid or circular, constricted at the base in such a way that the junction with the inner mitochondrial membrane is relatively narrow. Most of the cristae project radially inwards, but cristae from opposite sides of a mitochondrion rarely meet or overlap, and the finely granular matrix of the mitochondrial lumen is relatively large in volume.

With regards to mitochondrial ontogeny, the euglenoids show the simple situation of an observed sharing of mature mitochondria between two daughter cells at cell division (p. 104) and subsequent growth of the chondriome in each growing cell. The concept of chondriome continuity seems to be realised, though supporters of the theory of nuclear origin of mitochondria (see above, p. 160) might suggest a periodic replenishment of the chon-

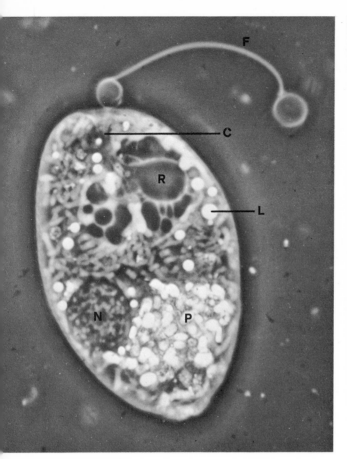

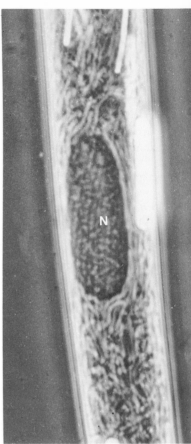

Fig. 143 Living cell of *Khawkinea quartana,* with many mitochondria in the anterior half of the cell. C canal, F locomotory flagellum, L lipid droplet, N nucleus, P paramylon, R reservoir surrounded by accessory vacuoles of the contractile vacuolar region. Anoptral contrast, ×2000.

Fig. 144 *Euglena acus* var. *hyalina:* mid-region of a living cell, showing the nucleus (N) surrounded by many filamentous mitochondria. Anoptral contrast, ×2000.

driome from the nuclear envelope. The unequivocal demonstration of plastid continuity in *Euglena* (p. 183) is of importance here, since neoformation of plastids from evaginations of the nuclear envelope is also suggested by Bell and Mühlethaler (1962, 1964) and linked to neoformation of mitochondria. The concepts of genetic continuity and nuclear origin of the chondriome both find support in suggestions that DNA is of general occurrence in mitochondria (Gibor and Granick, 1964; Nass, Nass and Afzelius, 1965), though this has not been conclusively proved. *Euglena gracilis* is an important research organism here: Ray and Hanawalt (1965) have demonstrated non-nuclear satellite DNA in cells without chloroplasts; Edelman,

Schiff and Epstein (1965) have discovered a non-nuclear satellite DNA different from that of the chloroplasts (p. 182) and associated with the mitochondrial cytochromes in fractionation.

Detailed studies on oxidative metabolism in euglenoid flagellates are virtually confined to *Astasia longa* and *Euglena gracilis* (strain *Z* and var. *bacillaris*). In a long series of papers, Buetow and co-workers have investigated respiratory pathways in these species (Buetow, 1961; Buetow and Levedahl, 1961; Buetow, 1963; Buetow and Padilla, 1963), the investigation culminating in the demonstration of oxidative phosphorylation in mitochondria isolated from *Euglena gracilis* by cell fractionation and differential centrifugation (Buetow and Buchanan, 1965). Danforth and co-workers have studied the oxidative assimilation of acetate and ethanol in *Astasia longa* and *Euglena gracilis* (Danforth, 1953, 1961; Danforth and Wilson, 1961; Eshleman and Danforth, 1964; Marzullo and Danforth, 1964). Glucose is generally supposed to be a less favourable substrate for euglenoids and other "acetate flagellates" (p. 202) but, providing suitable conditions are established, efficient glucose metabolism by *Astasia longa* (Barry, 1962) and *Euglena gracilis* (Hurlbert and Rittenberg, 1962) occurs by the Embden-Meyerhof-Parnas and pentose phosphate pathways and is thus similar to that in many other cells. Hunter and Lee (1962) have demonstrated that most tricarboxylic acid cycle intermediates are oxidised by intact cells of *Astasia longa*, while numerous enzymes of the cycle can be detected in cell-free extracts. Furthermore, the cytochromes of euglenoid mitochondria have been isolated and characterised (Gross and Wolken, 1960; Perini, Kamen and Schiff, 1964; Perini, Schiff and Kamen, 1964) as cytochrome type *c* (556) and cytochrome type *a* (605). From all these results the conclusion can be drawn that respiratory processes in *Astasia longa* and *Euglena gracilis* follow the general pattern known for many other organisms, probably with slight variations at specific points (Ohmann, 1963, 1964; Wilson, 1963).

Chapter 17

PHOSPHOLIPID VESICLES AND LYSOSOMES

Cells in old cultures of euglenoid flagellates contain numerous droplets (Fig. 145) which are charged with brown or orange pigments, show metachromasia with toluidine blue and give a positive lipid reaction. Such "metachromatic bodies" or "volutin granules" are constituents of many bacterial, fungal, protistan and algal cells and are known to contain large amounts of condensed inorganic phosphates (see Kuhl, 1962). In most organisms the phosphate condensations are polyphosphates with open-chain molecules, in contrast to metaphosphates which have closed-ring molecular structure. Cyclic metaphosphates have so far been recorded only for *Euglena*.

In euglenoid cells prepared for electron microscopy these droplets are represented by collapsed vesicles containing lipid bodies, myelin figures and proliferations of unit membranes (Fig. 140), hence the use here of the term *phospholipid vesicles*. Whether all the contents are condensation patterns of a liquid droplet, or whether the phospholipid vesicle has some solid components in the living cell is not certain. Each vesicle is bounded by a single unit membrane (Fig. 140).

In addition to the large phospholipid vesicles (which can be as much as 1 to 2μ in diameter), the cytoplasmic matrix of euglenoids also contains many smaller granules and droplets. These appear in electron micrographs of sectioned cells as single unit-membrane-limited vesicles of various sizes and content (Figs. 113, 126, 134) and need to be considered in terms of possible relation to lysosomes.

The concept of the lysosome has been discussed by Novikoff (1961b) and De Duve (1963). In terms of function the lysosome can be considered as an organelle of intracellular digestion, within which acid phosphatase, acid nucleases, cathepsin and β-glucuronase are safely delimited from the cytoplasmic matrix. In terms of structure, lysosomes are spherical vesicles, 0.5μ or less in diameter, characterised in electron micrographs by a single bounding unit membrane. Such vesicles occur in many types of animal cell, including by definition all pinocytotic and phagocytic vacuoles (for example, "food vacuoles" of protozoa). Release of the contained hydrolytic enzymes causes breakdown of phosphate and sulphate esters, nucleic acids, proteins and mucopolysaccharides, leading to autolysis and cell death. Frey-Wyssling and Mühlethaler (1965) discuss the possibility that the acid-phosphatase-containing spherosomes of plant cells are homologous to

166

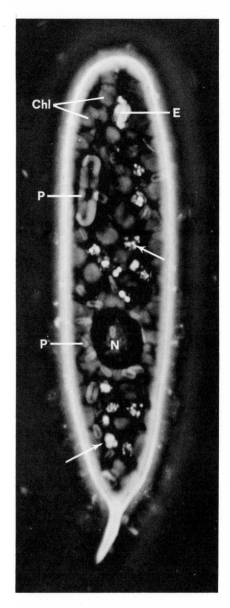

Fig. 145 Phospholipid vesicles (*arrows*, etc.) in a living cell of *Euglena spirogyra*. *Chl* chloroplasts, *E* eyespot, *N* nucleus, *P* paramylon. Anoptral contrast, ×1500.

lysosomes, though no lytic activity has yet been demonstrated for spherosomes.

Some of the unidentified vesicles in euglenoid cells correspond exactly to "identified" lysosomes in various animal tissues (as do some of the phospholipid vesicles, apart from their larger size). An interesting comparison is with lipofuscin granules which are found in human liver cells and which Novikoff regards as lysosomes charged with insoluble residues of the materials brought to the lysosomes by pinocytosis. Accumulation of lipofuscin granules is correlated with aging in human tissues and is regarded as a basic biological aging process. The accumulation of brown pigmented granules in euglenoid flagellates is also correlated with aging. It is now desirable for the cytochemist to determine the enzymatic status of these euglenoid cellular components.

Chapter 18

CHLOROPLASTS AND PYRENOIDS

Chloroplasts are organelles of photosynthesis, the process by which light energy is converted into chemical energy for storage in the cell or immediate use in cellular activity and metabolism. The chloroplasts of many algae (and the bryophyte *Anthoceros*) contain pyrenoids, regions usually associated with accumulation of reserve materials derived from photosynthates. Mature chloroplasts of higher plants contain small "particles" (grana, see below) but no pyrenoids.

Knowledge of chloroplast fine structure derives from electron microscopy and cytochemistry. In any plant cell a mature chloroplast contains the following components: (a) a semipermeable envelope of at least two unit membranes separated from one another by a region of low electron density, (b) protein-, lipid-, and chlorophyll-containing lamellations, (c) a proteinaceous stroma with granules slightly smaller than the ribosomes of the cytoplasmic matrix, and (d) various inclusions such as lipid globules and carbohydrates (usually starch). All chloroplast lamellations are constructed from flattened cisternae ("discs" *sensu* Sager and Palade, 1957; "thylakoids" *sensu* Menke, 1961). The thylakoid membrane is 25 to 50 Å thick, and its enclosed cavity is 25 to 75 Å wide. In chloroplasts of higher plants, cylindrical stacks of many superimposed thylakoids form the grana which are visible in the light microscope and which are linked by intergranal thylakoids.

Most or all of the enzyme systems and pigments involved in photosynthesis are located in the chloroplasts. There is good evidence (see Arnon, 1961) that the electron transport chain concerned with the synthesis of "assimilatory power" [ATP + NADPH$_2$ (reduced nicotinamide adenine dinucleotide phosphate)] by cyclic and noncyclic photophosphorylation is associated with the lamellar system, though there is considerable argument as to the exact location and orientation of the chlorophylls. Intensive current research is attempting to determine whether or not the chloroplast stroma contains the enzymes of the light-independent reactions in which the "assimilatory power" is used to condense atmospheric carbon dioxide into ribulose diphosphate and thence, after molecular cleavage and polymerisation, to hexose with regeneration of ribulose diphosphate (Calvin cycle). Reviews which specifically relate chloroplast chemistry and function to ultrastructure are those by Menke (1962) and Thomas (1960; 1965).

The chemical nature of the pyrenoids has not been fully investigated

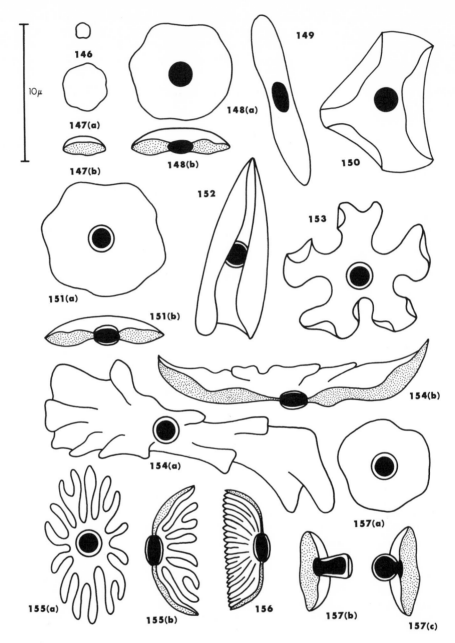

Figs. 146-157 Chloroplast types in euglenoid flagellates. 146–147, chloroplasts without pyrenoids, discoid in face view [146, 147(a)], lenticular in section [147(b)]; 148–150, flat chloroplasts with "naked" pyrenoids; 151–152, flat or shield-shaped chloroplasts with "double" pyrenoids; 153–156, lobed or dissected chloroplasts with "double" pyrenoids; 157, chloroplasts with "inner pyrenoids," discoid in face view [157(a)], lenticular in section with cylindrical [157(b)] or spherical [157(c)] pyrenoidal projection; see text for further details.

but staining reactions suggest that they are rich in proteins. Pyrenoids are thought to contain enzymes concerned with polysaccharide formation, since primary production (or, at least, accumulation) of starch and other such carbohydrates nearly always occurs around the pyrenoids (see p. 185).

Euglenoid Chloroplasts and Pyrenoids

Morphology and fine structure

Euglenoid chloroplasts show considerable diversity of size, shape and morphology (Figs. 146-157), and, as indicated in the first part of this book, these characters have proved valuable for species determination in certain genera. The five types of euglenoid plastidome (total chloroplast complement of a cell) are as follows:

1. Numerous discoid chloroplasts, each 2 to 5μ in diameter and 1 to 2μ thick, with no pyrenoids (Figs. 146 and 147); typical for species of *Phacus* (Figs. 39, 158), *Lepocinclis* (Fig. 38) and *Klebsiella* (Fig. 34), and certain species of *Euglena* (subgenera *Rigidae, Lentiferae,*Figs. 6-8, 10, 163), *Strombomonas* (Fig. 31) and, rarely, *Trachelomonas;* small discoid chloroplasts without pyrenoids are also the type found in many other groups of algae and nearly all higher plants.

2. Discoid, elongated or shield-shaped chloroplasts, 5 to 10μ in diameter, each with a central "naked pyrenoid" which has no direct association with paramylon (Figs. 148-150); found in *Euglena* subgenus *Serpentes* (Figs. 17, 18) and some species of *Trachelomonas.*

3. Large plate-chloroplasts, 5 to $10\mu \times 5$ to 20μ, each with a central pyrenoid which carries, on both plastid surfaces, a watchglass-shaped cap of paramylon (Figs. 151-156); chloroplast margin entire, lobed or finely dissected, the arms of the dissected type often showing helical arrangement in the cell (Fig. 159; see p. 23); such chloroplasts with "double-sheathed pyrenoids" are the feature used to define the subgenus *Catilliferae* of *Euglena* (Figs. 11-14) and are also encountered in some species of *Trachelomonas*.

4. Plate-chloroplasts with "inner pyrenoids," each chloroplast having projecting from its inner surface a large pyrenoid which is covered by a cylindrical or spherical cup of paramylon (Fig. 157); characteristic of all species of *Colacium* (Figs. 36, 160) and many species of *Trachelomonas* (Fig. 26), and recently reported for one species of *Euglena* (p. 27).

5. Chloroplast ribbons radiating from one, two or three "paramylon centres" (Figs. 1, 15, 16); the ribbons can convert into discrete, discoid, pyrenoid-less chloroplasts (Fig. 161); each paramylon centre, which stains and apparently functions as a pyrenoid, is often surrounded by a sheath of separate paramylon granules, recalling the starch sheath in other algae rather than the paramylon caps in other euglenoid flagellates; this type of plastidome occurs in the genus *Eutreptia* (Figs. 1, 161) and in *Euglena* subgenus *Radiatae* (Figs. 15, 16, 162).

Living euglenoid chloroplasts are grass-green in colour and appear homogeneous in the light microscope, apart from their pyrenoids. However,

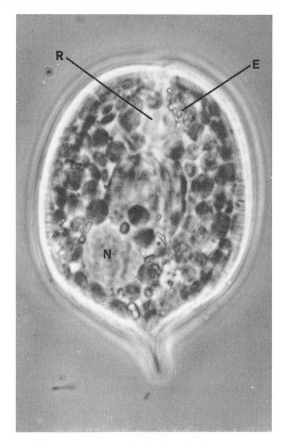

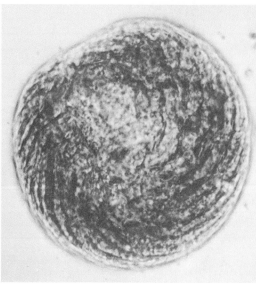

Fig. 158 Numerous discoid chloroplasts in a living cell of *Phacus triqueter*. *E* eyespot, *R* reservoir, *N* nucleus. Phase contrast, ×2000.

Fig. 159 Anterior view of a living cell of *Euglena magnifica*, showing the helically disposed ribbons of the diffused chloroplasts (see p. 23). ×1000.

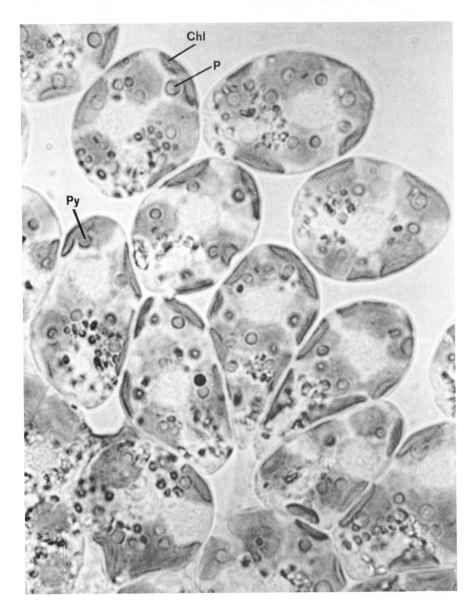

Fig. 160 Living cells of *Colacium cyclopicolum:* note the peripheral chloroplasts (*Chl*) with inwardly projecting pyrenoids (*Py*), each with a spherical cap of paramylon (*P*). ×2000.

when burst from a cell into water they swell to reveal a lamellate structure (Fig. 163), and continued swelling leads to the ballooning of several vesicles from each chloroplast (Fig. 164). These observations correlate with those on fine structure.

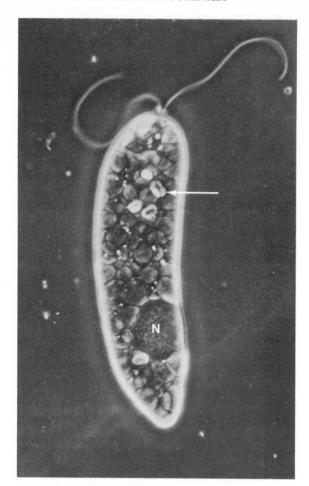

Fig. 161 Living cell of *Eutreptia pertyi*, showing the paramylon centre (arrow) and numerous chloroplasts in the discoid state throughout the cell; note also the two emergent flagella and the posteriorly placed nucleus (N). Anoptral contrast, ×1000.

Division of euglenoid chloroplasts (and pyrenoids) can be seen in the living organism. Chloroplasts of the small discoid type divide independently throughout the life of a cell, but in species with fewer large chloroplasts, plastid division may be synchronised with cell division. For example, the two chloroplasts in *Euglena pisciformis* (Fig. 12) divide simultaneously with the nucleus and other organelles, prior to cell cleavage. The specific number of chloroplasts is thus retained and in healthy cells is a reliable taxonomic character. Embedded pyrenoids divide as the plastid divides, but division of stalked pyrenoids begins at the distal end and this is followed by constriction and fission of the chloroplast body. In species of *Eutreptia* and *Euglena* subgenus *Radiatae*, the paramylon centre divides synchronously with the nucleus, but the behaviour of the associated chloroplast ribbons cannot be followed in living cells.

The euglenoid version of chloroplast ultrastructure is similar to that of many algal plastids (Gibbs, 1960, 1962a, 1962b, 1962c). The envelope is composed of three membranes (Figs. 140, 165), suggesting an association with endoplasmic reticulum such as is found in the *Chrysophyta* and *Phaeophyta*. The typical lamellation consists of three closely appressed thylakoids (Fig. 111), though patterns involving up to twelve thylakoids may occur (Fig. 165). This recalls the situation in the *Chlorophyta*, whereas plastids of other algae have lamellations of single thylakoids (*Rhodophyta*) or two or three thylakoids only (*Chrysophyta*, *Xanthophyta*, *Phaeophyta*). Photosynthetic procaryotic cells (bacteria and *Cyanophyta*) have chlorophyll-containing thylakoids free in the cytoplasmic matrix, not within membrane-bounded organelles (p. 4).

The sectioned three-thylakoid lamellation of the euglenoid chloroplast

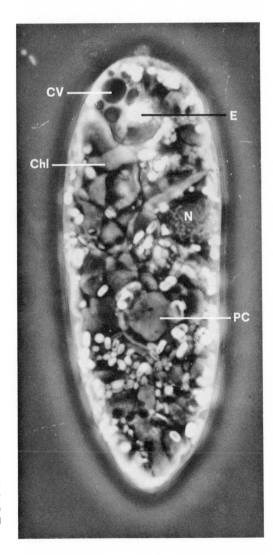

Fig. 162 *Euglena geniculata*: living cell, flattened to show chloroplast ribbons (*Chl*), paramylon centre (*PC*) with adjacent paramylon granules, eyespot (*E*), contractile vacuole (*CV*) and nucleus (*N*). Anoptral contrast, ×2000.

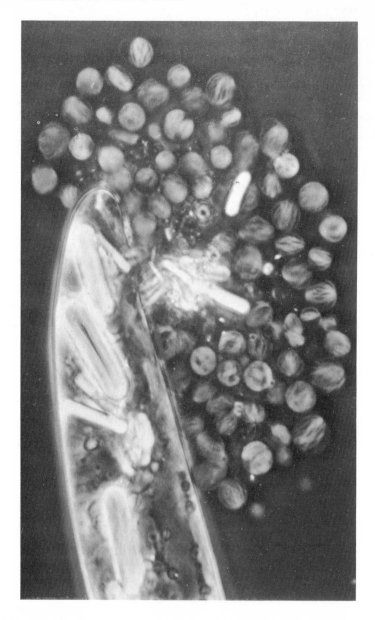

Fig. 163 Bursting cell of *Euglena acus*, with the liberated chloroplasts swelling in water to reveal their lamellate structure; also paramylon rods and links in the cell. Anoptral contrast, × 2000.

has the now familiar appearance of a thin line/space/thick line/space/thick line/space/thin line (Figs. 111, 140, 165), where a thin line is a single membrane, a thick line is the closely apposed membranes of neighbouring thylakoids, and each space is the cavity of one thylakoid. The compound

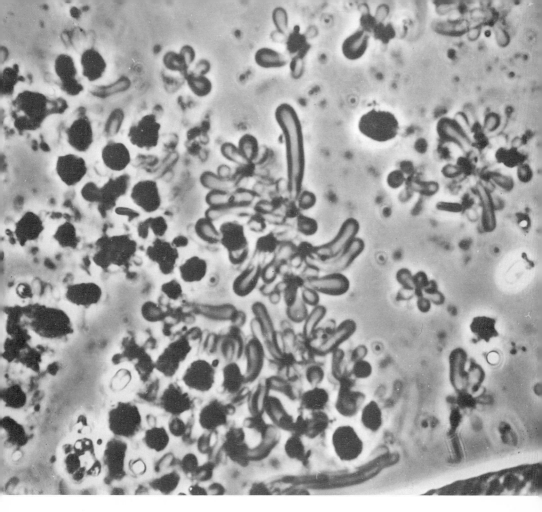

Fig. 164 Chloroplasts of *Euglena spirogyra* var. *fusca*, swelling in water to produce numerous vesicles. Phase contrast, ×2000.

lamellations often traverse the chloroplast, but individual thylakoids extend only partway and their "edges" are marked by small osmiophilic particles (Fig. 165) which are probably lipid stripped from the membranes during fixation. Osmiophilic globules, 2000 to 3000 Å in diameter, lie in the granular stroma (Fig. 165). Such globules are a characteristic component of many types of plastid, those in higher plants containing various lipids but no β-carotene or chlorophylls.

Pyrenoids in euglenoid chloroplasts are finely granular regions of stroma containing two-thylakoid lamellations which either traverse the pyrenoid matrix or appear to end within it (Fig. 166). Sections of the watchglass- or cup-shaped paramylon caps appear in electron micrographs as membrane-limited cavities, closely neighbouring the pyrenoids but clearly outside the plastid envelope and separated from it in places by a narrow region of cytoplasmic matrix (Fig. 166; see p. 185).

177

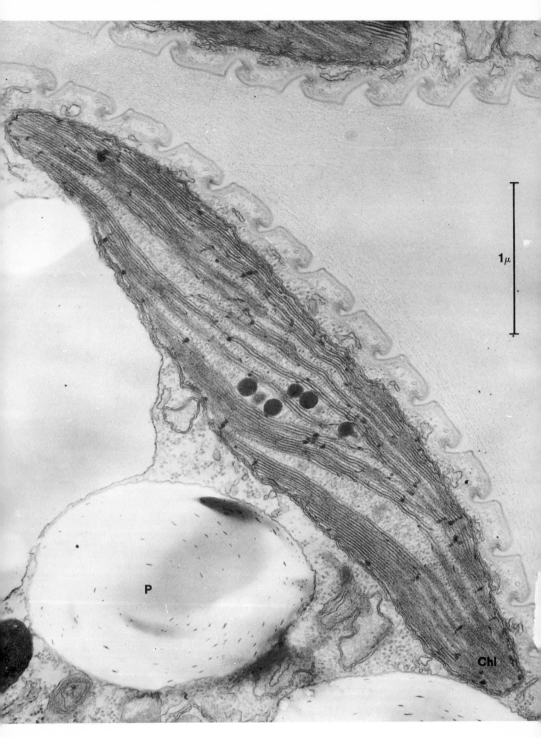

Chloroplast function in Euglena

Plastids of *Euglena gracilis* (and presumably other euglenoid flagellates) contain chlorophylls *a* and *b*, β-carotene, antheraxanthin, neoxanthin, small amounts of other carotenoids (Krinsky and Goldsmith, 1960) and quinones (Fuller, Smillie, Rigopoulos and Yount, 1961). The phylogenetic implications of the similarity of these pigments to those of the green plants have already been discussed (pp. 3 and 4). Experimental data (see numerous references below) suggest close similarity between the photosynthetic apparatus of *Euglena* and that of higher plants, and two of the physiological strains of *Euglena gracilis* isolated by Pringsheim (see p. 23), *Euglena gracilis* Z and *Euglena gracilis* var. *bacillaris*, have been much used to investigate chloroplast chemistry and development. The intensity of this research activity during the past ten years has produced a wealth of information; particular interest attaches to studies on the reduction and loss of chloroplasts during experimental etiolation and "bleaching" of these strains.

When dividing cells of *Euglena gracilis* are grown in the dark at room temperature in axenic culture (p. 199), the chloroplasts lose their chlorophyll and, over a span of eight generations (144 hours), the chloroplast lamellations become disorganised and disappear (Ben-Shaul, Epstein and Schiff, 1965). The cells then contain regressed plastids which resemble higher plant proplastids, the minute yellow or colourless "juvenile" plastids which occur, for example, in meristematic cells. These euglenoid "proplastids" divide in the dark to keep pace with cell division and on the return of an etiolated culture to the light (even after several years) all the cells, whether dividing or not, become green as the proplastids enlarge and synthesise chlorophyll. A dark-grown cell of *Euglena gracilis* var. *bacillaris* has approximately 30 proplastids (Epstein and Schiff, 1961), each 1μ in diameter with a two-membraned envelope but little internal structure. When such a cell is returned to optimal light intensity (100 foot-candles; Stern, Epstein and Schiff, 1964) thylakoids appear as invaginated blebs of each inner proplastid membrane and, after about six hours, the first lamella (lamellation) is produced by fusion of several thylakoids (Ben-Shaul, Schiff and Epstein, 1964). The fact that evolution of photosynthetic oxygen, fixation of carbon dioxide and synthesis of chlorophyll all begin from four to eight hours after illumination (Epstein and Schiff, 1961; Stern, Schiff and Epstein, 1964) suggests that the lamella is the structural (morphological) unit of photosynthesis. Though pyrenoids appear after 18 to 20 hours and rate of thylakoid formation gradually decreases, the rate of lamellar production is constant and linear from 14 to 72 hours. One lamella is formed every 6 hours (until the mature chloroplast has 13 or 14 lamellae) and, over this period of time, the

---

Fig. 165 *Colacium cyclopicolum:* sectioned chloroplast (Chl) showing the compound envelope, the stroma with granules slightly smaller than ribosomes of the cytoplasmic matrix, lipid globules (L) and lamellations composed of three or more thylakoids; deposition of flecks of lead gives some indication of helical organisation in the membrane-limited paramylon granule (P); the section also shows the pellicular strips, muciferous bodies and microtubules inside the plasmalemma (see Fig. 87) and mucilage of the cell sheath outside. Electron micrograph, × 40,000.

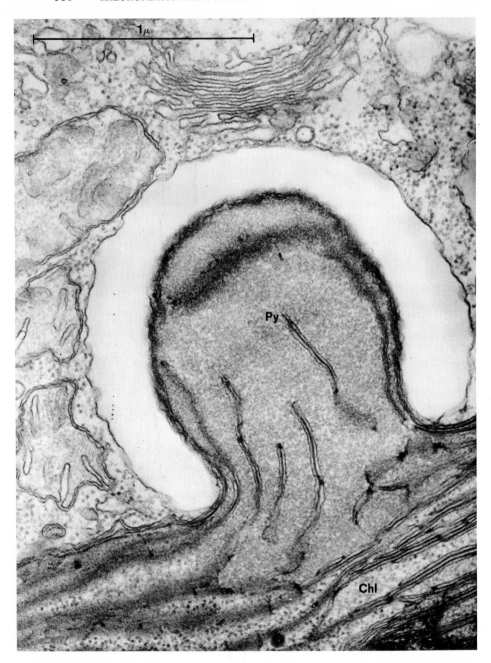

Fig. 166 Inner pyrenoid of *Colacium cyclopicolum*: compare the two-thylakoid lamellations and dense stroma of the pyrenoid diverticulum (*Py*) with the equivalent structures in the chloroplast proper (*Chl*); immediately surrounding the pyrenoid, but outside the plastid envelope, is the membrane-limited paramylon cap. Electron micrograph, ×50,000.

physiological parameters (oxygen evolution, carbon dioxide fixation, pigment synthesis) also show linear kinetics.*

This sequential development is known so far only in the *Euglena* chloroplast. In higher plants several lamellae form simultaneously (directly from the proplastid in light, or from a prolamellar body if proplastid development has taken place in darkness) and these replicate in geometrically parallel sequence (see von Wettstein, 1959). However, light is seen to be as essential for chlorophyll synthesis in *Euglena* as it is in angiosperms, whereas some algae (and gymnosperms) form chlorophyll in darkness as well as in light. Etiolated angiosperm leaves contain protochlorophyllide *a* as the known precursor of chlorophyll *a*, and protochlorophyll *a* of unknown fate. Dark-grown cells of *Euglena gracilis* var. *bacillaris* also contain one or perhaps both of these substances (Wolken and Mellon, 1956; Nishimura and Huzisige, 1959), the concentration of which decreases as chlorophyll is formed in the light. These and other data suggest that chlorophyll biosynthesis is possibly a similar process in *Euglena* and the flowering plants.

Non-dividing cells of *Euglena gracilis* show a different series of events when placed in the dark (Ben-Shaul, Epstein, and Schiff, 1965). Though 38 per cent of the chlorophyll is lost and another 50 per cent is converted to the degradation product, pheophytin (Wolken, Mellon and Greenblatt, 1955; Greenblatt and Schiff, 1959; Brown, 1963), the chloroplasts do *not* lose their lamellate structure over a 144 hour period. This agrees with the findings of von Wettstein (1961) that chlorophyll is not in itself an essential determinant of lamellar organisation. Retention of lamellate chloroplast structure in the non-dividing dark-grown *Euglena* is interpreted as of adaptive advantage by Ben-Shaul, Epstein and Schiff (1965): the cell cannot grow in the dark but is equipped for phototrophy as soon as light reappears. On the other hand, the dividing dark-grown *Euglena* (in a medium which supports heterotrophy; see p. 200) reduces "the excess baggage of chloroplast structure" to the proplastid state, becoming an efficient heterotroph until reappearance of light induces the formation of functional chloroplasts once more.

Other important work on the light-induced greening of etiolated *Euglena* includes studies on the photo-induction of enzyme biosynthesis (carboxylase and dehydrogenases, Fuller and Gibbs, 1959; transhydrogenase, Lazzarini and San Pietro, 1963; Lazzarini and Woodruff, 1964), demonstration by antigen-antibody reactions of extensive and varied protein and enzyme synthesis (Lewis, Schiff and Epstein, 1965), studies on lipid patterns and alterations (for example, a change from mainly saturated fatty acids in etiolated cells to mainly unsaturated fatty acids in green cells, Rosenberg and Pecker, 1964) and studies on carotenoid synthesis. Dark-grown cells of *Euglena gracilis* var. *bacillaris* have only 7 per cent of the carotenoid content

---

* A threefold increase in all parameters between 10 and 14 hours of development is interpreted as fusion of proplastids in threes, giving 10 mature chloroplasts from 30 proplastids. This unlikely cytological event has also been inferred from fluorescence studies (Epstein, Boy de la Tour and Schiff, 1960; Epstein and Schiff, 1961) and ultraviolet irradiation studies (Lyman, Epstein and Schiff, 1961). However, it has recently been suggested (Schiff and Epstein, 1965) that the proplastids are structurally linked in groups of three in the dark-grown cell.

of green cells in the light, with neoxanthin totally absent (Krinsky, Gordon and Stern, 1964). On placing etiolated cells in the light, carotenoid synthesis begins at once, except for a 4 hour lag before neoxanthin synthesis occurs. This correlates with the lag in appearance and development of photosynthetic competence (see above). Also, study of fluorescence and spectral changes during greening have led to calculations concerning molecular organisation of *Euglena* chloroplasts. For example, Brody, Brody and Levine (1965) have suggested that chlorophyll is present on the outer lamellar surfaces only and not between adjacent thylakoids.

Related research on the chloroplasts of *Euglena gracilis* concerns their nucleic acid content. It has been shown (Lyman, Epstein and Schiff, 1959, 1961; Schiff, Lyman and Epstein, 1961; Gibor and Granick, 1962) that non-lethal doses of ultraviolet (UV) irradiation specifically inhibit chloroplast replication [but not conversion of protochlorophyll(ide) into chlorophyll, nor the development of proplastids into chloroplasts, nor cell division] and that the probable site of inactivation is plastid-localised DNA-protein. Target analysis of the irradiation curves suggests there are 30 or multiplicities of 30 UV-sensitive entities in the cell, and this result has been correlated with the 30 proplastids of the dark-grown organism. Combination of the inhibition and photoreactivation data has led to the assumption (Schiff and Epstein, 1965) that each proplastid of the dark-grown *Euglena gracilis* var. *bacillaris* cell contains one DNA-protein entity, whereas each mature chloroplast of the green cell contains three DNA-protein entities (see footnote, p. 181). Leff, Mandel, Epstein and Schiff (1963) demonstrated two types of DNA for *Euglena*, a major component which occurs in both green and colourless cells (probably the nuclear DNA) and a minor component which is detectable only in green cells and is apparently localised in the chloroplasts. Demonstration of the minor component in dark-grown cells with proplastids (Edelman, Cowan, Epstein and Schiff, 1964) and in the chloroplast fraction of fractionated cells (Brawerman and Eisenstadt, 1964a; Ray and Hanawalt, 1964) helps to confirm its chloroplast localisation, as does autoradiographic demonstration of DNA in *Euglena* chloroplasts (Sagan, Ben-Shaul, Epstein and Schiff, 1965). Subsequently (Edelman, Schiff and Epstein, 1965; Ray and Hanawalt, 1965), it has been shown that the minor component DNA in fact contains two types, one being the chloroplast DNA and the other a species of DNA associated with the small-particle fraction of fractionated *Euglena* and possibly mitochondrial in origin (p. 165). The chloroplast DNA is quite different in base composition from the nuclear DNA (Brawerman and Eisenstadt, 1964b; Edelman, Cowan, Epstein and Schiff, 1964; Ray and Hanawalt, 1964, 1965; Edelman, Schiff and Epstein, 1965), but it remains to be shown whether or not it is informational for the formation of chloroplast structures. In their review, Schiff and Epstein (1965) speculate at length about possible control mechanisms for chloroplast development and replication in *Euglena*.

The extensive nucleic acid studies of Brawerman and his co-workers have also included work on the RNA of *Euglena gracilis* chloroplasts. Brawerman and Chargaff (1959a) have shown that *Euglena gracilis* Z can form chloroplasts in absence of growth and without net synthesis of protein and

RNA. During greening of non-growing etiolated cells, 17 per cent of cellular proteins appear in the chloroplast fraction and qualitative changes occur in nucleotide ratios in the RNA (Brawerman and Chargaff, 1959b). RNA of the green cells has higher proportions of adenylic and uridylic acids relative to cytidylic and guanylic acids. In greening non-dividing cells in which net synthesis of protein and nucleic acid is permitted to occur (Brawerman, Pogo and Chargaff, 1961) chloroplast RNA increases at once but chloroplast protein shows steep increase only after a delay of 24 hours, suggesting that the new RNA is responsible for protein formation. Isolation of the chloroplast ribosomes shows them to differ from the ribosomes of the cytoplasmic matrix (p. 116) in nucleotide ratios (Brawerman, 1963), sedimentation value (Eisenstadt and Brawerman, 1964b) and in higher content of template RNA (Brawerman and Eisenstadt, 1964a). It might be proposed that the significance of the *specific* RNA in the plastids is that it contains specific information for synthesis of chloroplast protein. However, messenger RNA theory (p. 115) states that ribosomal RNA does not determine protein specificity and would therefore suggest that the peculiar nucleotide composition of the ribosomal RNA of *Euglena* chloroplasts is fortuitous (Brawerman, 1963).

As indicated above, current research on *Euglena* chloroplasts is much concerned with the relation between the possibly informational nature of their nucleic acids (especially the DNA) and the concept of genetic continuity of plastids (see Schiff and Epstein, 1965). Such thoughts lead naturally to a consideration of "bleaching" experiments with *Euglena*.

When certain strains of *Euglena gracilis* are grown at high but sublethal temperatures (32–35°C), cell division continues but chloroplast replication is inhibited. At each cell cleavage, therefore, the number of chloroplasts per cell decreases and cells with no chloroplasts are soon produced (Pringsheim and Pringsheim, 1952). These aplastidic cells can then be isolated and grown as *permanently* colourless races. Once a cell has lost all its chloroplasts* *it can never form chloroplasts again.* This fact is of great significance, since it establishes unequivocally the concept of plastid continuity for *Euglena*. The controversial theory that chloroplasts are periodically regenerated from initials evaginated from the nuclear envelope (Mühlethaler and Bell, 1962; Bell and Mühlethaler, 1962; Frey-Wyssling and Mühlethaler, 1965) is certainly not applicable to *Euglena*. This organism exemplifies the widely accepted idea that plastids can arise only from other plastids.

Most of the heat-produced colourless races also lose the eyespot and flagellar swelling (pp. 23 and 146), but the Pringsheims were able to produce some aplastidic cells in which the eyespot and flagellar swelling were retained. The important phylogenetic implications of these experiments have been considered elsewhere (p. 73), as have studies on phototaxis using these races (p. 146).

Permanently colourless ("bleached") races of *Euglena gracilis* can also be produced by ultraviolet irradiation (Lyman, Epstein and Schiff, 1959), by the action of streptomycin (Provasoli, Hutner and Schatz, 1948) and

* Such a state can also be established under normal conditions by unequal distribution of organelles during cell cleavage (p. 104).

other antibiotics such as aureomycin (Robbins, Hervey and Stebbins, 1953), kanamycin, paromomycin and neomycin (Zahalsky, Hutner, Keane and Burger, 1962), erythromycin (Ebringer, 1962), carbomycin, spiramycin and viomycin (Ebringer, 1964), by the action of pyribenzamine (Gross, Jahn and Bernstein, 1955) and other antihistamines such as tripelennamine, methapyrilene and pyrilamine (Zahalsky, Hutner, Keane and Burger, 1962), by the action of β-methoxythreonine (Aaronson, 1960a) and O-methylthreonine (Aaronson and Bensky, 1962), and by the action of nitro-furantoin (McCalla, 1965). Of rather different significance is the non-permanent bleaching (with cells always regreening on removal of the agent) caused by aminotriazole (Aaronson, 1960b), picromycin and methamycin (Ebringer, 1964).

The mechanism of the bleaching action is still in dispute. Some authors consider the effect of streptomycin to be an arresting of chloroplast multipli-cation (as with heat treatment), dilution of chloroplasts at successive cell divisions leading to cells with none (Provasoli, Hutner and Pintner, 1951; Deken-Grenson and Messin, 1958; Schiff and Epstein, 1965). Other investi-gations suggest that the inhibition is biochemical but not structural and that irreversibly non-functional plastids persist and divide in some colourless races (Siegesmund, Rosen and Gawlik, 1962; Gibor and Granick, 1962; Moriber, Hershenov, Aaronson and Bensky, 1963). These authors and others (Deken-Grenson and Godts, 1960; Rosen and Gawlik, 1961) infer that streptomycin inhibits various steps of pigment synthesis; Kirk (1962a, 1962b) suggests an upset of general cellular biosynthesis by inactivation of the ribosomes; Zahalsky, Hutner, Keane and Burger (1962) deduce an interference with nucleic acid metabolism in the chloroplast. Similarly, bleaching with ultra-violet irradiation is believed to be due to selective damage of chloroplast DNA (Scher and Sagan, 1962; McCalla, 1965). Schiff and Epstein (1965) cast doubt upon the plastidial nature of the structures reported from bleached cells, but such reports are of interest in relation to the possible presence of leuco-plasts in some wild colourless species of *Khawkinea* (p. 29) and "*Hyalo-trachelomonas*" (p. 36).

Chapter 19

PARAMYLON

The various starches formed as reserve polysaccharides in green algae (*Chlorophyta*) and higher plants are all α-1:4-linked glucans. Closely related α-1:4-linked glucans include floridean starch and cyanophycean starch, the storage materials of certain red algae (*Rhodophyta*) and blue-green algae (*Cyanophyta*), respectively. Reserve polysaccharides in other algal groups are of a significantly different chemical nature, being β-1:3-linked glucans. Examples of such substances are laminarin of the brown algae (*Phaeophyta*) leucosin (chrysolaminarin) of the *Chrysophyta* and diatoms (*Bacillariophyta*) and paramylon of the euglenoids (*Euglenophyta*).* The chemistry and occurrence of these algal products are reviewed by Meeuse (1962), who points out that β-1:3-linked glucans are probably the most abundant polysaccharides in nature, also occurring in callose and many plant cell walls and forming as a response to injury in higher plants.

Paramylon, the characteristic storage product of euglenoid flagellates, was first identified as a β-1:3-linked glucan by Kreger and Meeuse (1952) on the basis of X-ray diffraction studies. The physical and chemical properties of this substance have been thoroughly investigated since and most recently reported on by Meeuse (Leedale, Meeuse and Pringsheim, 1965). Paramylon is soluble in anhydrous formic acid, 5 per cent formaldehyde, 5 per cent sodium hydroxide, and 55 per cent sulphuric acid. These reagents in lower concentration cause swelling of granules, as do various other substances (Leedale, Meeuse and Pringsheim, 1965). Unlike starch, paramylon is insoluble in boiling water and is not affected by diastase. Similarly, paramylon does not stain with iodine nor with any other reagent tested. Reaction is also negative with periodate-Schiff reagent, a result consistent with β-1:3-linked glucan structure which precludes the presence of the adjacent hydroxyl groups required for a positive reaction.

Another difference from most starch reserves is that paramylon is always formed in the cytoplasmic matrix of the cell, never inside the chloroplasts. In cells with pyrenoid-containing chloroplasts (see p. 171), paramylon forms independently of the pyrenoids in *all* species and also as sheaths around the pyrenoids in *some* species. Electron microscopy confirms that pyrenoid sheaths are formed outside the chloroplast membrane (Fig. 166). In species

---

* The recent observation that a species of *Eutreptiella* is probably storing carbohydrate as leucosin and not as paramylon is of great interest and potential taxonomic importance (see pp. 14 and 53).

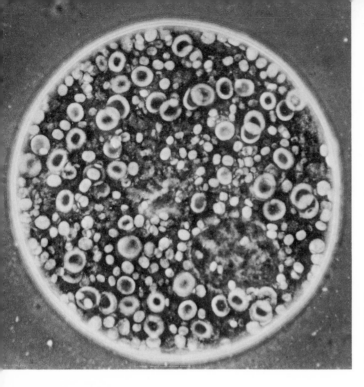

Fig. 167 *Euglena magnifica*: rounded-off living cell, flattened to show the watchglass-shaped paramylon caps of the double-sheathed pyrenoids (seen in slightly dissociated pairs). Anoptral contrast, ×1000.

of *Euglena* subgenus *Radiatae* and species of *Eutreptia*, paramylon is laid down around the pyrenoid-like paramylon centre (p. 171). A direct relation between paramylon formation and photosynthesis can be demonstrated for green species growing in the light, but paramylon is also, of course, the storage product of colourless euglenoids, and a direct relation between paramylon deposition and heterotrophy or phagotrophy can also be shown (see p. 192).

Since paramylon is a utilisable reserve material, it follows (Meeuse, 1962) that an enzyme to hydrolyse it, a paramylase, exists in euglenoid cells. This has not so far been isolated, but a laminarase capable of hydrolysing soluble laminarin has been prepared from *Euglena* extracts (Meeuse, 1962). Recently, Meeuse (Leedale, Meeuse and Pringsheim, 1965) obtained complete digestion of paramylon with enzyme preparations from the stomach glands of molluscs (*Anodonta*, *Dreissena* and *Unio*) which are natural predators on euglenoid flagellates. These preparations, which must contain a paramylase, digest large granules in regular fashion from the centre outwards, giving rings and loops with cavities of increasing size. This supports the observation (see below) that rings arise in living cells by lytic processes and not, as once thought, from pre-formed cytoplasmic structures. Meeuse deduces from his results that paramylon granules have very strict orientation of micelles and great internal uniformity of linkage types (with linkages other than β-1:3 rare or absent), and that paramylase attacks the chains of linked glucose residues in unidirectional fashion.

Granules of paramylon observed between crossed Nicol prisms show a dark cross, as do starch grains of higher plants. This is consistent with (but does not prove) a radial arrangement of crystallites. When paramylon granules are squashed or subjected to swelling, fissures appear (Figs. 169-171), and casual observation suggests that the granules consist of concentric lamellae, as do many starch grains. However, careful examination reveals that the granules have helical organisation (Fig. 171), a fact known for a hundred years but elegantly demonstrated by Pochmann (1956, 1958) in a photographic study of swollen paramylon from *Phacus* and *Euglena*. The granules grow peripherally, with central lysis leading to loops and rings and subsequent stretching and loss of the cavity resulting in solid rods. Cylindrical pyrenoid sheaths of paramylon (p. 171) have a helically wound biconvex base and tapering sides constructed from a flat helix of paramylon fibrils (Fig. 172).

In the light microscope, paramylon appears as refractive granules of various shapes and sizes (Figs. 69, 79, 84, 85, 97, 123, 145, 161-163, 167-170), and the shape and position of granules may be important taxonomic features. For example, cells of *Euglena spirogyra, oxyuris* and *tripteris* (Dujardin 1841) Klebs 1883 typically have two large paramylon granules, one anterior to and one posterior to the nucleus (Fig. 6). During cell division in these species, the nucleus migrates towards the reservoir (p. 84), and the two paramylon rings come to lie side by side posterior to the dividing

Fig. 168   Cell of *Trachelomonas grandis,* showing paramylon caps (P) of the inner pyrenoids (Py). Methanol fixed/Aceto-carmine stained, ×1500.

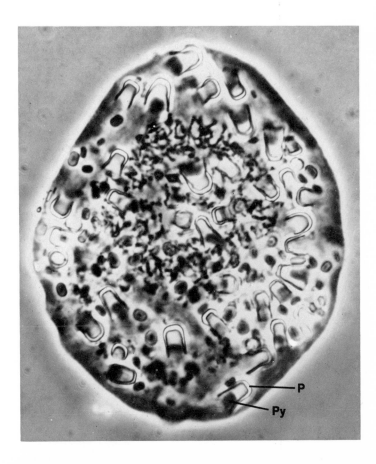

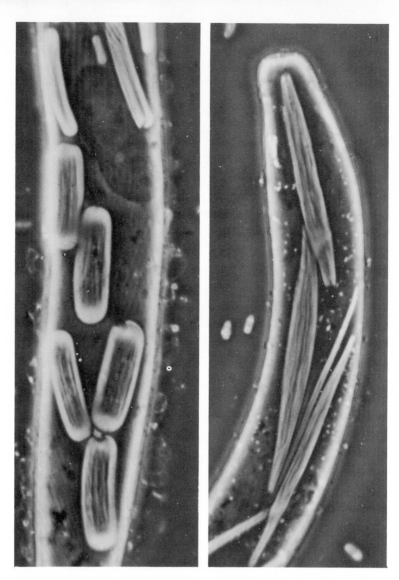

Figs. 169 and **170** Squashed paramylon granules, showing apparently longitudinal striations: cylindrical rods of *Euglena acus* var. *hyalina* in Fig. 169, tapering needles of *Cyclidiopsis acus* in Fig. 170. Anoptral contrast, ×2000.

nucleus. After mitosis, the cell divides longitudinally, and the helical cleavage plane passes between the two rings. Each daughter cell thus receives one paramylon ring which becomes the posterior ring in each case. After separation of the daughter cells, the second paramylon ring reforms in each cell in the characteristic position anterior to the nucleus. Electron microscopy provides no evidence of special cytoplasmic structures which could be developing centres for the "taxonomic" granules, and the cycle of movement and reformation of the rings in these species lends support to Pringsheim's (1956) suggestion that the important factor might be spatial, a cytoplasmic

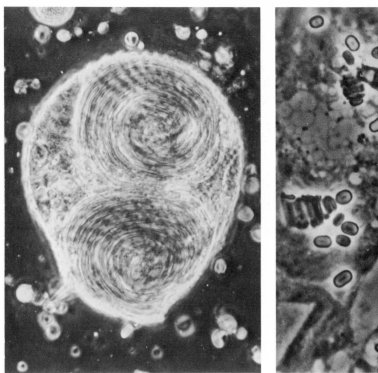 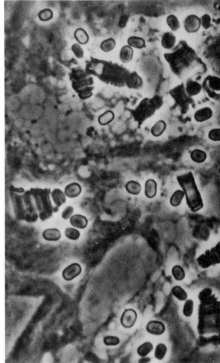

Fig. 171. Cell of *Euglena spirogyra* var. *fusca*, with squashed paramylon granules showing helical striations. Anoptral contrast, ×1000.

Fig. 172 Paramylon of *Trachelomonas grandis*, showing small oval granules and squashed pyrenoid caps (see text). Phase contrast, ×2000.

region free from large organelles automatically becoming a major centre of polysaccharide deposition. Nevertheless, it is difficult to see why this should apply to some species and not others.

In the electron microscope, surface replicas of paramylon granules reveal the helical organisation, but sectioned grains show little structure. Deposition of flecks of lead in stained preparations sometimes indicates internal helical structure (Fig. 165), and standard methods of processing (p. 203) show a unit membrane around each granule (Figs. 165, 166). In some micrographs, elements identical in appearance with the tubular endoplasmic reticulum (p. 115) arise from the membrane around the granule and join with elements of the vesicular endoplasmic reticulum (p. 116). At face value, the implication of these observations is that paramylon granules are formed either within the endoplasmic reticular cavity or else in vesicles which become connected with it. Further work on cells in various metabolic states should help to clarify the situation.

Chapter 20

INGESTION ORGANELLES

A number of colourless euglenoid flagellates possess the ability to ingest particulate food, either with or without the aid of a special organelle. Species of the genera *Heteronema, Peranema, Peranemopsis, Urceolus, Dinema* and *Entosiphon* ingest through a permanent cytostome, with skeletal rods or tubes actively participating in the capture and intake of food particles and living prey (see below). The cytostome and ingestion apparatus form an independent system lateral to the canal and reservoir and, despite reports to the contrary, ingestion does not occur via the reservoir in these genera. Phagotrophy also occurs in *Euglenopsis, Calycimonas, Petalomonas, Tropidoscyphus, Notosolenus* and *Anisonema*, but without the presence of ingestion rods or tubes. The mode of food intake is not established for these rarely studied organisms and, though there is evidence for an independent cytostome in some species, records of ingestion via canal and reservoir are less easily refuted than in the previous group. Recent observations (Christen, 1959) suggest, though do not yet prove, that ingestion of small algal cells by *Euglenopsis edax* (p. 34) occurs via the reservoir. However, in the original description of the genus, Klebs (1892) reported seeing an independent cytostome.

Euglenopsis is the only known phagotrophic genus in the order *Euglenales*, and it is virtually certain that no green members of this order ingest particulate food. Otherwise, in the classification used in the present account, all phagotrophic species are grouped in two wholly colourless orders of the *Euglenophyta*, forms with no ingestion apparatus in the order *Sphenomonadales* (p. 52) and forms with ingestion rods or tubes in the order *Heteronematales* (p. 59). Some species of this latter order have been described as lacking an ingestion organelle, but Christen (1963) is of the opinion that these records are suspect. The phylogenetic significance of phagotrophy and an ingestion apparatus is considered on p. 73.

Fig. 173 *Entosiphon sulcatum*, section of a cell in the region of the reservoir: lying within the reservoir (R) are transverse sections of the two flagella with their differing paraflagellar rods (see Fig. 122); lateral to the reservoir are transverse sections of the three ingestion rods (arrows) which form the siphon (see text), and central to the three rods are accessory bands (arrowhead) which are also part of the ingestion organelle; lateral to the reservoir, on the side away from the siphon, is the contractile vacuole (CV) with attendant accessory vacuoles; the pellicle is composed of 12 pellicular strips, seen here to be S-shaped in cross section (see Fig. 174 for more details); batteries of trichocysts (T) are seen in transverse and longitudinal section beneath the pellicle, also muciferous bodies (M). Electron micrograph by Dr. J.-P. Mignot, ×18,000.

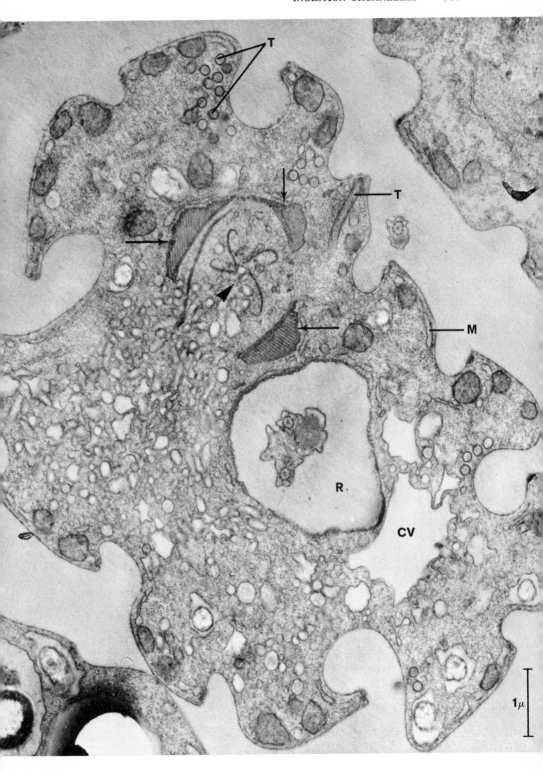

The most detailed study of the ingestion process in a euglenoid flagellate is that made by Chen (1950) on a species with an ingestion organelle, *Peranema trichophorum*. His experiments repay repetition, since the predatory behaviour of this organism is quite spectacular. The ingestion apparatus consists of two parallel tapering rods (Fig. 56), the hooked anterior ends of which are attached to the stiffened rim of the cytostome. This latter is a permanent "mouth" situated in a subapical position independent of the canal opening, but there is no permanent "gullet," and food vacuoles are formed at the cytostome only when feeding takes place. *Peranema* normally ingests food particles and living organisms (algae, bacteria, yeasts and even non-motile cells of *Euglena* as large as the predator itself) by engulfing them whole into food vacuoles. The ingestion rods are protruded and attached to the surface of the prey, which is then pulled some way through the cytostome in conjunction with a wave of euglenoid movement from the *Peranema* cell. With a large prey such as *Euglena*, the rods are detached, moved, and attached again further along the prey so that more of it can be pulled into the predator [Fig. 57(a)]. By repeated pullings the whole *Euglena* is engulfed [Fig. 57(b)], the process taking up to fifteen minutes. A second form of attack, reserved for large algal cells (sometimes much larger than *Peranema*), consists of cutting and sucking rather than engulfing. Several *Peranema* cells converge on the prey, and their ingestion rods are protruded and used to rasp a way through the prey's wall or periplast. *Euglena spirogyra* pellicle (see pp. 96–107) is cut through in approximately ten minutes, and the cell contents are then sucked out into a temporary food canal below the cytostome. If the prey is large enough, the predators finally enter its cell and engulf what remains of the contents, withdrawing when fully charged with food vacuoles. These decrease in size as digestion proceeds, and indigestible remains are finally ejected through a "defaecation area" of constant position at the posterior end of the cell. A whole cell of *Euglena gracilis* will be digested in one day, and the only part finally ejected is the pellicle. Chen (1950) experimentally demonstrated that *Peranema* can digest algal cells, yeast cells, fat (almond oil), protein (casein) and starch, ultimate conversion to paramylon and oil droplets being indicated in every case by the rapid accumulation of these inclusions in the feeding cell. That chemotaxis is

---

Fig. 174 Ingestion rods and trichocysts in *Entosiphon sulcatum*: part of a sectioned cell, showing the geometric structure of the ingestion rods in transverse section (*large arrowheads*); the accessory bands of the siphon (between the rods, see Fig. 173); the trichocysts (T), each in a unit-membrane-limited vesicle; and details of the pellicular complex (see Figs. 87 and 165) including the tripartite plasmalemma (*arrows*), material of the pellicular strip (*Pel*), microtubules (*small arrowheads*) and muciferous bodies (M); near to point A is an articulation between two strips, though the form of the articulation cannot be discerned. *Mit* mitochondrion. Electron micrograph by Dr. J.-P. Mignot, ×60,000.

Fig. 175 Siphon of *Entosiphon sulcatum*, cut in oblique longitudinal section: two of the three rods are sectioned (*arrowheads*), and between the rods can be seen the accessory bands of the ingestion apparatus forming a reticulum near the supposed cytostome; the cytostome (*arrow*) opens into a space which is continuous with the cell depression into which also opens the canal; the two flagella (F) emerge via this depression. Electron micrograph by Dr. J.-P. Mignot, ×30,000.

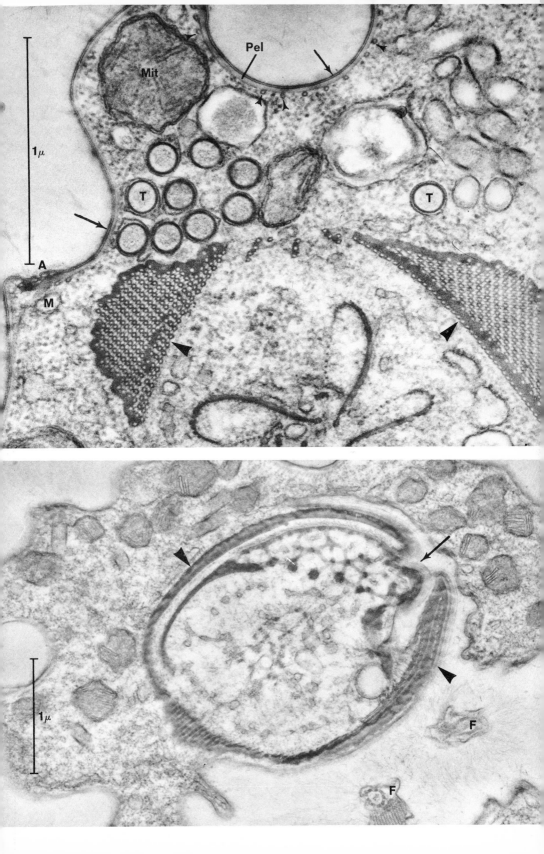

important in directing *Peranema* to its prey is also demonstrable: if living algal cells are burst open in a suspension of *Peranema*, the predators stream in for the meal from all directions.

In 1959, Roth made an electron microscopical study of *Peranema tricho-phorum* and reported on the fine structure of the ingestion apparatus. The two ingestion rods are each composed of a bundle of approximately 100 parallel fibrils or microtubules, averaging 260 Å in diameter, packed hexag-onally within the single groove of a dense column. The rods are joined at their anterior ends by a thick "membrane" (the rim of the cytostome) which is formed from sheetlike processes of fibrillar construction arising from the groove at two places along the rods. Roth points out that contraction of these sheets would move the rods forward (provided that the distal regions of the sheets were attached to, say, the pellicle; see Pitelka, 1963) and half-ingested matter would be compressed and pulled into the cell. Whether or not this is the mechanism of ingestion, it is of interest that those ubiquitous cytoplasmic structures, the microtubules (pp. 99 and 126), apparently figure in the construction of the ingestion rods and probably also in the putative contractile elements.

Light microscopy indicates that the ingestion apparatus in *Heteronema* (Fig. 58) and *Peranemopsis* (Fig. 59) is similar to that in *Peranema*, but in some species of the *Heteronematales* two or three ingestion rods are fused throughout their length to form a tube or "siphon." Phagotrophic behaviour has not been studied in detail in any of these organisms, but one of them, *Entosiphon sulcatum*, has been examined in the electron microscope (Mignot, 1963). Transverse sections of the ingestion organelle of *Entosiphon* (Fig. 173) show the three rods which form the siphon as triangular profiles situated in a ring to one side of the independent reservoir. Each rod is constructed from regularly arranged rows of fibrils or microtubules (200 to 250 Å in diameter) which touch one another in one direction but are separated in the other by fine processes (Fig. 174). The peripheries of the rods are homo-geneous but there is apparently no membrane delimiting these composite structures from the cytoplasmic matrix (Figs. 173, 174). The rods are not obviously fused to each other, but, in the region of cytoplasm between them, there are small groups of microtubules which probably link the rods laterally. In oblique longitudinal section (Fig. 175) the rods are seen to curve round and join posteriorly. The cytoplasmic region within the siphon contains fibrillar and membranous structures (Fig. 174) including a supplementary fibre which develops into a complex network at the mouth of the siphon (Fig. 175), beneath the supposed cytostome.

There are obvious resemblances between this ingestion apparatus and that in *Peranema*. The shape and morphology of the rods are different, but their ultrastructure is similar, and the structures in the centre of the siphon are not unlike the fibrillar sheets thought by Roth (1959) to be contractile in *Peranema*. These fine structures are also closely reminiscent of skeletal and other organelles in a variety of protozoa, such as the axostyle of *Trichomonas* and the rostral tube of *Trichonympha* (see Grimstone, 1961, for a review). The mode of ingestion in *Entosiphon* is not understood, and Mignot has not at-tempted a functional interpretation of the fine structure he has demonstrated so clearly. It is apparent from his sections (Fig. 175, for example) that the "cytostome" and canal opening are situated in a common groove or depression of the cell (as are those of *Peranema*), but there is no doubt that the ingestion apparatus is independent of the canal and reservoir (in fact, this independence can be clearly seen in the living cell). Detailed behavioural studies of *Entosiphon*, other genera of the *Heteronematales* and genera of the *Sphenomonadales* are now needed for comparison with Chen's (1950) study of *Peranema*.

Appendix 1

KEY FOR THE IDENTIFICATION OF THE
GENERA OF EUGLENOID FLAGELLATES

This dichotomous key is based upon the "natural" scheme of classification presented on pp. 11–71 (see also pp. 72–75). Features diagnostic for all euglenoid flagellates are listed on p. 6.

1. a. Cell with two or more flagella emergent from the canal.............. 2
    b. Cell with only one flagellum emergent from the canal 15

2. a. Two emergent flagella... 3
    b. More than two emergent flagella 14

3. a. Cell green... 4
    b. Cell colourless 5

4. a. The two flagella equal in length.................................... *Eutreptia*
    b. The two flagella markedly unequal in length..................... *Eutreptiella*

5. a. Cell with elastic pellicle.. 6
    b. Cell with rigid pellicle.. 10

6. a. Osmotrophic, no ingestion organelle.. 7
    b. Phagotrophic, ingestion organelle present (composed of separate rods) 8

7. a. Leucostigma present; cell probably parasitic.................... *Distigmopsis*
    b. No eyespot; cell free-swimming....................................... *Distigma*

8. a. The longer of the two flagella directed anteriorly during swimming, the shorter one curving posteriorly... 9
    b. The shorter of the two flagella directed anteriorly during swimming, the longer one trailing posteriorly (longer than the cell)... *Dinema*

9. a. The posteriorly directed flagellum pressed to the cell, usually lying in a groove.. *Peranema*
    b. The posteriorly directed flagellum lying free from the cell... *Heteronema*

10. a. The longer of the two flagella directed anteriorly during swimming, the shorter one curving posteriorly... 11
    b. The shorter of the two flagella directed anteriorly during swimming, the longer one trailing posteriorly (longer than the cell) 13

11. a. Cell elongated, not flattened....................................... *Sphenomonas*
    b. Cell slightly or markedly flattened.. 12

12. a. Cell slightly flattened, with 4 to 10 pronounced helical keels... *Tropidoscyphus*
    b. Cell ovoid, flattened, usually very compressed and leaf-shaped; mostly with strong ribs or keels .... *Notosolenus*

13. a. Cell ovoid, flattened, usually very compressed and leaf-shaped; phago-trophic and/or osmotrophic, but no ingestion organelle .... *Anisonema*
    b. Cell only slightly flattened; phagotrophic, ingestion organelle present (a conical tube composed of fused rods) .... *Entosiphon*

14. a. Cell parasitic in *Rana* tadpoles; with (typically) three flagella; cell green, but reduced colourless form also exists .... *Euglenamorpha*
    b. Cell parasitic in *Leptodactylus* tadpoles; with more than three flagella; cell colourless .... *Hegneria*

15. a. Cell green 16
    b. Cell colourless 23

16. a. Cell free-swimming, solitary 17
    b. Cell normally attached to a substratum 22

17. a. No envelope around the cell 18
    b. Cell with an external envelope 20

18. a. Cell non-rigid or semi-rigid, with pronounced euglenoid movement or, at least, some flexing of the cell; usually elongated .... *Euglena*
    b. Cell rigid 19

19. a. Cell not flattened, usually ovoid................................... *Lepocinclis*
    b. Cell flattened, usually very compressed and leaf-shaped............ *Phacus*

20. a. Envelope entirely enclosing the cell, except for an apical pore through which emerges the locomotory flagellum 21
    b. Envelope an open cup, only partially enclosing the cell......... *Klebsiella*

21. a. Envelope with a sharply defined neck or collar; envelope brown, orna-mented and brittle with ferric hydroxide .... *Trachelomonas*
    b. Envelope tapering gradually to the apical pore; envelope almost colour-less, non-brittle and without ornamentation except for brown particles of manganese peroxide .... *Strombomonas*

22. a. Cell attached to a substratum by its anterior end; usually grouped with other cells in bunches, sheets or dendroid colonies .... *Colacium*
    b. Cell enclosed in a flask-shaped envelope, the posterior end of which is attached to a substratum; solitary .... *Ascoglena*

23. a. Eyespot present 24
    b. Eyespot absent 27

24. a. No envelope around the cell 25
    b. Cell with an external envelope .... *"Hyalotrachelomonas"*

25. a. Cell non-rigid or semi-rigid; not flattened................................... 26
    b. Cell rigid; very compressed and leaf-shaped............... *Hyalophacus sp.*

26. a. Cell with pronounced euglenoid movement; canal opening subapi-cal .... *Khawkinea*
    b. Cell long, thin and cylindrical, with change of shape restricted to slight bending; canal opening apical .... *Cyclidiopsis*

27. a. Cell non-rigid or semi-rigid, with pronounced or slight euglenoid move-ment 28
    b. Cell rigid 31

28. a. Osmotrophic or phagotrophic, but no ingestion organelle 29

     b. Phagotrophic, ingestion organelle present (composed of separate rods)...   30

29. a. Exclusively osmotrophic ....   *Astasia*

     b. Phagotrophic ....   *Euglenopsis*

30. a. Cell elongated, not flattened, with no anterior extension; euglenoid movement pronounced ....   *Peranemopsis*

     b. Cell ovoid or urn-shaped, with a funnel-shaped extension of the anterior end; euglenoid movement only slight ....   *Urceolus*

31. a. The emergent flagellum mobile throughout its length during swimming...   32

     b. The emergent flagellum directed anteriorly, straight, during swimming, not mobile throughout its length   37

32. a. Cell not flattened, or only slightly so   33

     b. Cell very compressed   35

33. a. Cell not spiralled   34

     b. Cell irregularly spiralled, tapering ....   *Rhabdospira*

34. a. Cell cylindrical, curved, with shallow helical grooves ....   *Rhabdomonas*

     b. Cell ovoid or cylindrical, with pronounced helical keels.........   *Gyropaigne*

35. a. Cell elongated, curved, narrowly triangular or lenticular in cross-section; canal opening apical...   *Menoidium*

     b. Cell ovoid, very compressed; canal opening subapical   36

36. a. Cell leaf-shaped, with a keel...................................   *Hyalophacus sp.*

     b. Cell compressed, with a single shallow indentation on one flat side so that the cell is angularly concavo-convex in cross-section; no keel...   *Parmidium*

37. a. Cell not flattened   38

     b. Cell ovoid, flattened, usually very flat and leaf-shaped; mostly with strong ribs or keels ....   *Petalomonas*

38. a. Cell cylindrical, with longitudinal keels or grooves ....   *Atraktomonas*

     b. Cell ovoid, with 5 to 8 helical keels ....   *Calycimonas*

    See, also, notes on *Chlorachne, Ottonia, Protoeuglena, Cryptoglena, Euglenocapsa, Calkinsia, Clautriavia, Helikotropis, Jenningsia, Marsupiogaster, Pentamonas, Ploeotia, Protaspis, Rhizaspis, Rhynchopus, Scytomonas* and *Triangulomonas* (pp. 69–71).

Appendix 2

NOTES ON THE COLLECTION, CULTIVATION, NUTRITION AND MICROSCOPICAL EXAMINATION OF EUGLENOID FLAGELLATES

Collection

Euglenoid flagellates can be collected from most fresh-water habitats, from puddles, ditches, ponds, streams, lakes and rivers, particularly waters contaminated by animal pollution or decaying organic matter. Farmyard middens, greenhouse tanks, drainage channels, water butts, dew-ponds visited by cattle, peaty pools and damp mud along the banks of rivers and ponds are all habitats worth sampling for *Euglenophyta*, whereas larger bodies of purer water, such as rivers, lakes and reservoirs, often have sparse populations of less common species as planktonic organisms. Among the more bizarre habitats from which euglenoid flagellates have been recorded are the mucus secretions of aquatic animals, the barks and leaves of trees, the bladders of *Utricularia*, snow- and ice-fields, swimming pools, birdbaths and the public water supply of the city of New York.

Marine euglenoids are proving to be more abundant than hitherto supposed, with *Eutreptia*, *Eutreptiella* and *Klebsiella* occurring exclusively in marine or brackish conditions and many other genera having one or a few marine species. These occur in the open sea, in tidal zones among seaweeds and as sand inhabitants on beaches. Brackish species of *Euglena* often colour estuarine mud flats green when light intensity is low, the green colour disappearing in full sunlight as the euglenoids creep away from the mud surface.

Also, in addition to these free-living species there are several parasitic euglenoid flagellates, mostly species of *Khawkinea* (p. 29), *Euglenamorpha* (p. 67) and *Hegneria* (p. 67).

Cultivation

Very few euglenoid flagellates can be grown bacteria-free in a defined liquid medium, only *Euglena gracilis* growing sufficiently well to be used as a major research organism in physiological studies (see Cramer and Myers, 1952; Wolken, 1961; Kempner and Miller, 1965, for details of media for *E. gracilis*). Such axenic cultures are necessary for biochemical investigations but are unnecessary (and often undesirable) for cytological studies. Many phototrophic and osmotrophic euglenoids grow well in soil-water tubes (biphasic culture; Pringsheim, 1946a, 1946b), and most species kept in culture collections (see footnote, p. 11) can be grown only by this method (as unialgal cultures, but with bacteria present). Soil-water tubes are easily prepared for class use (see summary in Fig. 176). Cells from wild collections should be washed in diluted soil extract (by the pipetting method; Pringsheim, 1946b) and each culture tube inoculated with a single cell. Larger inocula can be introduced from named cultures. The resulting cultures grow best in warm conditions (20°C or higher), green species needing light (preferably northern daylight, in winter supplemented by incandescent lighting on a 16-hour-day/8-hour-night regime). There is usually no need to subculture such tubes more than twice a year.

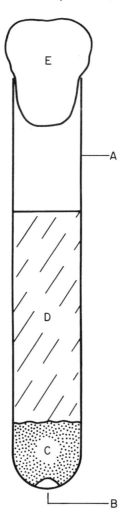

Fig. 176 Preparation of soil-water (biphasic) culture tubes. *A,* test-tube of heat-resistant glass; *B,* speck of nutritive substance (examples: ammonium magnesium phosphate for green species; starch, cheese, split pea or wheat grain for colourless species); *C,* soil (preferably a clay soil with pronounced iron content; pH can be adjusted by adding peat or chalk); *D,* water (glass-distilled for fresh-water species, or tap water if additives are few; equal volumes of distilled water and filtered sea water for brackish species; filtered sea water for marine species); *E,* plug of non-absorbent cotton wool, or plastic cap. A batch of tubes should be steamed for one hour on the day they are made up and for a second hour the next day (steam-bath only, not under pressure). Inoculations can be made on the third day.

Euglena gracilis (and, less easily, *Euglena anabaena* Mainx 1926, *deses*, *pisciformis*, *stellata* and *viridis*) can be conveniently grown bacteria-free in easily prepared undefined media (0.2 per cent beef extract, for example, or a mixture of 0.2 per cent tryptone, 0.1 per cent beef extract, 0.2 per cent yeast extract and 0.1 per cent sodium acetate) and the same media can be used for agar slopes (1 to 2 per cent agar). Some *Colacium* spp. grow bacteria-free in 0.2 per cent peptone or a mixture of peptone with sodium acetate and beef extract. *Peranema trichophorum*, the only phagotrophic species to be successfully cultivated, needs a supply of particulate food (milk, casein, living yeast or living *Euglena;* see Chen, 1950).

Nutrition

One of the fascinating features of euglenoid physiology is the subtle variety of nutritional characteristics displayed through the group, especially since some species have the ability to switch from one mode of nutrition to another. The classic papers on euglenoid nutrition by R. P. Hall, H. Dusi, A. Lwoff, T. Jahn, S. H. Hutner and L. Provasoli have been frequently summarised elsewhere (Hall, 1941, 1965; Hutner and Provasoli, 1951, 1955, 1964, 1965; Hutner, 1953; Provasoli, 1958; Pringsheim, 1963), and a review of this complex subject lies outside the scope of the present book. For our purpose it is necessary only to define terms used in earlier pages:

1. Phototrophy

(a) No euglenoid flagellate has yet been demonstrated to be fully **photoautotrophic**: capable of growing in a medium devoid of all organic compounds (including vitamins), with carbon dioxide as carbon source, nitrates or ammonium salts as nitrogen source, and light as energy source (through the agency of chlorophyll).

(b) All green euglenoid flagellates so far studied are **photoauxotrophic**: capable of growing in a medium devoid of organic nutrients, with carbon dioxide, ammonium salts and light, but needing at least one vitamin.

(c) Some of these photoauxotrophic euglenoids can also utilise amino acids, peptones and proteins as nitrogen source, but claims that certain green species *need* complex nitrogen sources remain unconfirmed.

2. Heterotrophy

(a) Colourless euglenoid flagellates are **obligately heterotrophic**: growing only in media furnished with organic nutrients as a source of carbon. The few colourless species so far studied need either ammonium salts or amino acids as nitrogen source. Light, of course, is not required.

(b) Some *green* euglenoids are **facultatively heterotrophic**: capable of growing *in the dark* if supplied with suitable organic carbon sources. These organic sources may enhance growth even in the light.

(c) Most green and many colourless euglenoids are **osmotrophic** (saprotrophic): absorbing their nutrients in soluble form only.

3. Phagotrophy

The remaining colourless euglenoid flagellates are **phagotrophic**: they ingest particulate food. Some species seem to depend solely on phagotrophy, others to combine osmotrophy and phagotrophy.

No green euglenoid is phagotrophic. In nature many green species, though photoauxotrophic, most probably combine phototrophy with osmotrophic heterotrophy (as is indicated by a preference for waters rich in decaying organic matter). Experiments on the facultative heterotrophy of green species (mostly *Euglena*) show that the organisms thrive on acetate, simple organic acids and alcohols as the carbon source, whereas more complex substances such as sugars are said to be less utilisable (but see p. 165). *Euglena* is, therefore, grouped with the "acetate flagellates" (Pringsheim, 1937b). Good growth of auxotrophs is obtained with ammonium salts as nitrogen source; no species tested so far can utilise nitrates. Requirements for vitamin B_{12} (cobalamin) is absolute in all species so far studied; most species also need vitamin B_1 (thiamin). The nutrition of *Euglena gracilis* is reviewed in detail by Hutner and Provasoli (1964), and growth characteristics are conveniently summarised by Cramer and Myers (1952). References to some aspects of growth physiology will be found on pp. 92, 140, 165, 181 and 186 of the present account.

Nutritional requirements of normally phagotrophic species are more complex. Storm and Hutner (1953) have shown that the requirements of *Peranema trichophorum* include plant and animal sterols, thiamin, cobalamin and riboflavin, nucleic acid constituents, amino acids, and unidentified factors from liver and cream. The principle substrate being used by *Peranema* in their cultures remained unidentified. Subsequently it has been demonstrated (Allen, Lee, Goldstone, Hutner and Diamond, 1964) that the essential factors from liver and cream can be replaced by linoleic, oleic and stearic acids, together with lysine, glycine, asparagine and glutamic acid. In the defined medium, methyl cellulose is supplied as a source of particulate food.

Microscopical Examination

The particular methods of microscopy which have proved most useful for studying the euglenoid flagellates may be summarised as follows (for practical details, reference should be made to the works cited):

1. Light microscopy

(a) *Living Cells*. It is desirable to examine living cells by several forms of light microscopy, especially phase contrast and the various systems using transmitted light, dark-ground illumination and polarized light. The most useful system is Reichert Anoptral contrast (a patented form of negative phase contrast), especially when used with a universal condenser (e.g., the Polyphos) which allows switching from contrast to bright field to dark-ground for the same cell.

(b) *Vital Staining*. Neutral red, cresyl blue and ruthenium red (2 per cent or weaker) are the most useful vital stains for muciferous bodies and, subsequently, other structures; 0.1 per cent methylene blue accumulates preferentially in muciferous bodies, pellicular ornamentation and other mucilaginous structures; Janus green B is useful for selectively staining the chondriome (see Jensen, 1962).

(c) *Chromosome Studies*. Material illustrated has been fixed in methanol or Carnoy's acetic-alcohol and stained with aceto-carmine following a ferric acetate mordant (see Godward, 1966), or by the Feulgen reaction. Other fixatives and stains are less satisfactory (Leedale, 1958b).

2. Electron microscopy

Standard methods have been used, and reference should be made to Kay (1965) and Pease (1965) for details of reagents and procedure. Material illustrated in the present account has preferentially been fixed in osmium tetroxide: as vapour for direct preparations and as a 2 per cent solution buffered to pH 7 for sections (potassium permanganate gives poor results with euglenoids, but organic fixatives such as glutaraldehyde are excellent for certain features). Fixed material has been embedded in Shell Epikote 812 resin and sections stained in Millonig's lead hydroxide (Millonig, 1961). Gold/palladium has been used for shadow-cast preparations, carbon/platinum for making replicas.

Appendix 3

LATIN DIAGNOSES OF EUGLENOID ORDERS

The following diagnoses of the six orders of the class *Euglenophyta*, as delimited in the classification introduced in the present account, have been constructed by Mr. R. Ross of the Department of Botany, British Museum (Natural History), London, S. W. 7. These orders are equivalent to the suborders of the order *Euglenida* in protozoological classification (see p. 10).

EUTREPTIALES

Cellula natans solitaria, sine integumento, elongata, non planata, non rigida, motione euglenoidea valde impegra, viridis aut incolorata, numquam phagotrophica. Flagella duo, ambo ex canale emergentia, aequaliter crassa, heterodynamica, mobilissima, numquam recta tenta, natantium alterum flagellum ad anteriorem alterum ad latus vel posteriorem tendens.

EUGLENALES

Cellula natans (Ascoglena et Colacio exceptis), viridis aut incolorata, phototrophica aut osmotrophica aut (Euglenopsis sola) phagotrophica sed sine apparatu ad cibum ingerendum. Flagella duo, alterum ex canale emergens et motionem efficiens, per totam longitudinem mobilissimum, alterum curtissimum neque ex cisterna emergens.

RHABDOMONADALES

Cellula natans, solitaria, sine integumento, rigida, sine motione euglenoidea, incolorata, osmotrophica, numquam phagotrophica. Ocellus et gibba flagellaris desunt. Flagellum emergens unum, natantium per totam longitudinem mobile, stantium plerumque recta tentum. Flagellum alterum in canale inclusum non reportatum sed possibiliter adest.

SPHENOMONADALES

Cellula natans, solitaria, sine integumento, rigida vel fere rigida, sine motione euglenoidea, plerumque carinis vel sulcis prominentibus ornata, incolorata, phagotrophica aut osmotrophica aut et phagotrophica et osmotrophica, sine apparatu ad cibum ingerendum. Ocellus et gibba flagellaris desunt. Aut unum flagellum emergens aut duo, unum semper ad anteriorem tendens et natantium pro parte immobile.

HETERONEMATALES

Cellula natans, solitaria, sine integumento, incolorata, phagotrophica, cum apparatu ad cibum ingerendum. Ocellus et gibba flagellaris desunt. Flagella emergentia unum vel duo; unum natantium ad anteriorem tendens, plerumque mobile solo in pars distalis et motionem prolabentem efficiens.

EUGLENAMORPHALES

Cellula solitaria, sine integumento, elongata, non planata, non rigida, motione euglenoidea impegra, viridis vel incolorata, non phagotrophica, endozoica, in intestinis ranularum habitans. Flagella tres vel plura, omnia ex canale emergentia, aequaliter longa et crassa et mobilia.

BIBLIOGRAPHY

AARONSON, S. (1960a), "β-Methoxythreonine, a new *Euglena*-bleaching agent," *Journal of Protozoology*, **7** (*Supplement*), 12.

AARONSON, S. (1960b), "Mode of action of 3-amino-1,2,4-triazole on photosynthetic microorganisms," *Journal of Protozoology*, **7**, 289–294.

AARONSON, S. and B. BENSKY (1962), "O-Methylthreonine, a new bleaching agent for *Euglena gracilis*," *Journal of General Microbiology*, **27**, 75–98.

AFZELIUS, B. (1963), "Cilia and flagella that do not conform to the $9 + 2$ pattern," *Journal of Ultrastructure Research*, **9**, 381–392.

ALLEN, J. R., J. J. LEE, E. GOLDSTONE, S. H. HUTNER, and J. H. DIAMOND (1964), "Prolonged culture of *Peranema trichophorum*," *Journal of Protozoology*, **11** (*Supplement*), 21.

ARNON, D. I. (1961), "Cell-free photosynthesis and the energy conversion process," *Light and Life*, ed. W. D. McElroy and B. Glass, 489–566. Baltimore: The John Hopkins Press.

BARRAS, D. R. and B. A. STONE (1965), "The chemical composition of the pellicle of *Euglena gracilis* var. *bacillaris*," *Biochemical Journal*, **97**, 14–15.

BARRY, J. M. (1964), *Molecular Biology: Genes and the Chemical Control of Living Cells.* Englewood Cliffs, New Jersey: Prentice-Hall, Inc.

BARRY, S. C. (1962), "Utilization of glucose by *Astasia longa*," *Journal of Protozoology*, **9**, 395–400.

BATRA, P. P. and G. TOLLIN (1964), "Phototaxis in *Euglena*. I. Isolation of the eye-spot granules and identification of the eye-spot pigments," *Biochimica et biophysica acta*, **79**, 371–378.

BEHRE, K. (1961), "Die Algenbesiedlung der Unterweser unter Berücksichtigung ihrer Zuflüsse (ohne die Kieselalgen)," *Veröffentlichungen des Instituts für Meeresforschung in Bremerhaven*, **7**, 71–263.

BELL, P. R. and K. MÜHLETHALER (1962), "The fine structure of the cells taking part in oogenesis in *Pteridium aquilinum* (L.) Kuhn," *Journal of Ultrastructure Research*, **7**, 452–466.

BELL, P. R. and K. MÜHLETHALER (1964), "The degeneration and reappearance of mitochondria in the egg cells of a plant," *Journal of Cell Biology*, **20**, 235–248.

BENDIX, S. (1960), "Phototaxis," *Botanical Review*, **26**, 145–208.

BEN-SHAUL, Y., H. T. EPSTEIN, and J. A. SCHIFF (1965), "Studies of chloroplast development in *Euglena*. 10. The return of the chloroplast to the proplastid condition during dark adaptation," *Canadian Journal of Botany*, **43**, 129–136.

BEN-SHAUL, Y., J. A. SCHIFF, and H. T. EPSTEIN (1964), "Studies of chloroplast development in *Euglena*. VII. Fine structure of the developing plastid," *Plant Physiology*, **39**, 231–240.

BLUM, J. J. and G. M. PADILLA (1962), "Studies on synchronized cells. The time course of DNA, RNA, and protein synthesis in *Astasia longa*," *Experimental Cell Research*, **28**, 512–523.

BLUM, J. J., J. R. SOMMER, and V. KAHN (1965), "Some biochemical, cytological and morphogenetic comparisons between *Astasia longa* and a bleached *Euglena gracilis*," *Journal of Protozoology*, **12**, 202–209.

BOLD, H. C. (1964), *The Plant Kingdom*, 2nd ed. Englewood Cliffs, New Jersey: Prentice-Hall, Inc.

BOURNE, G. H. and H. B. TEWARI (1964), "Mitochondria and the Golgi complex," *Cytology and Cell Physiology*, 3rd ed., ed. G.H. Bourne, 377–421. New York and London: Academic Press.

BOURRELLY, P. (1947), "Algues rares ou nouvelles de la forêt de Sénart," *Bulletin du Muséum d'Histoire naturelle, Paris*, 2ᵉ Ser., **19**, 464–470.

BOURRELLY, P. and M. CHADEFAUD (1948), *Catalogues des Collections Vivantes, Herbiers et Documents. I. L'Algothèque*, Laboratoire de Cryptogamie, Muséum d'Histoire naturelle, Paris.

BOURRELLY, P. and G. GEORGES (1951), "Un nouvel Euglénien incolore, *Gyropaigne lefèvrei*," *Bulletin du Muséum d'Histoire naturelle, Paris*, 2ᵉ Ser., **23**, 453–455.

BRAWERMAN, G. (1963), "The isolation of a specific species of ribosomes associated with chloroplast development in *Euglena gracilis*," *Biochimica et biophysica acta*, **72**, 317–331.

BRAWERMAN, G. and E. CHARGAFF (1959a), "Changes in protein and ribonucleic acid during the formation of chloroplasts in *Euglena gracilis*," *Biochimica et biophysica acta*, **31**, 164–171.

BRAWERMAN, G. and E. CHARGAFF (1959b), "Relation of ribonucleic acid to the photosynthetic apparatus in *Euglena gracilis*," *Biochimica et biophysica acta*, **31**, 172–177.

BRAWERMAN, G. and J. M. EISENSTADT (1964a), "Template and ribosomal ribonucleic acids associated with the chloroplasts and the cytoplasm of *Euglena gracilis*," *Journal of Molecular Biology*, **10**, 403–411.

BRAWERMAN, G. and J. M. EISENSTADT (1964b), "Deoxyribonucleic acid from the chloroplasts of *Euglena gracilis*," *Biochimica et biophysica acta*, **91**, 477–485.

BRAWERMAN, G., A. O. POGO, and E. CHARGAFF (1961), "Synthesis of novel ribonucleic acids and proteins during chloroplast formation in resting *Euglena* cells," *Biochimica et biophysica acta*, **48**, 418–420.

BRODY, M., S. S. BRODY, and J. H. LEVINE (1965), "Fluorescence changes during chlorophyll formation in *Euglena gracilis* (and other organisms) and an estimate of lamellar area as a function of age," *Journal of Protozoology*, **12**, 465–476.

BROWN, F. and J. F. DANIELLI (1964), "The cell surface and cell physiology," *Cytology and Cell Physiology*, 3rd ed., ed. G. H. Bourne, 239–310. New York and London: Academic Press.

BROWN, J. S. (1963), "The separation of the forms of chlorophyll a and the absorption changes in *Euglena* during aging," *Biochimica et biophysica acta*, **75**, 299–305.

BROWN, V. E. (1930), "The cytology and binary fission of *Peranema trichophorum*," *Quarterly Journal of Microscopical Science*, **73**, 403–420.

BRUCE, V. G. and C. S. PITTENDRIGH (1956), "Temperature independence in a unicellular 'clock,'" *Proceedings of the National Academy of Sciences, Washington*, **42**, 676–682.

BRUMPT, E. and G. LAVIER (1924), "Un nouvel Euglénien polyflagellé parasite du têtard de *Leptodactylus ocellatus* au Brésil," *Annales de Parasitologie*, **2**, 248–252.

BUCHER, O. (1959), "Die Amitose der tierischen und menschlichen Zelle," *Protoplasmatologia*, **6.E.1**, 1–159.

BUETOW, D. E. (1961), "Ethanol stimulation of oxidative metabolism in *Euglena gracilis*," *Nature*, **190**, 1196.

BUETOW, D. E. (1963), "Linear relationship between temperature and uptake of oxygen in *Euglena gracilis*," *Lancet*, **199**, 196–197.

BUETOW, D. E. and P. J. BUCHANAN (1965), "Oxidative phosphorylation in mitochondria isolated from *Euglena gracilis*," *Biochimica et biophysica acta*, **96**, 9–17.

BUETOW, D. E. and B. H. LEVEDAHL (1961), "The action of testosterone at the cell level. Testosterone stimulation of the respiration of *Euglena gracilis*," *Archives of Biochemistry and Biophysics*, **94**, 358–363.

CHADEFAUD, M. (1937), "Anatomie comparée des Eugléniens," *Le Botaniste*, **28**, 85–185.

CHADEFAUD, M. (1938), "Nouvelles recherches sur l'anatomie comparée des Eugléniens: les Péranémines," *Revue Algologique*, **11**, 189–220.

CHEN, Y. T. (1950), "Investigations of the biology of *Peranema trichophorum* (*Euglenineae*)," *Quarterly Journal of Microscopical Science*, **91**, 279–308.

CHRISTEN, H. R. (1958), "Farblose Euglenalen aus dem Hypolimnion des Hausersees," *Schweizerische Zeitschrift für Hydrologie*, **20**, 141–176.

CHRISTEN, H. R. (1959), "New colorless Eugleninae," *Journal of Protozoology*, **6**, 292–303.

CHRISTEN, H. R. (1960), "*Gyropaigne* Skuja, eine bemerkenswerte Gattung der farblosen Eugleninen," *Beihefte zu den Zeitschriften des Schweizerischen Forstvereins*, **30**, 31–37.

CHRISTEN, H. R. (1962), "Neue und wenig bekannte Eugleninen und Volvocalen," *Revue Algologique*, 162–202.

CHRISTEN, H. R. (1963), "Zur Taxonomie der farblosen Eugleninen," *Nova Hedwigia*, **4**, 437–464.

CHRISTENSEN, T. (1962), *Botanik, Bind II: Systematisk Botanik, Nr. 2, Alger*, Copenhagen: Munksgaard.

CHRISTENSEN, T. (1966), *Botanik, Bind II: Systematisk Botanik, Nr. 2, Alger*, 2nd ed. Copenhagen: Munksgaard.

CHU, S. P. (1946), "Contributions to our knowledge of the genus *Euglena*," *Sinensia*, **17**, 75–134.

COBB, H. D. (1963), "An *in vivo* absorption spectrum of the eyespot of *Euglena mesnili*," *Texas Journal of Science*, **15**, 231–235.

CONRAD, W. (1916), "Révision des éspèces indigènes et françaises du genre *Trachelomonas* Ehrenbg.," *Annales de Biologie Lacustre*, **8**, 193–212.

CONRAD, W. (1934), "Matériaux pour une monographie du genre *Lepocinclis* Perty," *Archiv für Protistenkunde*, **82**, 203–249.

CONRAD, W. (1935), "Étude systématique du genre *Lepocinclis* Perty," *Mémoires du Musée royale d'histoire naturelle de Belgique*, 2ᵉ Ser., **1**, 1–84.

CONRAD, W. and L. VAN MEEL (1952), "Matériaux pour une monographie de *Trachelomonas* Ehrenberg, C., 1834, *Strombomonas* Deflandre, G., 1930 et *Euglena* Ehrenberg, C., 1832, genres d'Euglénacées," *Institut royal des sciences naturelles de Belgique*, Mémoire No. **124**, 1–176.

COOK, J. R. (1961), "*Euglena gracilis* in synchronous division. II. Biosynthetic rates over the life cycle," *Biological Bulletin of the Marine Biological Laboratory, Wood's Hole*, **121**, 277–289.

CRAMER, M. and J. MYERS (1952), "Growth and photosynthetic characteristics of *Euglena gracilis*," *Archiv für Mikrobiologie*, **17**, 384–402.

DA CUNHA, A. M. (1913), Not traced. da Cunha mentions 1913 in his 1914 paper (see below) but gives no reference; the 1913 paper in *Memórias do Instituto Oswaldo Cruz*, cited by most authorities, contains no reference to *Eutreptiella*.

DA CUNHA, A. M. (1914), "Contribuição para o conhecimento da fauna de Protozoarios do Brazil. II.," *Memórias do Instituto Oswaldo Cruz*, **6**, 169–179.

DALTON, A. J. (1961), "Golgi apparatus and secretion granules," *The Cell*, Vol. 2, eds. J. Brachet and A. E. Mirsky, 603–619. New York and London: Academic Press.

DANFORTH, W. F. (1953), "Oxidative metabolism of *Euglena*," *Archives of Biochemistry and Biophysics*, **46**, 164–173.

DANFORTH, W. F. (1961), "Oxidative assimilation of acetate by *Euglena*. Carbon balance and effects of ethanol," *Journal of Protozoology*, **8**, 152–158.

DANFORTH, W. F. and B. W. WILSON (1961), "The endogenous metabolism of *Euglena gracilis*," *Journal of General Microbiology*, **24**, 95–105.

DANGEARD, P.-A. (1901), "Recherches sur les Eugléniens," *Le Botaniste*, **8**, 97–357.

DAVSON, H. and J. F. DANIELLI (1943), *The Permeability of Natural Membranes*. Cambridge: University Press.

DE DUVE, C. (1963), "The lysosome," *Scientific American*, May, 1963, 64–72.

DEFLANDRE, G. (1926), *Monographie du genre Trachelomonas Ehr.* Nemours: Imprimerie André Lesot.

DEFLANDRE, G. (1930), "*Strombomonas*, nouveau genre d'Euglénacées (*Trachelomonas* Ehrb. pro parte)," *Archiv für Protistenkunde*, **69**, 551–614.

DEKEN-GRENSON, M. DE and A. GODTS (1960), "Descendance of *Euglena* cells isolated after various bleaching treatments," *Experimental Cell Research*, **19**, 376–382.

DEKEN-GRENSON, M. DE and S. MESSIN (1958), "La continuité génétique des chloroplastes chez les euglénes. I. Mécanisme de l'apparition des lignées blanches dans les cultures traitées par la streptomycine," *Biochimica et biophysica acta*, **27**, 145–155.

DODGE, J. D. (1963), "The nucleus and nuclear division in the *Dinophyceae*," *Archiv für Protistenkunde*, **106**, 442–452.

DUJARDIN, F. (1841), *Histoire Naturelle des Zoophytes-Infusoires*. Paris: Roret.

EBRINGER, L. (1962), "Erythromycin-induced bleaching of *Euglena gracilis*," *Journal of Protozoology*, **9**, 373–374.

EBRINGER, L. (1964), "Bleaching of Euglenas by antibiotics: A specific form of antagonism in Actinomycetes," *Folia Microbiologica, Praha*, **9**, 249–255.

EDELMAN, M., J. A. SCHIFF, and H. T. EPSTEIN (1965), "Studies of chloroplast development in *Euglena*. XII. Two types of satellite DNA," *Journal of Molecular Biology*, **11**, 769–774.

EDELMAN, N., C. A. COWAN, H. T. EPSTEIN, and J. A. SCHIFF (1964), "Studies of chloroplast development in *Euglena*. VIII. Chloroplast-associated DNA," *Proceedings of the National Academy of Sciences, Washington*, **52**, 1214–1219.

EDMUNDS, L. N. (1964), "Replication of DNA and cell division in synchronously dividing cultures of *Euglena gracilis*," *Science*, **145**, 266–268.

EHRENBERG, C. G. (1829), "Die geographische Verbreitung der Infusionsthierchen in Nord-Afrika und West-Asien, beobachtet auf Hemprich und Ehrenbergs Reisen," *Physikalische Abhandlungen der Königlichen Akademie der Wissenschaften zu Berlin*, 1–20.

EHRENBERG, C. G. (1830a), "Neue Beobachtungen über blutartige Erscheinungen in Aegypten, Arabien und Sibirien, nebst einer Uebersicht und Kritik der früher bekannnten," (*sic*), *Annalen der Physik*, **18**, 477–514.

EHRENBERG, C. G. (1830b), "Beiträge zur Kenntniss der Organisation der Infusorien und ihrer geographischen Verbreitung, besonders in Sibirien," *Physikalische Abhandlungen der Königlichen Akademie der Wissenschaften zu Berlin*, 1–88.

EHRENBERG, C. G. (1831), "Über die Entwickelung und Lebensdauer der Infusionsthiere; nebst ferneren Beiträgen zu einer Vergleichung ihrer organischen Systeme," *Physikalische Abhandlungen der Königlichen Akademie der Wissenschaften zu Berlin*, 1–154.

EHRENBERG, C. G. (1832), "Zweiter Beitrag zur Erkenntnis der Organisation in der Richtung des Kleindes Raumes," *Physikalische Abhandlungen der Königlichen Akademie der Wissenschaften zu Berlin*.

EHRENBERG, C. G. (1833), Dritter Beitrag zur Erkenntnis grosser Organisation in der Richtung des Kleinsten Raumes," *Physikalische Abhandlungen der Königlichen Akademie der Wissenschaften zu Berlin*, 145–336.

EHRENBERG, C. G. (1838), *Die Infusionsthierchen als vollkommene Organismen*. Leipzig: Verlag von Leopold Voss.

EHRENBERG, C. G. (1840), "Charakteristik vom 274 neuen Arten von Infusorien," *Bericht über die zur Bekanntmachung geeigneten Verhandlungen (Königlichen Akademie der Wissenschaften zu Berlin)*, **5**, 157–262.

EISENSTADT, J. and G. BRAWERMAN (1964a), "Characteristics of a cell-free system from *Euglena gracilis* for the incorporation of amino acids into protein," *Biochimica et biophysica acta*, **80,** 463–472.

EISENSTADT, J. and G. BRAWERMAN (1964b), "The protein-synthesizing systems from the cytoplasm and the chloroplasts of *Euglena gracilis*," *Journal of Molecular Biology*, **10,** 392–402.

ENGELMAN, T. W. (1882), "Über Licht- und Farbenperzeption niederster Organismen," *Pfügers Archiv für die gesamte Physiologie d. Menschen u. d. Tiere*, **29,** 387–400.

EPSTEIN, H. T. and J. A. SCHIFF (1961), "Studies of chloroplast development in *Euglena*. 4. Electron and fluorescence microscopy of the proplastid and its development into a mature chloroplast," *Journal of Protozoology*, **8,** 427–432.

EPSTEIN, H. T., E. BOY DE LA TOUR, and J. A. SCHIFF (1960), "Fluorescence studies of chloroplasts in *Euglena*," *Nature*, **185,** 825–826.

ESHLEMAN, J. N. and W. F. DANFORTH (1964), "Some characteristics of ethanol metabolism in *Euglena gracilis* var. *bacillaris*," *Journal of Protozoology*, **11,** 394–399.

FAURÉ-FREMIET, E. (1958), "The origin of the Metazoa and the stigma of the phyto-flagellates," *Quarterly Journal of Microscopical Science*, **99,** 123–129.

FAWCETT, D. (1961), "Cilia and flagella," *The Cell*, Vol. 2, eds. J. Brachet and A. E. Mirsky, 217–297. New York and London: Academic Press.

FRANCÉ, R. (1897), "Protozoen," *Resultate der Wissenschaftlichen Erforschung des Balatonsees*, Vol. II, 1, ed. G. Entz, Section I, 1–64. Vienna: Commissioverlag von Ed. Hölzel.

FRESENIUS, G. (1858), "Beiträge zur Kenntniss mikroskopischer Organismen," *Abhandlungen herausgegeben von der Senckenbergischen naturforschenden Gesellschaft*, **2,** 211–242.

FREY-WYSSLING, A. and K. MÜHLETHALER (1965), *Ultrastructural Plant Cytology*. Amsterdam, London and New York: Elsevier Publishing Company.

FRITSCH, F. E. (1935), *The Structure and Reproduction of the Algae*, Vols. 1 and 2. Cambridge: University Press.

FULLER, R. C. and M. GIBBS (1959), "Intracellular and phylogenetic distribution of ribulose 1,5-diphosphate carboxylase and D-glyceraldehyde-3-phosphate dehydrogenases," *Plant Physiology*, **34,** 324–329.

FULLER, R. C., R. M. SMILLIE, N. RIGOPOULOS, and V. YOUNT (1961), "Comparative studies of some quinones in photosynthetic systems," *Archives of Biochemistry and Biophysics*, **95,** 197–202.

GIBBONS, I. R. and A. V. GRIMSTONE (1960), "On flagellar structure in certain flagellates," *Journal of Biophysical and Biochemical Cytology*, **7,** 697–716.

GIBBS, S. P. (1960), "The fine structure of *Euglena gracilis* with special reference to chloroplasts and pyrenoids," *Journal of Ultrastructure Research*, **4,** 127–148.

GIBBS, S. P. (1962a), "The ultrastructure of the chloroplasts of algae," *Journal of Ultrastructure Research*, **7,** 418–435.

GIBBS, S. P. (1962b), "The ultrastructure of the pyrenoids of algae, exclusive of the green algae," *Journal of Ultrastructure Research*, **7,** 247–261.

GIBBS, S. P. (1962c), "The ultrastructure of the pyrenoids of green algae," *Journal of Ultrastructure Research*, **7,** 262–272.

GIBOR, A. and S. GRANICK (1962), "The plastid system of normal and bleached *Euglena gracilis*," *Journal of Protozoology*, **9,** 327–334.

GIBOR, A. and S. GRANICK (1964), "Plastids and mitochondria: inheritable systems," *Science*, **145,** 890–897.

GICKLHORN, J. (1920), "Über eine neue Euglenacee (*Amphitropis aequiciliata*, nov. gen. et spec.)," *Österreichische Botanische Zeitschrift*, **69,** 193–199.

GICKLHORN, J. (1925), "Notiz über *Euglena cyclopicola* n. sp.," *Archiv für Protistenkunde*, **51,** 542–548.

GODWARD, M. B. E. (1966), *The Chromosomes of the Algae*. London: Edward Arnold Ltd.

GOJDICS, M. (1953), *The Genus* **Euglena.** Madison, Wisconsin: The University of Wisconsin Press.

GÖSSEL, I. (1957), "Über das Aktionsspektrum der Phototaxis chlorophyllfreier Euglenen und über die Absorption des Augenflecks," *Archiv für Mikrobiologie,* **27,** 288–305.

GREEN, J. (1963), "The occurrence of astaxanthin in the euglenoid *Trachelomonas volvocina,*" *Comparative Biochemistry and Physiology,* **9,** 313–316.

GREENBLATT, C. L. and J. A. SCHIFF (1959), "A pheophytin-like pigment in dark-adapted *Euglena gracilis,*" *Journal of Protozoology,* **6,** 23–28.

GRELL, K. G. (1964), "The protozoan nucleus," *The Cell,* Vol. 6, eds. J. Brachet and A. E. Mirsky, 1–79. New York and London: Academic Press.

GRIMSTONE, A. V. (1961), "Fine structure and morphogenesis in protozoa," *Biological Reviews and Biological Proceedings of the Cambridge Philosophical Society,* **36,** 97–150.

GROSS, J. A. and J. J. WOLKEN (1960), "Two c-type cytochromes from light- and dark-grown *Euglena,*" *Science,* **132,** 357–358.

GROSS, J. A., T. L. JAHN, and E. BERNSTEIN (1955), "The effect of antihistamines on the pigments of green protista," *Journal of Protozoology,* **2,** 71–74.

HALL, R. P. (1941), "Food requirements and other factors influencing growth of Protozoa in pure cultures," *Protozoa in Biological Research,* eds. G. N. Calkins and F. M. Summers, 475–516. New York: Columbia University Press.

HALL, R. P. (1965), *Protozoan Nutrition.* New York, London and Toronto: Blaisdell Publishing Company.

HALL, R. P. and W. N. POWELL (1928), "Morphology and binary fission of *Peranema trichophorum* Ehrbg. Stein," *Biological Bulletin of the Marine Biological Laboratory, Wood's Hole,* **54,** 36–65.

HALLDAL, P. (1964), "Phototaxis in protozoa," *Biochemistry and Physiology of Protozoa,* Vol. 3, ed. S. H. Hutner, 277–296. New York and London: Academic Press.

HAMBURGER, C. (1911), "Studien über *Euglena ehrenbergii,* inbesondere über die Körperhülle," *Sitzungsberichte der Heidelberger Akademie der Wissenschaften,* **2,** 1–22.

HARKER, J. (1963), "Diurnal rhythms in the animal kingdom," *Biological Reviews and Biological Proceedings of the Cambridge Philosophical Society,* **33,** 1–52.

HARTMAN, P.E. and S. SUSKIND (1965), *Gene Action.* Englewood Cliffs, New Jersey: Prentice-Hall, Inc.

HEIDT, K. (1934), "Haematochrom-Wanderung bei *Euglena sanguinea* Ehrenberg," *Bericht der deutschen Botanischen Gesellschaft,* **52,** 607–612.

HOLLANDE, A. (1937), "Quelques données nouvelles sur la cytologie d'une Astasiacée peu connue: *Distigma proteus* Ehrbg.," *Bulletin de la Société zoologique de France,* **62,** 236–241.

HOLLANDE, A. (1942), "Étude cytologique et biologique de quelques flagellés libres. Volvocales, Cryptomonadines, Eugléniens, Protomastigines," *Archives de Zoologie expérimentale et générale,* **83,** 1–268.

HOLLANDE, A. (1952), "Classe des Eugléniens (*Euglenoidina* Bütschli, 1884)," *Traité de Zoologie,* Vol. I, fasc. 1, ed. P. P. Grassé, 238–284. Paris: Masson et Cie.

HOLWILL, M. E. J. (1967), "The motion of *Euglena viridis*: The role of flagella," *Journal of Experimental Biology* (in the press).

HONIGBERG, B. M., W. BALAMUTH, E. C. BOVEE, J. O. CORLISS, M. GOJDICS, R. P. HALL, R. R. KUDO, N. D. LEVINE, A. R. LOEBLICH, Jr., J. WEISER, and D. H. WENRICH (1964), "A revised classification of the phylum *Protozoa,*" *Journal of Protozoology,* **11,** 7–20.

HUBER-PESTALOZZI, G. (1955), *Das Phytoplankton des Süsswassers.* 4. *Euglenophyceen.* Stuttgart: E. Schweizerbart'sche Verlagsbuchhandlung.

HUNTER, F. R. and J. W. LEE (1962), "On the metabolism of *Astasia longa* (Jahn)," *Journal of Protozoology*, **9**, 74–78.

HURLBERT, R. E. and S. C. RITTENBERG (1962), "Glucose metabolism of *Euglena gracilis* var. *bacillaris;* growth and enzymatic studies," *Journal of Protozoology*, **9**, 170–182.

HURRY, S. W. (1965), *The Microstructure of Cells. An Introduction for Sixth Forms.* London: John Murray Publishers, Ltd.

HUTNER, S. H. (1953), "Growth of protozoa," *Annals of the New York Academy of Sciences*, **56**, 851–1094.

HUTNER, S. H. and L. PROVASOLI (1951), "The phytoflagellates," *Biochemistry and Physiology of Protozoa*, Vol. 1, ed. A. Lwoff, 27–128. New York: Academic Press.

HUTNER, S. H. and L. PROVASOLI (1955), "Comparative biochemistry of flagellates," *Biochemistry and Physiology of Protozoa*, Vol. 2, eds. S. H. Hutner and A. Lwoff, 1–40. New York: Academic Press.

HUTNER, S. H. and L. PROVASOLI (1964), "Nutrition of Algae," *Annual Review of Plant Physiology*, **15**, 37–56.

HUTNER, S. H. and L. PROVASOLI (1965), "Comparative physiology: Nutrition," *Annual Review of Physiology*, **27**, 19–50.

IYENGAR, M. O. P. (1962), "*Euglena* studies from Madras," *Archiv für Mikrobiologie*, **42**, 322–332.

JAHN, T. L. (1951), "Euglenophyta," *Manual of Phycology*, ed. G. M. Smith, 69–81. Waltham: Chronica Botanica Company.

JAHN, T. L. and E. C. BOVEE (1964), "Protoplasmic movements and locomotion of protozoa," *Biochemistry and Physiology of Protozoa*, Vol. 3, ed. S. H. Hutner, 61–129. New York and London: Academic Press.

JAHN, T. L. and W. R. McKIBBEN (1937), "A colorless euglenoid flagellate, *Khawkinea halli* N. Gen., N. Sp.," *Transactions of the American Microscopical Society*, **56**, 48–54.

JAHN, T. L., M. D. LANDMAN, and J. R. FONSECA (1964), "The mechanism of locomotion of flagellates. II. Function of the mastigonemes of *Ochromonas*," *Journal of Protozoology*, **11**, 291–296.

JAMES, T. W. (1965), "Dynamic respirometry of division synchronized *Astasia longa*," *Experimental Cell Research*, **38**, 439–453.

JENSEN, W. A. (1962), *Botanical Histochemistry.* San Francisco and London: W. H. Freeman and Company.

JOHN, B. and K. R. LEWIS (1965), "The meiotic system," *Protoplasmatologia*, **5.F.1**, 1–335.

JOHNSON, D. F. (1934), "Morphology and life history of *Colacium vesiculosum* Ehrbg.," *Archiv für Protistenkunde*, **83**, 241–263.

JOHNSON, L. P. and T. L. JAHN (1942), "Cause of the green-red color change in *Euglena rubra*," *Physiological Zoölogy*, **15**, 89–94.

KAY, D. H., ed. (1965), *Techniques for Electron Microscopy*, 2nd ed. Oxford: Blackwell.

KEMPNER, E. S. and J. H. MILLER (1965), "The molecular biology of *Euglena gracilis*. I. Growth conditions and cellular composition. II. Utilization of labelled carbon, sulfur, and phosphorus," *Biochimica et biophysica acta*, **104**, 11–24.

KIRK, J. T. O. (1962a), "Effect of streptomycin on greening and biosynthesis in *Euglena gracilis*," *Biochimica et biophysica acta*, **56**, 139–151.

KIRK, J. T. O. (1962b), "Effect of streptomycin on (^{14}C) leucine incorporation in *Euglena gracilis*," *Biochimica et biophysica acta*, **59**, 476–479.

KITCHING, J. A. (1956), "Contractile vacuoles of protozoa," *Protoplasmatologia*, **3.D.3a**, 1–45.

KLEBS, G. (1883), "Über die Organisation einiger Flagellaten-Gruppe und ihre Beziehungen zu Algen und Infusorien," *Untersuchungen aus dem botanisches Institut zu Tübingen*, **1**, 233–362.

KLEBS, G. (1892), "Flagellatenstudien," *Zeitschrift für wissenschaftliche Zoologie* (*Leipzig*), **55**, 265–445.

KORSHIKOV, A. (1917), "Contributions a l'étude des algues de la Russie. Recherches algologiques aux environs de la station biologique «Borodinskaja» pendant l'été 1915," *Travaux de la Station Biologique "Borodinskaja,"* **4**, 265–267.

KORSHIKOV, A. (1928) "Notes on some new flagellates," *Archives russes de protistologie*, **7**, 155–158.

KREGER, D. R. and B. J. D. MEEUSE (1952), "X-ray diagrams of *Euglena*-paramylon, of the acid-insoluble glucan of yeast cell walls and of laminarin," *Biochimica et biophysica acta*, **9**, 699–700.

KRICHENBAUER, H. (1937), "Beitrag zur Kenntnis der Morphologie und Entwicklungeschichte der Gattungen *Euglena* und *Phacus*," *Archiv für Protistenkunde*, **90**, 88–123.

KRINSKY, N. I. and T. H. GOLDSMITH (1960), "The carotenoids of the flagellated alga, *Euglena gracilis*," *Archives of Biochemistry and Biophysics*, **91**, 271–279.

KRINSKY, N. I., A. GORDON, and A. I. STERN (1964), "The appearance of neoxanthin during the regreening of dark-grown *Euglena*," *Plant Physiology*, **39**, 441–445.

KUHL, A. (1962), "Inorganic phosphorus uptake and metabolism," *Physiology and Biochemistry of Algae*, ed. R. A. Lewin, 211–229. New York and London: Academic Press.

LACKEY, J. B. (1929), "Studies on the life histories of Euglenida. II. The life cycles of *Entosiphon sulcatum* and *Peranema trichophorum*," *Archiv für Protistenkunde*, **67**, 128–156.

LACKEY, J. B. (1933), "Studies on the life histories of Euglenida. III. The morphology of *Peranema trichophorum* Ehrbg., with special reference to its kinetic elements and the classification of the Heteronemidae," *Biological Bulletin of the Marine Biological Laboratory, Wood's Hole*, **65**, 238–248.

LACKEY, J. B. (1934), "Studies on the life histories of Euglenida. IV. A comparison of the structure and division of *Distigma proteus* Ehrb. and *Astasia Dangeardi* Lemm., a study in phylogeny," *Biological Bulletin of the Marine Biological Laboratory, Wood's Hole*, **67**, 145–162.

LACKEY, J. B. (1940), "Some new flagellates from the Wood's Hole area," *American Midland Naturalist*, **23**, 463–471.

LACKEY, J. B. (1960), "*Calkinsia aureus* gen. et sp. nov., a new marine euglenid," *Transactions of the American Microscopical Society*, **79**, 105–107.

LACKEY, J. B. (1962), "Three new colorless Euglenophyceae from marine situations," *Archiv für Mikrobiologie*, **42**, 190–195.

LANJOUW, J., ed. (1952), *International Code of Botanical Nomenclature adopted by the Seventh International Botanical Congress, Stockholm, July 1950*. Utrecht: International Bureau for Plant Taxonomy and Nomenclature.

LAZZARINI, R. A. and A. SAN PIETRO (1963), "The biosynthesis of transhydrogenase in *Euglena gracilis*," *Studies on Microalgae and Photosynthetic Bacteria*, ed. Japanese Society of Plant Physiologists, 453–464. Tokyo: University of Tokyo Press.

LAZZARINI, R. A. and M. WOODRUFF (1964), "The photoinduction of transhydrogenase in *Euglena*," *Biochimica et biophysica acta*, **79**, 412–415.

LEEDALE, G. F. (1958a), "Mitosis and chromosome numbers in the *Euglenineae* (Flagellata)," *Nature*, **181**, 502–503.

LEEDALE, G. F. (1958b), "Nuclear structure and mitosis in the *Euglenineae*," *Archiv für Mikrobiologie*, **32**, 32–64.

LEEDALE, G. F. (1959a), "Periodicity of mitosis and cell division in the *Euglenineae*," *Biological Bulletin of the Marine Biological Laboratory, Wood's Hole*, **116**, 162–174.

LEEDALE, G. F. (1959b), "The time-scale of mitosis in the *Euglenineae*," *Archiv für Mikrobiologie*, **32**, 352–360.

LEEDALE, G. F. (1959c), "Amitosis in three species of *Euglena*," *Cytologia*, **24**, 213–219.

LEEDALE, G. F. (1959d), "Formation of anucleate cells of *Euglena gracilis* by miscleavage," *Journal of Protozoology*, **6**(*Supplement*), 26.

LEEDALE, G. F. (1962), "The evidence for a meiotic process in the *Euglenineae*," *Archiv für Mikrobiologie*, **42**, 237–245.

LEEDALE, G. F. (1964), "Pellicle structure in *Euglena*," *British Phycological Bulletin*, **2**, 291–306.

LEEDALE, G. F., B. J. D. MEEUSE, and E. G. PRINGSHEIM (1965), "Structure and physiology of *Euglena spirogyra*. I and II. III–VI.," *Archiv für Mikrobiologie*, **50**, 68–102, 133–155.

LEFÈVRE, M. (1932), "Sur la structure de la membrane des Euglènes du groupe *spirogyra*," *Comptes rendus des séances de l'Académie des sciences*, **195**, 1308–1309.

LEFF, J., M. MANDEL, H. T. EPSTEIN, and J. A. SCHIFF (1963), "DNA satellites from cells of green and aplastidic algae," *Biochemical and Biophysical Research Communications*, **13**, 126–130.

LEHNINGER, A. L. (1964), *The Mitochondrion*. New York and Amsterdam: W. A. Benjamin, Inc.

LEMMERMANN, E. (1901), "Beiträge zur Kenntniss der Planktonalgen. XII. Notizen über einige Schwebalgen," *Berichte der deutschen Botanischen Gesellschaft*, **19**, 85–95.

LEMMERMANN, E. (1910), *Kryptogamenflora der Mark Brandenburg. III. Algen I. (Schizophyceen, Flagellaten, Peridineen)*. Leipzig: Verlag von Gebrüder Borntraeger.

LEMMERMANN, E. (1913), "Eugleninae," *Die Susswasserflora Deutschlands, Österreichs und der Schweiz*, ed. A. Pascher, Vol. 2, 115–174. Jena: Gustav Fischer Verlag.

LEWIS, S., J. A. SCHIFF, and H. T. EPSTEIN (1965), "Studies of chloroplast development in *Euglena*. 9. Chloroplast antigens and their appearance during chloroplast development," *Journal of Protozoology*, **12**, 281–290.

LOEFER, J. B. (1931), "Morphology and binary fission in *Heteronema acus* (Ehrb.) Stein," *Archiv für Protistenkunde*, **74**, 449–470.

LOEWY, A. G. and P. SIEKEVITZ (1963), *Cell Structure and Cell Function*. New York: Holt, Rinehart and Winston, Inc.

LOWNDES, A. G. (1936), "Flagella movement," *Nature*, **138**, 210–211.

LOWNDES, A. G. (1941), "On flagellar movement in unicellular organisms," *Proceedings of the Zoological Society of London*, Ser. A., **111**, 111–134.

LYMAN, H., H. T. EPSTEIN, and J. A. SCHIFF (1959), "Ultraviolet inactivation and photoreactivation of chloroplast development in *Euglena* without cell death," *Journal of Protozoology*, **6**, 264–265.

LYMAN, H., H. T. EPSTEIN, and J. A. SCHIFF (1961), "Studies of chloroplast development in *Euglena*. I. Inactivation of green colony formation by U.V. light," *Biochimica et biophysica acta*, **50**, 301–309.

McCALLA, D. R. (1965), "Effect of nitrofurans on the chloroplast system of *Euglena gracilis*," *Journal of Protozoology*, **12**, 34–41.

McELROY, W. (1964), *Cell Physiology and Biochemistry*, 2nd ed. Englewood Cliffs, New Jersey: Prentice-Hall, Inc.

MAINX, F. (1926), "Einige neue Vertreter der Gattung *Euglena* Ehrenberg," *Archiv für Protistenkunde*, **54**, 150–162.

MANTON, I. (1959), "Electron microscopical observations on a very small flagellate: the problem of *Chromulina pusilla* Butcher," *Journal of the Marine Biological Association of the United Kingdom*, **38**, 319–333.

MANTON, I. (1964a), "Observations with the electron microscope on the division cycle in the flagellate *Prymnesium parvum* Carter," *Journal of the Royal Microscopical Society*, **83**, 317–325.

MANTON, I. (1964b), "The possible significance of some details of flagellar bases in plants," *Journal of the Royal Microscopical Society*, **82**, 279–285.

MANTON, I. (1964c), "Observations on the fine structure of the zoospore and young germling of *Stigeoclonium*," *Journal of Experimental Botany*, **15**, 399–411.

MANTON, I. (1965), "Some phyletic implications of flagellar structure in plants," *Advances in Botanical Research*, Vol. 2, ed. R. D. Preston, 1–34. New York and London: Academic Press.

MANTON, I. and B. CLARKE (1955), "Observations with the electron microscope on the internal structure of the spermatozoid of *Fucus*," *Journal of Experimental Botany*, **7**, 416–432.

MANTON, I. and G. F. LEEDALE (1961), "Observations on the fine structure of *Paraphysomonas vestita*, with special reference to the Golgi apparatus and the origin of scales," *Phycologia*, **1**, 37–57.

MANTON, I. and H. A. VON STOSCH (1966), "Observations on the fine structure of the male gamete of the marine centric diatom *Lithodesmium undulatum*," *Journal of the Royal Microscopical Society*, **85**, 119–134.

MARTIN, G. W. (1955), "Are fungi plants?" *Mycologia*, **47**, 779–792.

MARZULLO, G. and W. F. DANFORTH (1964), "Kinetic studies of the oxidative assimilation of acetate by a non-photosynthetic strain of *Euglena gracilis*," *Journal of General Microbiology*, **34**, 9–20.

MASSART, J. (1900), "*Clautriavia*, un nouveau genre de flagellates," *Bulletin des séances de la Société royale des sciences medicales et naturelles de Bruxelles*, **58**, 133–134.

MAST, S. O. (1917), "The relation between spectral colour and stimulation in the lower organisms," *Journal of Experimental Zoology*, **22**, 471–528.

MAST, S. O. (1941), "Motor response in unicellular animals," *Protozoa in Biological Research*, eds. G. N. Calkins and F. M. Summers, 271–351. New York: Columbia University Press.

MAZIA, D. (1961), "Mitosis and the physiology of cell division," *The Cell*, Vol. 3, eds. J. Brachet and A. E. Mirsky, 77–412. New York and London: Academic Press.

MEEUSE, B. J. D. (1962), "Storage products," *Physiology and Biochemistry of Algae*, ed. R. A. Lewin, 289–313. New York and London: Academic Press.

MENKE, W. (1961), "Über die Chloroplasten von *Anthoceros punctatus*," *Zeitschrift für Naturforschung*, **16b**, 334–336.

MENKE, W. (1962), "Structure and chemistry of plastids," *Annual Review of Plant Physiology*, **13**, 27–44.

MERESCHKOWSKY, C. VON (1879), "Studien über Protozoen des nördlichen Russland," *Archiv für mikroskopische Anatomie (und Entwicklungsmechanik)*, **16**, 153–248.

MIGNOT, J.-P. (1962), "Étude du noyau de l'Euglénien *Scytomonas pusilla* (Stein) pendant la division et la copulation," *Comptes rendus des séances de l'Académie des sciences*, **254**, 1864–1866.

MIGNOT, J.-P. (1963), "Quelques particularités de l'ultrastructure d'*Entosiphon sulcatum* (Duj.) Stein, flagellé Euglénien," *Comptes rendus des séances de l'Académie des sciences*, **257**, 2530–2533.

MIGNOT, J.-P. (1964), "Observations complémentaires sur la structure des flagelles d'*Entosiphon sulcatum* (Duj.) Stein, flagellé Euglénien," *Comptes rendus des séances de l'Académie des sciences*, **258**, 3360–3363.

MIGNOT, J.-P. (1965), "Étude ultrastructurale des Eugléniens: II. A, Dictyosomes et dictyocinèse chez *Distigma proteus* Ehrbg. B, Mastigonèmes chez *Anisonema costatum* Christen," *Protistologica*, **1**(2), 17–22.

MILLONIG, G. (1961), "A modified procedure for lead staining of thin sections," *Journal of Biophysical and Biochemical Cytology*, **11**, 736–739.

MIRSKY, A. E. and S. OSAWA (1961), "The interphase nucleus," *The Cell*, Vol. 2, eds. J. Brachet and A. E. Mirsky, 677–770. New York and London: Academic Press.

MOOR, H. and K. MÜHLETHALER (1963), "Fine structure in frozen-etched yeast cells," *Journal of Cell Biology*, **17**, 609–628.

MOORE, R. T. and J. H. McALEAR (1963), "Fine structure of Mycota. 4. The occurrence of the Golgi dictyosome in the fungus *Neobulgaria pura* (Fr.) Petrak," *Journal of Cell Biology*, **16**, 131–141.

MORIBER, L. G., B. HERSHENOV, S. AARONSON, and B. BENSKY (1963), "Teratological chloroplast structures in *Euglena gracilis* permanently bleached by exogenous physical and chemical agents," *Journal of Protozoology*, **10**, 80–86.

MOROFF, T. (1904), "Beitrag zur Kenntnis einiger Flagellaten," *Archiv für Protistenkunde*, **3**, 69–106.

MOSES, M. J. (1964), "The nucleus and chromosomes: A cytological perspective," *Cytology and Cell Physiology*, 3rd ed., ed. G. H. Bourne, 423–558. New York and London: Academic Press.

MÜHLETHALER, K. and P. R. BELL (1962), "Untersuchungen über die Kontinuität von Plastiden und Mitochondrien in der Eizelle von *Pteridium aquilinum* (L.) Kuhn," *Naturwissenschaften*, **49**, 63–64.

NASS, M. M. K., S. NASS, and B. A. AFZELIUS (1965), "The general occurrence of mitochondrial DNA," *Experimental Cell Research*, **37**, 516–539.

NISHIMURA, M. and H. HUZISIGE (1959), "Studies on the chlorophyll formation in *Euglena gracilis* with special reference to the action spectrum of the process," *Journal of Biochemistry*, **46**, 225–234.

NOVIKOFF, A. B. (1961a), "Mitochondria (chondriosomes)," *The Cell*, Vol. 2, eds. J. Brachet and A. E. Mirsky, 299–421. New York and London: Academic Press.

NOVIKOFF, A. B. (1961b), "Lysosomes and related particles," *The Cell*, Vol. 2, eds. J. Brachet and A. E. Mirsky, 423–488. New York and London: Academic Press.

OHMANN, E. (1963), "Über den Ausfall glykolytischer Enzyme in *Euglena gracilis*," *Naturwissenschaften*, **50**, 552–553.

OHMANN, E. (1964), "Acetataktivierung in Grünalgen, I. Oxydation und Aktivierung des Acetats in *Euglena gracilis*," *Biochimica et biophysica acta*, **82**, 325–335.

PADILLA, G. M. and T. W. JAMES (1964), "Continuous synchronous cultures of protozoa," *Methods in Cell Physiology*, Vol. 1, ed. D. M. Prescott, 141–157. New York and London: Academic Press.

PALMER, T. C. (1902), "Five species of *Trachelomonas*," *Proceedings of the Academy of Natural Sciences of Philadelphia*, **54**, 791–795.

PASCHER, A. (1927), "Neue oder wenig bekannte Protisten. XX. Neue oder wenig bekannte Flagellaten. XVIII," *Archiv für Protistenkunde*, **58**, 577–598.

PASCHER, A. (1931), "Über die Verfestigung des Protoplasten im Gehäuse einer neuen Euglenine (*Klebsiella*)," *Archiv für Protistenkunde*, **73**, 315–322.

PAUL, J. (1965), *Cell Biology*. London: Heinemann Educational Books, Ltd.

PEASE, D. C. (1965), *Histological Techniques for Electron Microscopy*, 2nd ed. New York and London: Academic Press.

PERINI, F., M. D. KAMEN, and J. A. SCHIFF (1964), "Iron-containing proteins in *Euglena*. I. Detection and characterization," *Biochimica et biophysica acta*, **88**, 74–90.

PERINI, F., J. A. SCHIFF, and M. D. KAMEN (1964), "Iron-containing proteins in *Euglena*. II. Functional localization," *Biochimica et biophysica acta*, **88**, 91–98.

PERTY, M. (1849), "Über verticale Verbreitung mikroskopischer Lebensformen," *Mittheilungen der naturforschenden Gesellschaft in Bern* (Nr. 146–149), 17–45.

PERTY, M. (1852), *Zur Kenntnis Kleinster Lebensformen nach Bau, Funktionen, Systematik, mit Spezialverzeichnis der in der Schweiz beobachteten*. Bern: Verlag von Jent und Reinert.

PICKEN, L. (1960), *The Organization of Cells and Other Organisms*. Oxford: University Press.

PIGON, A. (1947), "Spostrzezenia nad pellikula *Euglena viridis* Ehrbg.—On the pellicle of *Euglena viridis* Ehrbg.," *Bulletin international de l'Académie polonaise des sciences et des lettres*, B. II, 1946, 111–120.

PITELKA, D. R. (1963), *Electron-Microscopic Structure of Protozoa*. Oxford: Pergamon Press.

PITELKA, D. R. and F. M. CHILD (1964), "The locomotor apparatus of ciliates and flagellates: relations between structure and function," *Biochemistry and Physiology of Protozoa*, Vol. 3, ed. S. H. Hutner, 131–198. New York and London: Academic Press.

PITELKA, D. R. and C. N. SCHOOLEY (1955), "Comparative morphology of some protozoan flagella," *University of California Publications in Zoology*, **61**, 79–128.

PLAYFAIR, G. J. (1915), "The genus *Trachelomonas*," *Proceedings of the Linnean Society of New South Wales*, **40**, 1–41.

POCHMANN, A (1942), "Synopsis der Gattung *Phacus*," *Archiv für Protistenkunde*, **95**, 81–252.

POCHMANN, A. (1953), "Struktur, Wachstum und Teilung der Körperhülle bei den Eugleninen," *Planta*, **42**, 478–548.

POCHMANN, A. (1955), "*Helikotropis okteres* n. gen. n. spec. (*Peranemataceae*) und die Frage de Ätiologie der Kielbildungen bei farblosen Eugleninen," *Österreichische Botanische Zeitschrift*, **102**, 1–17.

POCHMANN, A. (1956), "Untersuchungen über Plattenbau und Spiralbau, über Wachstum und Zerteilung der Paramylon-körner," *Österreichische Botanische Zeitschrift*, **103**, 110–141.

POCHMANN, A. (1958), "Zweiter Beitrag zur Kenntnis der Struktur, Entwicklung und Zerteilung der Paramylon-körner," *Österreichishe Botanische Zeitschrift*, **104**, 321–341.

POHL, R. (1948), "Tagesrhythmus im phototaktischen Verhalten der *Euglena gracilis*," *Zeitschrift für Naturforschung*, **3b**, 367–374.

PORTER, K. R. (1961a), "The endoplasmic reticulum: some current interpretations of its forms and functions," *Biological Structure and Function*, Vol. 1, eds. T. W. Goodwin and O. Lindberg, 127–155. New York and London: Academic Press.

PORTER, K. R. (1961b), "The ground substance; observations from electron microscopy," *The Cell*, Vol. 2, eds. J. Brachet and A. E. Mirsky, 621–675. New York and London: Academic Press.

PORTER, K. R. (1963), "Diversity at the subcellular level and its significance," *The Nature of Biological Diversity*, ed. J. M. Allen, 121–163. New York, Toronto, and London: McGraw-Hill Book Company.

PRINGSHEIM, E. G. (1936), "Zur Kenntnis saprotropher Algen und Flagellaten. I. Über Anhäufungskulturen polysaprober Flagellaten," *Archiv für Protistenkunde*, **87**, 43–96.

PRINGSHEIM, E. G. (1937a), "Über das Stigma bei farblosen Flagellaten," *Cytologia*, *Fujii-Jubilaumsband*, 234–255.

PRINGSHEIM, E. G. (1937b), "Beiträge zur Physiologie saprotropher Algen und Flagellaten. 3. Die Stellung der Azetatflagellaten in einem physiologischen Ernährungssystem," *Planta*, **27**, 61–92.

PRINGSHEIM, E. G. (1942), "Contributions to our knowledge of saprotrophic algae and flagellata. III. *Astasia, Distigma, Menoidium* and *Rhabdomonas*," *New Phytologist*, **41**, 171–205.

PRINGSHEIM, E. G. (1946a), "The biphasic or soil-water culture method for growing algae and flagellates," *Journal of Ecology*, **33**, 193–204.

PRINGSHEIM, E. G. (1946b), *Pure Cultures of Algae*. Cambridge: University Press.

PRINGSHEIM, E. G. (1948), "Taxonomic problems in the *Euglenineae*," *Biological Reviews and Biological Proceedings of the Cambridge Philosophical Society*, **23**, 46–61.

PRINGSHEIM, E. G. (1953a), "Salzwasser-Eugleninen," *Archiv für Mikrobiologie*, **18**, 149–164.

PRINGSHEIM, E. G. (1953b), "Observations on some species of *Trachelomonas* grown in culture," *New Phytologist*, **52,** 93–113, 238–266.

PRINGSHEIM, E. G. (1953c), "Notiz über *Colacium (Euglenaceae)*," *Österreichische Botanische Zeitschrift*, **100,** 270–275.

PRINGSHEIM. E. G. (1956), "Contributions towards a monograph of the genus *Euglena*," *Nova Acta Leopoldina*, **18,** 1–168.

PRINGSHEIM, E. G. (1957), "Two species of *Trachelomonas (Euglenineae)* without chlorophyll," *Nature*, **180,** 1296–1297.

PRINGSHEIM, E. G. (1963), *Farblose Algen. Ein Beitrag zur Evolutionsforschung.* Stuttgart: Gustav Fischer Verlag.

PRINGSHEIM, E. G. and O. PRINGSHEIM (1952), "Experimental elimination of chromatophores and eye-spot in *Euglena gracilis*," *New Phytologist*, **51,** 65–76.

PROVASOLI, L. (1958), "Nutrition and ecology of protozoa and algae," *Annual Review of Microbiology*, **12,** 279–308.

PROVASOLI, L., S. H. HUTNER, and I. J. PINTNER (1951), "Destruction of chloroplasts by streptomycin," *Cold Spring Harbor Symposia on Quantitative Biology*, **16,** 113–120.

PROVASOLI, L., S. H. HUTNER, and A. SCHATZ (1948), "Streptomycin-induced chlorophyll-less races of *Euglena*," *Proceedings of the Society for Experimental Biology and Medicine*, **69,** 279–282.

RAY, D. S. and P. C. HANAWALT (1964), "Properties of the satellite DNA associated with the chloroplasts of *Euglena gracilis*," *Journal of Molecular Biology*, **9,** 812–824.

RAY, D. S. and P. C. HANAWALT (1965), "Satellite DNA components in *Euglena gracilis* cells lacking chloroplasts," *Journal of Molecular Biology*, **11,** 760–768.

RHOADES, M. M. (1961), "Meiosis," *The Cell*, Vol. 3, eds. J. Brachet and A. E. Mirsky, 1–75. New York and London: Academic Press.

ROBBINS, W. J., A. HERVEY, and M. E. STEBBINS (1953), "*Euglena* and vitamin B_{12}," *Annals of the New York Academy of Sciences*, **56,** 818–830.

ROBERTSON, J. D. (1959), "The ultrastructure of cell membranes and their derivatives," *Symposia, Biochemical Society*, **16,** 3–43.

ROBERTSON, J. D. (1964), "Unit membranes: A review with recent new studies of experimental alterations and a new subunit structure in synaptic membranes," *Cellular Membranes in Development*, ed. M. Locke, 1–81. New York and London: Academic Press.

ROBINOW, C. F. (1962), "Some observations on the mode of division of somatic nuclei of *Mucor* and *Allomyces*," *Archiv für Mikrobiologie*, **42,** 369–377.

ROSEN, W. G. and S. R. GAWLIK (1961), "Effect of streptomycin on chlorophyll accumulation in *Euglena gracilis*," *Journal of Protozoology*, **8,** 90–96.

ROSENBAUM, J. L. (1965), "Effect of cycloheximide on flagellar regeneration in *Euglena gracilis*," *Journal of Cell Biology*, **27,** 89A–90A.

ROSENBAUM, J. L. and F. M. CHILD (1964), "Incorporation of tritiated precursors into regenerating flagella of two flagellates," *Journal of Protozoology*, **11**(*Supplement*), 22.

ROSENBAUM, J. L. and F. M. CHILD (1966), private communication.

ROSENBERG, A. and M. PECKER (1964), "Lipid alterations in *Euglena gracilis* cells during light-induced greening," *Biochemistry*, **3,** 254–258.

ROTH, L. E. (1959), "An electron-microscope study of the cytology of the protozoan *Peranema trichophorum*," *Journal of Protozoology*, **6,** 107–116.

ROTH, T. F. and K. R. PORTER (1964), "Yolk protein uptake in the oocyte of the mosquito *Aedes aegypti* L.," *Journal of Cell Biology*, **20,** 313–332.

ROUILLER, C. and E. FAURÉ-FREMIET (1958), "Structure fine d'un flagellé chrysomonadien: *Chromulina psammobia*," *Experimental Cell Research*, **14,** 47–67.

SAGAN, L., Y. BEN-SHAUL, H. T. EPSTEIN, and J. A. SCHIFF (1965), "Studies of chloroplast development in *Euglena*. XI. Radioautographic localization of chloroplast DNA," *Plant Physiology*, **40**, 1257–1260.

SAGER, R. and G. E. PALADE (1957), "Structure and development of the chloroplast in *Chlamydomonas*," *Journal of Biophysical and Biochemical Cytology*, **3**, 463–488.

SATIR, P. (1965), "Structure and function in cilia and flagella," *Protoplasmatologia* **III. E.**, 1–52.

SCHAEFFER, A. A. (1918), "A new and remarkable diatom-eating flagellate, *Jenningsia diatomophaga* nov. gen., nov. spec.," *Transactions of the American Microscopical Society*, **37**, 177–182.

SCHER, S. and L. SAGAN (1962), "Comparative studies of chloroplast replication: Ultraviolet inactivation and photoreactivation of cytoplasmic DNA synthesis associated with chloroplast replication in *Euglena gracilis*," *Journal of Protozoology*, **9**(*Supplement*), 13.

SCHEWIAKOFF, W. (1893), "Über die geographische Verbreitung der Süsswasser-Protozoën," *Mémoires de l'Académie impériale des sciences de St.-Petersbourg*, **41**, 1–201.

SCHIFF, J. A. and H. T. EPSTEIN (1965), "The continuity of the chloroplast in *Euglena*," *Reproduction: Molecular, Subcellular, and Cellular*, ed. M. Locke, 131–189. New York and London: Academic Press.

SCHIFF, J. A., H. LYMAN, and H. T. EPSTEIN (1961), "Studies of chloroplast development in *Euglena*. III. Experimental separation of chloroplast development and chloroplast replication," *Biochimica et biophysica acta*, **51**, 340–346.

SCHILLER, J. (1925), "Die planktonischen Vegetationen des adriatischen Meeres. B. *Chrysomonadina, Heterokontae, Cryptomonadina, Eugleninae, Volvocales*. 1. Systematischer Teil," *Archiv für Protistenkunde*, **53**, 59–123.

SCHMARDA, L. K. (1846), *Kleine Beiträge zur Naturgeschichte der Infusorien*. Wien: Verlag der Carl Haas'schen Buchhandlung.

SCHMITZ, Fr. (1884), "Beiträge zur Kenntniss der Chromatophoren," *Jahrbücher für wissenschaftliche Botanik*, **15**, 1–177.

SHAWHAN, F. M. and T. L. JAHN (1947), "A survey of the genus *Petalomonas* Stein (*Protozoa: Euglenida*)," *Transactions of the American Microscopical Society*, **66**, 182–189.

SIEGESMUND, K. A., W. G. ROSEN, and S. R. GAWLIK (1962), "Effects of darkness and of streptomycin on the fine structure of *Euglena gracilis*," *American Journal of Botany*, **49**, 137–145.

SINGH, K. P. (1956), "Studies in the genus *Trachelomonas*. I. Description of six organisms in cultivation," *American Journal of Botany*, **43**, 258–266.

SJÖSTRAND, F. S. (1964), "The endoplasmic reticulum," *Cytology and Cell Physiology*, 3rd ed., ed. G. H. Bourne, 311–375. New York and London: Academic Press.

SKUJA, H. (1939), "Beitrag zur Algenflora Lettlands II," *Acta Horti botanici Universitatis latviensis*, **11/12**, 41–169.

SKUJA, H. (1948), "Taxonomie des Phytoplanktons einiger Seen in Uppland, Schweden," *Symbolae botanicae upsalienses*, **9, 3**, 1–399.

SKUJA, H. (1956), "Taxonomische und biologische studien über das Phytoplankton schwedischer Binnengewässer," *Nova acta Regiae Societatis scientarium upsaliensis*, Ser. 4, **16**, 1–404.

SLAUTTERBACK, D. B. (1963), "Cytoplasmic microtubules," *Journal of Cell Biology*, **18**, 367–388.

SLEIGH, M. A. (1962), *The Biology of Cilia and Flagella*. Oxford: Pergamon Press.

SMITH, G. M. (1933), *The Fresh-water Algae of the United States*. New York: McGraw-Hill Book Company.

STANIER, R. Y. and C. B. VAN NIEL (1962), "The concept of a bacterium," *Archiv für Mikrobiologie*, **42**, 17–35.

STEIN, F. R. VON (1878), *Der Organismus der Infusionsthiere. III. Der Organismus der Flagellaten. I.* Leipzig: Verlag von Wilhelm Engelmann.

STEINECKE, F. (1932), "Algologische Notizen II. *Heterodendron pascheri, Euglenocapsa ochracea, Stylodinium cerasiforme,*" *Archiv für Protistenkunde,* **70,** 589–594.

STERN, A. I., H. T. EPSTEIN, and J. A. SCHIFF (1964), "Studies of chloroplast development in *Euglena.* VI. Light intensity as a controlling factor in development," *Plant Physiology,* **39,** 226–231.

STERN, A. I., J. A. SCHIFF, and H. T. EPSTEIN (1964), "Studies of chloroplast development in *Euglena.* V. Pigment biosynthesis, photosynthetic oxygen evolution and carbon dioxide fixation during chloroplast development," *Plant Physiology,* **39,** 220–226.

STOKES, A. C. (1884a), "Notes on some apparently undescribed forms of fresh-water Infusoria," *American Journal of Science,* 3rd Ser., **28,** 38–49.

STOKES, A. C. (1884b), "Change of the generic name *Solenotus,*" *American Journal of Science,* 3rd Ser., **28,** 158.

STOKES, A. C. (1887), "Notices of new fresh-water Infusoria," *Proceedings of the American Philosophical Society,* **24,** 244–255.

STORM, J. and S. H. HUTNER (1953), "Nutrition of *Peranema,*" *Annals of the New York Academy of Sciences,* **56,** 901–909.

STROTHER, G. K. and J. J. WOLKEN (1961), "In vivo absorption spectra of *Euglena*: Chloroplast and eyespot," *Journal of Protozoology,* **8,** 261–265.

SUBRAHMANYAN, R. (1954), "A new member of the *Euglenineae, Protoeuglena noctilucae* gen. et sp. nov., occurring in *Noctiluca miliaris* Suriray, causing green discoloration of the sea off Calicut," *Proceedings of the Indian Academy of Sciences,* **39,** 118–127.

SWANSON, C. P. (1964), *The Cell,* 2nd ed. Englewood Cliffs, New Jersey: Prentice-Hall, Inc.

TAMM, S. L. (1965), "Flagellar development in the protozoan *Peranema trichophorum,*" *Journal of Cell Biology,* **27,** 104A.

TAMM, S. L. (1966), private communication.

THOMAS, J. B. (1960) "Chloroplast structure," *Encyclopedia of Plant Physiology,* Vol. V, Part 1, ed. W. Ruhland, 511–565. Berlin: Springer-Verlag.

THOMAS, J. B. (1965), *Primary Photoprocesses in Biology.* Amsterdam: North-Holland Publishing Company.

TRAGER, W. (1964), "The cytoplasm of protozoa," *The Cell,* Vol. 6, eds. J. Brachet and A. E. Mirsky, 81–137. New York and London: Academic Press.

TSCHERMAK-WOESS, E. (1963), "Strukturtypen der Ruhekerne von Pflanzen und Tieren," *Protoplasmatologia,* **5.1,** 1–158.

WAYLAND, F. (1963), "Some observations on *Scytomonas pusilla* and *S. klebsi,*" *Journal of Protozoology,* **11** (*Supplement*), 39.

WENRICH, D. H. (1924), "Studies on *Euglenamorpha hegneri* N. G., N. SP., a euglenoid flagellate found in tadpoles," *Biological Bulletin of the Marine Biological Laboratory, Wood's Hole,* **47,** 149–175.

WETTSTEIN, D. VON (1959), "Developmental changes in chloroplasts and their genetic control," *Developmental Cytology,* ed. D. Rudnick, 123–160. New York: The Ronald Press Company.

WETTSTEIN, D. VON (1961), "Nuclear and cytoplasmic factors in development of chloroplast structure and function," *Canadian Journal of Botany,* **39,** 1537–1545.

WICHTERMAN, R. (1961), "Biological effects of X-irradiation in some representative protozoa," *Progress in Protozoology. Proceedings of the First International Congress on Protozoology,* 231–237.

WILSON, B. W. (1963), "The oxidative assimilation of acetate by *Astasia longa* and the regulation of cell respiration," *Journal of Cellular and Comparative Physiology,* **62,** 49–56.

WILSON, B. W. and T. W. JAMES (1963), "The respiration and growth of synchronized populations of the cell *Astasia longa,*" *Experimental Cell Research,* **32,** 305–319.

WITTEKIND, D. (1963), "Pinozytose," *Naturwissenschaften*, **50**, 270–277.

WOLKEN, J. J. (1956), "A molecular morphology of *Euglena gracilis* var. *bacillaris*," *Journal of Protozoology*, **3**, 211–221.

WOLKEN, J. J. (1961), *Euglena. An Experimental Organism for Biochemical and Biophysical Studies*. New Brunswick, New Jersey: Rutgers University Press.

WOLKEN, J. J. and A. D. MELLON (1956), "The relationship between chlorophyll and the carotenoids in the algal flagellate *Euglena*," *Journal of General Physiology*, **39**, 675–685.

WOLKEN, J. J. and E. SHIN (1958), "Photomotion in *Euglena gracilis*. I. Photokinesis. II. Phototaxis," *Journal of Protozoology*, **5**, 39–46.

WOLKEN, J. J., A. D. MELLON, and C. L. GREENBLATT (1955), "Environmental factors affecting growth and chlorophyll synthesis in *Euglena*. I. Physical and Chemical. II. The effectiveness of the spectrum for chlorophyll synthesis," *Journal of Protozoology*, **2**, 89–96.

ZAHALSKY, A. C., S. H. HUTNER, M. KEANE, and R. N. BURGER (1962), "Bleaching *Euglena gracilis* with antihistamines and streptomycin-type antibiotics," *Archiv für Mikrobiologie*, **42**, 46–55.

AUTHOR INDEX

(Numbers in bold type indicate page on which full reference is listed.)

A

Aaronson, S., 184, **206, 216**
Afzelius, B., 128, 164, **206, 216**
Allen, J. R., 202, **206**
Arnon, D. I., 169, **206**

B

Balamuth, W., **211**
Barras, D. R., 99, **206**
Barry, J. M., 115, 165, **206**
Batra, P. P., 143, **206**
Behre, K., 71, **206**
Bell, P. R., 160, 164, 183, **206, 216**
Bendix, S., 146, **206**
Ben-Shaul, Y., 179, 181, 182, **206, 218**
Bensky, B., 184, **206, 216**
Bernstein, E., 184, **211**
Blum, J. J., 89, 92, **206, 207**
Bold, H. C., 3, **207**
Bourne, G. H., 163, **207**
Bourrelly, P., 41, 50, **207**
Bovee, E. C., 99, 141, 142, **211, 212**
Boy de la Tour, E., 181, **210**
Brawerman, G., 116, 117, 182, 183, **207, 210**
Brody, M., 182, **207**
Brody, S. S., 182, **207**
Brown, F., 79, **207**
Brown, J. S., 181, **207**
Brown, V. E., 56, 59, 64, **207**
Bruce, V. G., 146, **207**
Brumpt, E., 67, 68, **207**
Buchanan, P. J., 165, **207**
Bucher, O., 92, **207**
Buetow, D. E., 165, **207, 208**
Burger, R. N., 184, **221**

C

Chadefaud, M., 17, 23, 41, 60, 99, **207, 208**
Chargaff, F. M., 182, 183, **207**
Chen, Y. T., 60, 141, 142, 192, 195, 201, **208**
Child, F. M., 128, 140, 141, **217, 218**
Christen, H. R., 9, 31, 32, 34, 41, 46, 48, 50, 52, 53, 54, 55, 56, 60, 64, 65, 66, 69, 74, 190, **208**
Christensen, T., 3, 4, **208**
Chu, S. P., 17, **208**
Clark, B., 147, **215**
Cobb, H. D., 146, **208**
Conrad, W., 17, 35, 36, 38, 43, **208**
Cook, J. R., 92, **208**
Corliss, J. O., **211**
Cowan, C. A., 182, **209**
Cramer, M., 199, 202, **208**

D

Da Cunha, A. M., 12, 14, **208**
Dalton, A. J., 153, 155, **208**
Danforth, W. F., 165, **208, 209, 210, 215**
Dangeard, P.-A., 17, 21, 25, 60, **209**
Danielli, J. F., 79, **207, 209**
Davson, H., 79, **209**
De Duve, C., 166, **209**
Deflandre, G., 35, 38, 111, **209**
Deken-Grenson, M. de, 184, **209**
Diamond, J. H., 202, **206**
Dodge, J. D., 89, **209**
Dujardin, F., 25, 29, 31, 43, 45, 56, 57, 59, 60, 66, 71, 187, **209**
Dusi, H., 201

223

E

Ebringer, L., 184, **209**
Edelman, M., 164, 182, **209**
Edmunds, L. N., 92, **209**
Ehrenberg, C. G., 16, 17, 18, 25, 27, 31, 35, 41, 43, 45, 60, 69, 143, **209**
Eisenstadt, J. M., 116, 117, 182, 183, **207, 210**
Engelman, T. W., 146, **210**
Epstein, H. T., 165, 179, 181, 182, 183, 184, **206, 209, 210, 214, 218, 219, 220**
Eshleman, J. N., 165, **210**

F

Fauré-Fremiet, E., 147, **210, 218**
Fawcett, D., 128, 139, **210**
Fonseca, J. R., 139, **212**
Francé, R., 41, **210**
Fresenius, G., 46, **210**
Frey-Wyssling, A., 79, 81, 115, 153, 160, 163, 166, 183, **210**
Fritsch, F. E., 3, 74, **210**
Fuller, R. C., 179, 181, **210**

G

Gawlik, S. R., 184, **218, 219**
Georges, G., 50, **207**
Gibbons, I. R., 128, 139, **210**
Gibbs, M., 181, **210**
Gibbs, S. P., 147, 174, **210**
Gibor, A., 164, 182, 184, **210**
Gicklhorn, J., 41, 69, **210**
Godts, A., 184, **209**
Godward, M. B. E., 203, **210**
Gojdics, M., 17, 108, 146, 151, **211**
Goldsmith, T. H., 143, 179, **213**
Goldstone, S. H., 202, **206**
Gordon, A., 182, **213**
Gössel, I., 146, **211**
Granick, S., 164, 182, 184, **210**
Green, J., 143, **211**
Greenblatt, C. L., 181, **211, 221**
Grell, K. G., 89, **211**
Grimstone, A. V., 126, 128, 139, 194, **210, 211**
Gross, J. A., 165, 184, **211**

H

Hall, R. P., 60, 201, **211**
Halldal, P., 146, **211**
Hamburger, C., 99, **211**
Hanawalt, P. C., 164, 182, **218**
Harker, J., 146, **211**
Hartman, P. E., 115, **211**
Heidt, K., 25, **211**

Hershenov, R., 184, **216**
Hervey, A., 184, **218**
Hollande, A., 9, 14, 16, 17, 59, 64, 67, 151, **211**
Holwill, M. E. J., 142, **211**
Honigberg, B. M., 3, 5, **211**
Huber-Pestalozzi, G., 8, 11, 34, 35, 40, 43, 62, 67, 69, 71, **211**
Hunter, F. R., 165, **212**
Hurlbert, R. E., 165, **212**
Hurry, S. W., 80, **212**
Hutner, S. H., 183, 184, 201, 202, **206, 212, 218, 220, 221**
Huzisige, H., 181, **216**

I

Iyengar, M. O. P., 27, **212**

J

Jahn, T. L., 25, 27, 29, 41, 56, 99, 139, 141, 142, 184, 201, **211, 212, 219**
James, T. W., 92, **212, 216, 220**
Jensen, W. A., 203, **212**
John, B., 81, **212**
Johnson, D. F., 41, **212**
Johnson, L. P., 25, **212**

K

Kahn, V., 89, **207**
Kamen, M. D., 165, **216**
Kay, D. H., 203, **212**
Keane, M., 184, **221**
Kempner, E. S., 199, **212**
Kirk, J. T. O., 184, **212**
Kitching, J. A., 148, **212**
Klebs, G., 9, 21, 23, 34, 36, 99, 100, 126, 187, 190, **212, 213**
Korshikov, A., 34, 48, **213**
Kreger, D. R., 185, **213**
Krichenbauer, H., 92, 93, 94, **213**
Krinsky, N. I., 143, 179, 182, **213**
Kudo, R. R., **211**
Kuhl, A., 166, **213**

L

Lackey, J. B., 16, 60, 62, 69, 71, **213**
Landman, M. D., 139, **212**
Lanjouw, J., 43, 56, **213**
Lavier, G., 67, 68, **207**
Lazzarini, R. A., 181, **213**
Lee, J. J., 202, **206**
Lee, J. W., 165, **212**
Leedale, G. F., 18, 83, 85, 87, 89, 91, 92, 96, 99, 100, 104, 139, 153, 155, 185, 186, 203, **213, 214, 215**

Lefèvre, M., 100, **214**
Leff, J., 182, **214**
Lehninger, A. L., 163, **214**
Lemmerman, E., 32, 41, 43, **214**
Levedahl, B. H., 165, **208**
Levine, J. H., 182, **207**
Levine, N. D., **211**
Lewis, K. R., 81, **212**
Lewis, S., 181, **214**
Loeblich, A. R., **211**
Loefer, J. B., 60, **214**
Loewy, A. G., 80, **214**
Lowndes, A. G., 142, **214**
Lwoff, A., 201
Lyman, H., 181, 182, 183, **214, 219**

M

McAlear, J. H., 155, **216**
McCalla, D. R., 184, **213**
McElroy, W., 80, **213**
McKibben, W. R., 27, 29, **212**
Mainx, F., 25, 27, **214**
Mandel, M., 182, **214**
Manton, I., 89, 128, 139, 147, 153, 155, 156, 161, **214, 215**
Martin, G. W., 89, **215**
Marzullo, G., 165, **215**
Massart, J., 69, **215**
Mast, S. O., 146, **215**
Mazia, D., 81, 128, **215**
Meel, L. van, 17, 38, **208**
Meeuse, B. J. D., 18, 99, 100, 139, 153, 185, 186, **213, 214, 215**
Mellon, A. D., 181, **221**
Menke, W., 169, **215**
Mereschkowsky, C. von, 62, **215**
Messin, S., 184, **209**
Mignot, J.-P., 92, 109, 134, 158, 190, 192, 194, **215**
Miller, J. H., 199, **212**
Millonig, G., 203, **215**
Mirsky, A. E., 81, **215**
Moor, H., 79, **216**
Moore, R. T., 155, **216**
Moriber, L. G., 184, **216**
Moroff, T., 29, **216**
Moses, M. J., 81, **216**
Mühlethaler, K., 79, 81, 115, 153, 160, 163, 164, 166, 183, **206, 210, 216**
Myers, J., 199, 202, **208**

N

Nass, M. M. K., 164, **216**
Nass, S., 164, **216**
Niel, C. B. van, 81, **219**
Nishimura, M., 181, **216**
Novikoff, A. B., 160, 163, 166, 167, **216**

O

Ohmann, E., 165, **216**
Osawa, S., 81, **215**

P

Padilla, G. M., 92, 165, **206, 216**
Palade, E., 169, **219**
Palmer, T. C., 36, **216**
Pascher, A., 36, 38, 40, **216**
Paul, J., 80, **216**
Pease, D. C., 203, **216**
Pecker, M., 181, **218**
Perini, F., 165, **216**
Perty, M., 12, 25, 43, 50, 64, **216**
Picken, L., 104, **216**
Pigon, A., 99, **216**
Pintner, I. J., 184, **218**
Pitelka, D. R., 109, 128, 139, 148, 194, **217**
Pittendrigh, C. S., 146, **207**
Playfair, G. J., 38, **217**
Pochmann, A., 45, 69, 72, 104, 105, 187, **217**
Pogo, S. S., 183, **207**
Pohl, R., 146, **217**
Porter, K. R., 115, 153, **217, 218**
Powell, W. N., 60, **211**
Pringsheim, E. G., 8, 9, 12, 16, 17, 18, 21, 23, 25, 27, 29, 32, 34, 35, 36, 38, 41, 46, 48, 50, 73, 74, 99, 100, 102, 108, 110, 139, 146, 147, 153, 179, 183, 185, 186, 188, 200, 201, 202, **214, 217, 218**
Pringsheim, O., 73, 183, **218**
Provasoli, L., 183, 184, 201, 202, **212, 218**

R

Ray, D. S., 164, 182, **218**
Rhoades, M. M., 81, **218**
Rigopoulos, N., 179, **210**
Rittenberg, S. C., 165, **212**
Robbins, W. J., 184, **218**
Robertson, J. D., 79, **218**
Robinow, C. F., 89, **218**
Rosen, W. G., 184, **218, 219**
Rosenbaum, J. L., 140, 141, **218**
Rosenberg, A., 181, **218**
Ross, R., 204
Roth, T. F., 153, **218**
Rothe, L. E., 132, 194, **218**
Rouiller, C., 147, **218**

S

Sagan, L., 182, 184, **218, 219**
Sager, R., 169, **219**
San Pietro, A., 181, **213**

Satir, P., 128, **219**
Schaeffer, A. A., 69, **219**
Schatz, A., 183, **218**
Scher, S., 184, **219**
Schewiakoff, W., 71, **219**
Schiff, J. A., 165, 179, 181, 182, 183, 184,
    **206, 209, 210, 211, 214, 216, 218,
    219, 220**
Schiller, J., 14, 69, **219**
Schmarda, L. K., 102, **219**
Schmitz, Fr., 23, 27, **219**
Schooley, C. N., 139, **217**
Shawhan, F. M., 56, **219**
Shin, E., 146, **221**
Siegesmund, K. A., 184, **219**
Siekevitz, P., 80, **214**
Singh, K. P., 36, **219**
Sjöstrand, F. S., 115, **219**
Skuja, H., 34, 48, 52, 53, 55, 56, 57, 58, 59,
    62, 63, 64, 70, 71, **219**
Slautterback, D. B., 100, 126, **219**
Sleigh, M. A., 128, 139, 142, **219**
Smillie, R. M., 179, **210**
Smith, G. M., 41, **219**
Sommer, J. R., 89, **207**
Stanier, R. Y., 81, **219**
Stebbins, M. E., 184, **218**
Stein, F. R. von, 38, 40, 45, 53, 55, 56, 60,
    64, 66, 71, 96, 111, **219**
Steinecke, F., 69, **220**
Stern, A. J., 179, 182, **213, 220**
Stokes, A. C., 57, 62, **220**
Stone, B. A., 99, **206**
Storm, J., 202, **220**
Stosch, H. A. von, 128, **215**

Strother, S. K., 146, **220**
Subrahmanyan, R., 69, **220**
Suskind, S., 115, **211**
Swanson, C. P., 80, **220**

T

Tamm, S. L., 140, **220**
Tewari, H. B., 163, **207**
Thomas, J. B., 169, **220**
Tollin, G., 143, **206**
Trager, W., 148, 153, **220**
Tschermak-Woess, E., 81, **220**

W

Wayland, F., 71, **220**
Weiser, J., **217**
Wenrich, D. H., 66, 67, 68, 92, **211, 220**
Wettstein, D. von, 181, **220**
Wichterman, R., 87, **220**
Wilson, B. W., 92, 165, **209, 220**
Wittekind, D., 153, **221**
Wolken, J. J., 146, 147, 165, 181, 199, **211,
    220, 221**
Woodruff, M., 181, **213**

Y

Yount, V., 179, **210**

Z

Zahalsky, A. C., 184, **221**

SUBJECT INDEX

(Page numbers in bold type refer to figures.)

A

Absorption spectrum, of *Euglena* eyespot, 146
Acetate:
  as carbon source for *Euglena*, 202
  oxidative assimilation of by euglenoids, 165
Acetate flagellates, 165, 202
Aceto-carmine, 203
Aconta, 4
Action spectrum, of phototaxis in *Euglena*, 146
Adenylic acid, proportion in *Euglena* RNA, 183
Aging, 168 (*see also* Phospholipid vesicles)
Algae:
  blue-green, 4, 185 (*see also* Cyanophyta)
  brown, 4, 147, 185 (*see also* Phaeophyta)
  chlorophyll synthesis in darkness, 181
  chloroplasts and pyrenoids, 169, 171, 174–175
  contractile vacuoles, 153
  euglenoids epiphytic on, 40, 41
  eyespots, 143
  flagella, 127, 139
  flagellar swelling, 147
  in food vacuoles of euglenoids, 60, 192
  green, 3, 4, 34, 153, 185 (*see also* Chlorophyta)
  ingestion of by euglenoids, 34, 190, 192, 194
  phototaxis, 146
  red, 4, 185 (*see also* Rhodophyta)
  taxonomic position of euglenoids in, 3–4, 6
  water uptake, 148
Alveolate vesicles (*see* Contractile vacuole)
Amino acids:
  as nitrogen source, 201, 202

Amino acids (*cont.*):
  oxidation of, 163
Aminotriazole, non-permanent "bleaching" of *Euglena* by, 184
Amitosis, 18, 25, 67, **91,** 92
Ammonium salts, as nitrogen source, 201, 202
Amoebae:
  contractile vacuoles, 148
  taxonomic position in relation to euglenoids, 5
Amphitropis aequiciliata, notes on, 69
Anaphase (*see* Mitosis, euglenoid, anaphase)
Animal kingdom, taxonomic position of euglenoids in, 3
Anisonema, 52, 57, 197
  flagellar activity, 141
  ingestion organelle, 64
  phagotrophy, 190
  prosgeobium, notes and drawing of, **58, 59**
  relationships, 64, 66, 75
Annelids, *Khawkinea* parasitic in, 29
Anodonta, paramylon digestion by enzymes from, 186
Antheraxanthin, in euglenoid chloroplasts, 179
Antibiotics (aureomycin, carbomycin, erythromycin, kanamycin, paromomycin, neomycin, spiramycin, viomycin), permanent "bleaching" of *Euglena* by, 184 (*see also* Streptomycin)
Antihistamines (methapyrilene, pyribenzamine, pyrilamine, tripelennamine), permanent "bleaching" of *Euglena* by, 184
Aplastidic race:
  increase of mitochondrial volume, 163
  production in *Euglena gracilis*, 183
Ascoglena, 16, 40, 197

227

Ascoglena (*cont.*):
  amphoroides, 40, 41
  envelope formation, 110
  flagellar swelling, 145
  relationships, 75
  vaginicola, notes and drawing of, **39**, 40–41
Astasia, 16, 29, 31, 198
  concinna, 32
  edax, 32, 34 (*see also Euglenopsis edax*)
  euglenoid movement, **31**, 99
  flagellar regeneration, 141
  flagellar structure, 129
  klebsii:
    chromosome   orientation   during mitosis, 85
    interphase nuclei, **82**
    notes and drawings of, **31**, 32, **33**
  longa:
    notes and drawing of, 32, **33**
    oxidative metabolism, 165
    regrowth of emergent flagellum, 141
    relationship to *Euglena gracilis*, 27
    synchronised cultures, 92
  muciferous bodies, 109
  quartana, 29 (*see also Khawkinea quartana*)
  relationships, 32, 34, 73, 75
  subgenus *Astasia devorantes*, 32
  subgenus *Euastasia*, 31
  subgenus *Euglenoidea*, 32
  subgenus *Phytophaga*, 32, 34
  vacuolata, 34
Astasiae, 9
Astaxanthin, in euglenoid eyespots, 143
ATP (adenosine triphosphate), 163, 169
Atraktomonas, 52, 53, 55, 198
  flagellar activity, 141
  laevis, notes and drawing of, **54**, 55
  relationships, 75
Autogamy, 7, 92, 94
Axostyles, microtubular construction of, 126, 194

B

B_1 (*see* Vitamin B_1)
B_{12} (*see* Vitamin B_{12})
Bacillariophyceae, 3, 4
Bacillariophyta, 4
  reserve polysaccharides, 185
Bacteria, 36, **132**, 166, 175, 200
  flagella, 127, 128, **133**
  in food vacuoles of euglenoids, 60, 192
Basal bodies, 128, 160 (*see also* Flagella, of euglenoids, basal bodies)
β-carotene:
  in chloroplasts, 177, 179
  in eyespots, 143

Binucleate cell, following amitosis in *Euglena*, 92, **93**
Biological clock, control of phototactic response in *Euglena*, 146
Biological nomenclature, rules and problems, 17n, 60, 69n
"Bleaching," 183–184 (*see also Euglena gracilis*, "bleaching" of)
β-methoxythreonine, permanent "bleaching" of *Euglena* by, 184

C

Calkinsia, 69, 198
  aureus, notes on, 69
  flagellar activity, 141
Callose, β-1:3-linked glucans in, 185
Calvin cycle, 169
Calycimonas, 52, 55, 198
  flagellar activity, 141
  phagotrophy, 190
  physaloides, notes and drawing of, **54**, 55
  relationships, 75
Canal (of euglenoids), 120–126
  diagnostic form, 6
  endoplasmic reticular sheath, 116, **117**, 121, **123**, **124**, **134**, **136**
  form in particular species, **13–70**, **121**, **122**, **144**, **149**, **156**, **162**
  independence of ingestion organelle from, 190, 192
  microtubules, 99, 116, **117**, 120, 121, **123**, **124**, 126, **136**
  opening, 96, **101**, 104, 192, 195
  pellicular lining, 96, **97**, **101**, **123**, 126, **136**, **144**
  relation to contractile vacuolar function, **150**, 151
  taxonomic use of features, 9, 12–71, 197, 198
Carbohydrate, in pellicle of *Euglena*, 99
Carbohydrate reserves, 79, 169, 171, 185 (*see also* Laminarin, Leucosin, Paramylon, Starch)
Carbon dioxide:
  as carbon source, 201
  fixation of, 169, 179, 181
Carbon/platinum replicas, 100, 203 (*see also* Surface replicas)
Carboxylase, photo-induction of in *Euglena*, 181
Carnoy's acetic-alcohol, 203
Carotenoids (*see* Pigments, carotenoid)
Catenula, Khawkinea parasitic in, 29
Cell, 79 (*see also* Eucaryotic cell, Procaryotic cell)
Cell fractionation, of *Euglena gracilis*, 116, 165, 182

Cell of euglenoids:
  cleavage (and division), 41, 90, 93, 104–107, **105,** 114
    delay of, 27, 104
    relation of various organelles to, 89, 104, 140, 143, 145, 158, 161, 163, 174, 179, 182–184, 187, 188
  contortion, 18, 27, 34, 96
  flattening, 72, 73, 74, 104, 196, 197, 198
  gyration during swimming, 12, 18, 21, 23, 25, 45, 46, 50, 52, 53, 56, 141, 142
  invagination, 6, 120, 128, 140, 147 (*see also* Canal, Reservoir)
  rigidity, 72, 73, 74, 99
    as a taxonomic feature, 9, 12–71, 196, 197
  shape, 99, 148
    in particular species, 18–67
    as a taxonomic feature, 9, 12–71, 196, 197, 198
  symmetry, 43, 102, 104 (*see also* Symmetry)
Cellulose, absence of in euglenoids, 4, 99
Cell wall, 4, 79, 96, 148, 155, 185
Centrioles, 89, 128, 139
Centromeres, 81
  apparent absence of in euglenoids, 85, 87, 89
Chaetogaster, Khawkinea parasitic in, 29
Chaetomorpha, Klebsiella in samples of, 40
Chemoreception, possible mechanism in euglenoids, 122, 153
Chemosensitivity, of *Peranema,* 142
Chemotaxis, by *Peranema,* 192
Chlorachne, 69, 198
Chloromonadida, 5
Chlorophacus, 45
Chlorophyceae, 3, 4 (*see also* Chlorophyta)
Chlorophyll, 169, 177, 201
  in *Euglena,* 179, 181, 182
  synthesis, 179, 181
Chlorophylls *a* and *b,* 3, 4, 179
Chlorophyta, 3, 4, 69, 143, 175
Chloroplasts, 79, 161, 169
  of *Euglena:*
    chemistry, development, function, nucleic acids and replication, 179, 181–184
    continuity, 164, 183
    fluidity, 23, 25
    helical arrangement, 23, 102, **172**
    loss of, 8, 73, 179, 183, 184
    perforated, 23
    ribosomes, 116, 117, 183
  of euglenoids, 170–184
    discoid, 12, 14, 17, 25, 36, 38, 40, 45, 66, **98, 103, 109, 170,** 171, **172,** 174, **174, 176**
    dissected, 17, 23, **170,** 171

Chloroplasts, of euglenoids (*cont.*):
    distribution at cell cleavage, 104, 174, 183, 184
    division, 174
    flat, plate- or shield-shaped, 17, 21, 23, 25, 36, 38, 41, 45, **170,** 171, **173**
    form in particular species, **13–69, 98, 103, 109, 170,** 171, **172, 173, 174, 175, 176**
    independence of eyespot from, 143
    living, **98, 103, 109,** 119, 171, **172,** 173, **173,** 174, **174, 175, 176, 177**
    loss of, 73, 74
    presence or absence, and form, as a taxonomic feature, 9, 12–71, 114, 171, 196, 197
    ribbon-shaped, 12, 17, 25, **26,** 171, **172,** 174, **175**
    ultrastructure, **117, 123, 161, 167,** 174–182, **178, 180**
Chondriome, 50, 60, 66, 160, **162,** 163, 203 (*see also* Mitochondria)
Chromatids, 81
  of euglenoids, 12, 36, **84,** 85, **86,** 89, **93**
    segregation of during mitosis, 81, 85, **86,** 87, 89
    velocity of during mitosis, 85, 89
Chromophyta, 3, 4
Chromosomes, 81
  of euglenoids, 82–89, 92–95, 203 (*see also* Mitosis, euglenoid)
    fixation and staining, 203
    form in particular species, 12, 13, **22,** 32, 36, 38, **65, 82, 84, 86, 88, 91, 93, 94**
    nucleolar-organising, 87
    number, 9*n,* 12, 18, 23, 25, 32, 36, 43, 46, 62, 92, 94, 95
    orientation during mitosis, 6, **84,** 85, **86,** 89, 92
    replication, 81, 85, 87, 92
Chromulina psammobia, non-emergent flagellum of, 147
Chrysolaminarin (*see* Leucosin)
Chrysomonadida, 5
Chrysophyceae, 3, 4 (*see also* Chrysophyta)
Chrysophyta, 4, 143, 175, 185
Cilia (Cilium), 127, 128, 129 (*see also* Flagella)
Ciliary derivatives, 128*n,* 147
Ciliates:
  contractile vacuoles, 148
  taxonomic position of in relation to euglenoids, 5
  trichocysts, 108
Ciliophora, 5
Classification (*see* Taxonomy)
Clautriavia, 69, 198
  mobilis, notes on, 69

Cleavage (*see* Cell of euglenoids, cleavage)

Clone, 8, 48 (*see also* Culture, clonal)

Cnidospora, 5

Co⁶⁰, irradiation of euglenoids, 87*n*

Cobalamin (*see* Vitamin B₁₂)

Coccolithophorida, 5

Colaciaceae, 41

Colacium, 16, 41, 197
  bacteria-free culture, 201
  cyclopicolum, 41
    contractile vacuolar region, **124, 152**
    living, **173**
    ultrastructure, **124, 137, 152, 178, 180**
    envelope and stalk formation, 100, 110
    flagellar structure, **124,** 129, **137, 152**
    flagellar swelling, 145
    inner pyrenoids, 27, 171, **173, 180**
    muciferous bodies, 109, **178**
  mucronatum:
    chromosome orientation during mitosis, 85
    living colony, **111**
    long chromosome, **86,** 95
    notes and drawings of, 41, **42,** 43
    relationships, 75

Colchicine, absence of effect on euglenoid mitosis, 87, 89

Collection, of euglenoids, 199

Colonial habit of euglenoids, 9, 41, **42,** 71, 73, 74, **111,** 197

Conjugation, in *Scytomonas*, 71, 92

Contophora, 4

Contractile vacuole, 148
  of euglenoids, 149–154
    accessory vacuoles, **15, 30,** 55, **125, 136,** 148, 149, **149,** 151, **152, 154, 191**
    activity (functioning), 122, 126, 148, 149, **149, 150,** 151, 153, 159
    alveolate vesicles, **125, 136,** 151, **152,** 153, **154**
    diagnostic form, 6
    form in particular species, **13–70, 121, 129, 135, 144,** 149, **156, 162, 175**
    presence or absence as a taxonomic feature, 9, 12–71
    relation to cell symmetry, 104, 149
    ultrastructure, **125, 136,** 151–155, **152, 154, 191**

Copepods, *Khawkinea* parasiticin, 29

Craspedophyceae, 4

Creeping locomotion, by euglenoids, 21, 23, 27, 199 (*see also* Gliding)

Cresyl blue, 108, 202

Cristae (*see* Mitochondria, of euglenoids, ultrastructure)

Crumenula, 43 (*see also Lepocinclis*)

Cryptoglena, 69, 198

Cryptomonadida, 5

Cryptophyceae, 4

Cryptoxanthin, in euglenoid eyespots, 143

Crystallites, in paramylon, 186

Culture collections, 11*n*, 200
  euglenoid species available in, 11, 12, 16, 18, 21, 23, 25, 27, 29, 32, 34, 36, 38, 41, 43, 45, 46, 48, 50, 60, 71

Culture (Cultivation), of euglenoids, 199–201
  agar, 23, 201
  axenic, 179, 199
  bacteria-free, 21, 199, 201
  biphasic, 12, 21, 27, 90, 91, 200
    preparation of, **200**
  clonal, 38, 43, 104
  importance in taxonomic studies, 8, 36
  pure, 32, 36
  synchronised, 91, 92
  unialgal, 200

Culture media, 199–201

Cultures, old, 43, 166

Cyanophyceae, 4 (*see also Cyanophyta*)

Cyanophyta, 4, 175, 185

Cyclidiopsidaceae, 34

Cyclidiopsis, 16, 34, 197
  acus:
    apical canal opening, **121, 144**
    eyespot, 143, **144**
    flagellar basal bodies, **135**
    Golgi bodies, 159
    living, **121, 135, 188**
    notes and drawings of, **30,** 34–35
    paramylon, **188**
    apical canal opening, 120, **121, 144**
    flagellar swelling, **121, 144,** 145
    relationships, 18, 29, 75

Cyclidium, 56 (*see also Petalomonas*)

Cyclops:
  Colacium zoophytic on, 43
  Khawkinea parasitic in, 29

Cyclosis, in euglenoids, 117, 119 (*see also* Cytoplasmic streaming)

Cysts, of euglenoids:
  formation, 95, 114
  formation or not as a taxonomic feature, 9, 16–60

Cytidilic acid, proportion in *Euglena* RNA, 183

Cytochrome oxidase, in mitochondria, 163

Cytochromes, of euglenoid mitochondria, 165

"Cytopharynx," 121

Cytoplasm and cytoplasmic matrix, 79
  delimitation of nucleus from, 79, 80, 81, **84**
  in euglenoids, 82, **84,** 104, 115–119, **117, 123,** 145, 149, 151, 153, 155, 163, 169, 175, 177, 179, **183, 185,** 194

Cytoplasmic flow, in euglenoids, 12, **13**, 99, 104, 117
Cytoplasmic streaming, in euglenoids, 21, 50, 119, 162
Cytostome, of euglenoids, 34, 59, 60, **61**, 62, 64, **65**, 190, 192, **193**, 194, 195

D

Daphnia, *Colacium* zoophytic on, 43
Dark-grown *Euglena*, 179, 181, 182
Defaecation area, of *Peranema*, 192
Dehydrogenases, photo-induction of in *Euglena*, 181
"*De novo*" origin (formation), 128, 141, 146, 155, 160*n*
Diastole, 148, 151 (*see also* Contractile vacuole, of euglenoids, activity)
Diatoms, 4, 128*n*, 185
   in food vacuoles of euglenoids (ingestion of), 59, 64, **65**, 69
Digestion:
   of food by *Peranema*, 192
   of paramylon, 186
Dinema, 59, 64, 196
   flagellar activity, 141
   ingestion by, 190
   relationships, 64, 71, 75
   sulcatum, notes and drawing of, 64, **65**
Dinoflagellates, relationship to euglenoids, 4, 71, 89
Dinoflagellida, 5
Dinophyceae, 3, 4
Dinophyta, 4
Discs, in chloroplasts, 169 (*see also* Thylakoids)
Distigma, 11, 14, 16, 196
   cysts, 114
   euglenoid movement, 99
   flagellar structure, 129, **131**, **133**, 140
   Golgi bodies, **156**, 158, 159
   gracile:
      dismembered flagellum, **131**
      pellicle architecture, **102**
   proteus:
      chromosome orientation during mitosis, 85
      flagellar structure, **133**, 140
      Golgi bodies, **156**, 158
      living, **156**
      notes and drawing of, **15**, 16
      relationships, 75
Distigmopsis, 11, 14, 196
   grassei, notes and drawing of, **15**, 16
   relationships, 75
Division (*see* Cell of euglenoids, cleavage; Mitosis)
Division axis, during euglenoid mitosis, 84, 85, 88

DNA (Deoxyribonucleic acid):
   absence from euglenoid endosomes, 87
   in chromosomes, 81
   doubling, prior to euglenoid mitosis, 92
   in euglenoid chloroplasts, 182–183
   in euglenoid mitochondria, 164–165
   in mitochondria, 164
Dreissena, paramylon digestion by enzymes from, 186
Drug resistance, of euglenoids, 9*n*

E

Ebriida, 5
Echinenone, in euglenoid eyespots, 143
Ecological forms, of euglenoid species, 8
Ecology of euglenoids:
   brackish habitats, 12, 23, 27, 59, 199
   freshwater habitats, 16, 18, 21, 23, 25, 27, 29, 32, 36, 41, 43, 45, 46, 48, 50, 52, 55, 56, 57, 60, 62, 64, 66, 67, 148, 199
   marine habitats, 12, 40, 69, 199
   as a taxonomic feature, 10, 12–71
Embden-Meyerhof-Parnas pathway, in *Astasia* and *Euglena*, 165
Embedding for electron microscopy, 203
Endoplasmic reticulum, 115
   of euglenoids, 115–118
      possible association with chloroplasts, 175
      relation to muciferous bodies, 7, 109
      tubular, 82, 115, **116**, **118**, 189
      vesiculate, 116, **117**, **123**, **134**, **158**, 189
   relation to Golgi bodies, 155, 159
   "rough" (granular), 115, 116
   "smooth" (agranular), 115, 116
Endosome, of the euglenoid nucleus:
   behaviour during mitosis, 6, 18, 84, **84**, 85, **86**, 87, **88**
   form in particular species, **13**, **15**, **22**, **61**, **65**
   homology and function, 87
   in interphase nuclei, 82, **82**, **83**, **91**
   as a taxonomic feature, 10
Endozoic habit of euglenoids, 66, 67
Entosiphon, 59, 64, 197
   flagellar activity, 141, 142
   flagellar structure, 129, 134, **134**, **191**, **193**
   Golgi bodies, 159
   ingestion by, 190, 194, 195
   microtubules, 99, **191**, **193**, 194
   relationships, 66, 75
   sulcatum:
      flagellar structure, **134**, **191**, **193**
      ingestion organelle, **191**, **193**, 194
      muciferous bodies, 109, **191**, **193**

Entosiphon, sulcatum (cont.):
  notes and drawing of, **65,** 66
  pellicle, **191, 193**
  trichocysts, 109, **191, 193**
  ultrastructure, **134, 191, 193**
Envelope, 79
  of euglenoids:
    absence of cellulose from, 4
    acquisition of, 73, 74
    form in particular species, 36, **37,** 38,
      39, 40, **111**
    formation, 100, 110, **112**
    presence or absence as a taxonomic
      feature, 9, 12–66, 197
    structure, 35, 36, 110, **112, 114**
Enzyme biosynthesis in euglenoids, photo-
  induction of, 181
Enzymes, 79, 115, 163, 166, 169, 171
  in euglenoids, 165, 181, 186
Epikote 812 resin, 203
Epiphytic habit of euglenoids, 40, 41
ER, 115 (*see also* Endoplasmic reticulum)
Ergastic materials, 79
Ethanol, oxidative assimilation of by
  euglenoids, 165
Etiolation, of *Euglena gracilis*, 179, 181, 182,
  183
Eucaryota, 4
Eucaryotic cell, 79, 81, 115, 127, 128, 155,
  160, 161
Euglena, 8, 16, 17, 197
  acus:
    amitosis, **91,** 92
    canal region, **121**
    chloroplasts, **176**
    interphase nucleus, **91**
    living, **121, 176**
    mitosis, 84, 85
    notes and drawing of, 18, **19**
    relationship with *Cyclidiopsis acus*, 35
  acus var. *hyalina*, 18
    canal region, **121**
    paramylon, **188**
  anabaena, bacteria-free culture, 201
  archaeoplastidiata, 23
  brackish species, 199
  chloroplast continuity, 164, 183
  chloroplast function, 179, 181–184
  colourless derivatives, 27, 29, 73
  cysts and palmellae, 114
  cytoplasmic streaming, 117
  deses:
    bacteria-free culture, 201
    cell cleavage, **105, 106**
    mitosis, 84, 85
    notes and drawing of, 27, **28**
  ecology (*see* Ecology of euglenoids)
  ehrenbergii:
    interphase nucleus, **82**

Euglena, ehrenbergii (cont.):
    notes and drawing of, **20,** 21
  experimental studies on, 23, 27, 32, 73,
    116, 141, 146, 164–165, 179, 181–184
  flagellar activity, 142
  flagellar replication, 140
  geniculata:
    living, **175**
    notes and drawing of, 25, **26**
    paramylon centre, **175**
  gracilis:
    "bleaching" of, 23, 27, 32, 73, 146, 183,
      184
    chloroplast studies on, 179, 181–184
    cultivation, 199, 201, 202
    digestion of by *Peranema*, 192
    endosome, **83, 84, 86,** 87
    eyespot pigments, 143
    flagellar structure, **130, 145**
    flagellar swelling, **129, 135, 145,** 146
    living, **129, 135**
    mitochondrial DNA, 164–165
    mitosis, **84,** 85, **86,** 91
    muciferous bodies, **110**
    notes and drawing of, 21, **22, 23**
    oxidative metabolism, 165
    photoreception and phototaxis, 146
    physiological strains, 23, 179
    ribosomes, 116
    ultrastructure, **83, 110, 130, 136, 145,**
      179, 181
  gracilis strain *Z*, 23
    chloroplast RNA, 183
    chloroplast studies on, 179, 182, 183
    flagellar regeneration, 141
    oxidative metabolism, 165
    synchronised cultures, 92
  gracilis var. *bacillaris*, 23
    chemical composition of pellicle, 99
    chloroplast DNA, 182
    chloroplast studies on, 179, 181, 182
    oxidative metabolism, 165
  gracilis var. *hyalina*, 23
    flagellar basal bodies, **135**
    flagellar bases, **129**
    living, **129, 135**
  ingestion of, **61,** 192
  laciniata, chloroplast fluidity, 24–25
  magnifica:
    chloroplasts, **172**
    living, **108, 172, 186**
    muciferous bodies, **108**
    notes and drawing of, 23, **24**
    paramylon, **186**
  mucifera, 27
  mutabilis, notes and drawings of, 27, **28**
  obtusa:
    canal system, **24,** 120
    notes and drawing of, 23, **24**

Euglena (cont.):
  oxyuris:
    paramylon, 187
    Z-helix of pellicle, 102
  pisciformis:
    bacteria-free culture, 201
    chloroplast division, 174
    notes and drawing of, 23, **24**
    pellicular striations, **101**
  polyploidy, 94
  pringsheimii, inner pyrenoids, 27
  proxima:
    notes and drawing of, 20, **21**
    palmella, **113**
  relationships, 32, 34, 73, 75
  sanguinea:
    chloroplast organisation, 23, 25
    movement of carotenoid pigment in, 25
  spirogyra:
    alveolate vesicles, **154**
    amitosis, 92
    canal region, 120, 121, **123, 124**
    chloroplasts, **109, 123, 161, 167, 177**
    contractile vacuolar region, **154**
    endoplasmic reticulum, **116, 117, 118,**
      121, **123, 124, 158**
    euglenoid movement, 99
    eyespot, **109, 144, 167**
    flagellar structure, **138,** 139–140
    Golgi bodies, **118, 154, 157, 158**
    interphase nucleus, **83, 109, 116, 167**
    living, **109, 167**
    microtubules, **100, 117,** 120, 121,
      123, 124, 144
    mitochondria, **123, 124, 154, 161**
    mitosis, 85, 90, **93**
    muciferous bodies, **100, 109, 117, 124**
    notes and drawing of, 18, **19**
    nuclear envelope, **83, 116**
    paramylon, **109, 167,** 187, **189**
    pellicle, 96, **97, 98,** 99, 100, **100, 103,**
      104, **105, 106,** 114, **124, 144,** 192
    phospholipid vesicles, **158, 161, 167**
    ultrastructure, **83,** 96, 100, **100, 105,**
      116, 117, 118, 120, 121, **123, 124,**
      138, 144, 154, 157, 158, 161
  spirogyra var. *fusca*:
    chloroplasts, **177**
    paramylon, **189**
    pellicle, **98, 103**
  splendens, chloroplast fluidity, 25
  stellata:
    bacteria-free culture, 201
    muciferous bodies, 25
  subgenus *Catilliferae*, 21, 171
  subgenus *Lentiferae*, 18, 171
  subgenus *Limpidae*, 27
  subgenus *Radiatae*, 25, 171, 174, 186
  subgenus *Rigidae*, 17, 18, 171

Euglena (cont.):
  subgenus *Serpentes*, 25, 27, 171
  tripteris, paramylon, 187
  viridis:
    amitosis, 92
    bacteria-free culture, 201
    chromosome   orientation   during
      mitosis, 85
    notes and drawing of, 25, **26**
Euglenaceae, 9
Euglenae, 9
Euglenales, 10, 16, 46, 74, 204
  flagellar movement, 141
  flagellar replication, 140
  non-emergent flagellum, 135, 141
  phagotrophy, 190
Euglenamorpha, 66, 197, 199
  flagellar proliferation, 72, 73
  hegneri:
    amitosis, 92
    flagellar swellings, 145
    notes and drawing of, 67, **68**
  relationships, 67, 75
Euglenamorphales, 10, 66, 74, 205
  flagellar activity, 141
Euglenamorphina, 10, 66 (*see also Euglena-*
  morphales)
Euglenanone, in euglenoid eyespots, 143
Euglenida, 3, 5, 72 (*see also Euglenophyta*)
Euglenina, 10, 16 (*see also Euglenales*)
Euglenineae, 3 (*see also Euglenophyta*)
Euglenocapsa, 69, 198
  ochracea, notes on, 69
Euglenoid mitosis (*see* Mitosis, euglenoid)
Euglenoid movement, 99–100
  in particular species, 12–71
  in relation to ingestion, 192
  in relation to pellicle, 96, 97, 99, 100, 104
  as a taxonomic feature, 14–64, 197, 198
Euglenophyceae, 3, 4 (*see also Euglenophyta*)
Euglenophyta:
  cell components and inclusions, 81–195
  diagnostic features, 6–7
  key to genera, 196–199
  phylogeny, 72–75
  taxonomy, 8–71, 72, 74, 204–205
  taxonomic position, 3–5
  techniques for study of, 200–203
Euglenopsis, 16, 17, 32, 34, 198
  edax:
    ingestion by, 190
    notes and drawing of, **33,** 34
Eutreptia, 11, 12, 196, 199
  euglenoid movement, **13,** 99
  in euglenoid phylogeny, 73, 75
  eyespot, 143
  flagellar structure, 129
  flagellar swelling, 145
  Golgi bodies, 159

Eutreptia (*cont.*):
muciferous bodies, 109
palmellae, 114
paramylon centre and chloroplasts, 171, **174**, 186
pertyi:
chromosome orientation during mitosis, 85
living, **174**
notes and drawings of, 12, **13**
paramylon centre, 174, **174**
viridis, 12
chromosome orientation during mitosis, 85
Eutreptiales, 10, 11, 204
flagellar activity, 141
Eutreptiella, 11, 12, 196, 199
flagellar swelling, 145
leucosin storage, 14, 185*n*
marina, notes and drawing of, 14, **15**
sp., 14
Eutreptiina, 10, 11 (*see also Eutreptiales*)
Evolutionary trends, in euglenoids, 8, 9, 72, 73
Eyespot, 143
of euglenoids, 143–147
diagnostic form, 6, 143
division, **105**, 143
form in particular species, **13**–69, **109, 121, 135, 144, 149, 167, 172, 175**
loss of, 73, 74, 183
in phylogeny, 73, 74
presence or absence as a taxonomic feature, 9, 12–71, 196, 197
relation to cell symmetry, 104, **136**, 151
relation to photoreception, 126, 146–147
ultrastructure, **136, 144, 152**

F

Fat (*see* Lipid)
Fatty acids:
in green and etiolated *Euglena*, 181
oxidation of, 163
Ferric hydroxide, in euglenoid ornamentation and envelopes, 35, 100, 197
Feulgen reaction, 87, 203
Fibrils, 79, 127, 132, 194 (*see also* Microtubules)
Flagella (Flagellum), 127–128
activity, mechanism of, 128
appendages, 3, 139
basal bodies, 128, 160*n*
of euglenoids, 128–142
activity, 141, 142

Flagella, of euglenoids (*cont.*):
appendages (hairs), 3, 6, **131,133,**134, **134, 138,** 139, 140, 153
arrangement, 72, 128
basal bodies, **13, 22, 54, 63,** 84, 89, 135, **135, 137,** 139, 140
bases, 6, **37, 50, 51,** 52, 56, **68,** 104, **121, 136,** 140, **144, 149, 152**
bifurcation of, 41, 140
diagnostic form, 6, 128, 140
form in particular species, **13–68,** 72, **156, 174**
growth, 43, 140
leading, **58,** 60, **61, 63, 65,** 129, 132, 134, 139, 140, 141, 142
living, **121, 122, 129, 135, 144, 149, 156, 164, 174**
locomotory (emergent), 3, 6, 18*n*, 120, **122, 123, 125, 129, 130, 131, 132,** 135, **135, 136, 138,** 139, 140, 141, 145, **145,** 146, **149, 152, 174,** 198
non-emergent, 6, 16, **22,** 23, **24,** 27, **30, 33,** 40, 41, **42,** 43, **44, 47,** 53, 55, 62, 72, **129,** 135, 141, 147, **152**
reduction of, in relation to phylogeny, 72, 73
regeneration, 140, 141
replication, 140, 141, 145*n*
shedding of, 21, 27, 29, 35, **122, 129,** 132, **132, 135,** 140, 141
taxonomic use of number, lengths, activity, etc., 4, 9, 11–71, 141, 196, 198
trailing, 56, 57, **58,** 59, **61,** 62, **63,** 64, **65,** 66, 134, 141, 142, 196
ultrastructure, **125,** 129, **130, 131,** 132, **133,** 134, **134,** 135, **136, 137, 138,** 139, 140, 145, **145, 152, 191, 193**
functions, 127
replication, 128
ultrastructure, 127, 128
Flagellar grooves, 3, 59, 62, 196
Flagellar scales, 132, 139, 155
Flagellar swelling:
of euglenoids, 6, 145–147
behaviour during flagellar growth, 140, 145*n*
form in particular species, 12–68, **121, 129, 135, 144, 149**
living, **121, 129, 135, 144, 149**
loss of, 74, 183
in phylogeny, 73, 74
presence or absence as a taxonomic feature, 9, 12–71
relation to photoreception, 126, 146–147
ultrastructure, 145, **145**

Flagellar swelling (*cont.*):
of non-euglenoid flagellates, 147
Flagellata, 3
Flagellates, other than euglenoid:
basal bodies, 139
contractile vacuoles, 148, 153
eyespots, 143
flagellar scales, 132, 155, 156
taxonomic position in relation to euglenoids, 3, 4, 5
Flatworms, *Khawkinea* parasitic in, 29
Flavoprotein, in mitochondria, 163
Fluorescence studies on euglenoids, 181*n*, 182
Food vacuoles, 166
in euglenoids, 52, 53, **54**, 55, 57, **58, 61, 63,** 64, **65,** 66, 192
Fucus, flagellar swelling in spermatozoids of, 147
Fungi, 89, 127, 155, 166

G

Gametes, 92, 94, 127, 148
Genetic continuity, of mitochondria and plastids, 164, 183
Genetic information, storage and transfer of, 81, 115, 160
Gliding, by euglenoids, 21, 25, 35, 59, 141, 142 (*see also* Creeping locomotion)
Glucan:
α-1:4-linked, 185
β-1:3-linked, 3, 6, 185, 186
Glucose, oxidative assimilation of by euglenoids, 165
Glutaraldehyde, 203
Gold/palladium, shadowcast preparations, 203
Golgi bodies, 155–156, 161
of euglenoids, 158–159
fission, 158
form in particular species, **15**–66, **156,** 158, 159, **162**
living, **156, 162**
relation to contractile vacuole, 153, **154,** 159
relation to endoplasmic reticulum, 116, **118,** 159
ultrastructure, **118, 136, 154,** 155, **157, 158,** 159
Grana, 169
Greening, of etiolated *Euglena* (*see Euglena gracilis*, chloroplast studies on)
Guanylic acid, proportion in *Euglena* RNA, 183
"Gullet," 121, 192
Gymnastica, 14 (*see also Eutreptiella*)
Gyropaigne, 46, 48, 198
lefevrei, notes and drawing of, **49,** 50

Gyropaigne (*cont.*):
phylogeny, 72*n*, 75
relationships, 50, 69, 75

H

"Half-nuclei," of *Euglena* following amitosis, **91,** 92
Haploid condition, in euglenoids, 94, 95
Haptophyceae, 4
Hegneria, 66, 67, 197, 199
flagellar proliferation, 72
leptodactyli, notes and drawing of, 67, **68**
relationships, 67, 75
Helikotropis, 69, 198
okteres, notes on, 69
Heterochlorida, 5
Heteronema, 59, 196
acus, notes and drawing of, 60, **63**
flagellar activity, 141
ingestion organelle, 190, 194
Heteronematales, 10, 59, 71, 74, 205
flagellar structure, 129
ingestion organelle, 190, 194, 195
Heteronematina, 10, 59 (*see also Heteronematales*)
Heterotrophy, in euglenoids, 73, 91, 163, 181, 186, 201, 202
Higher plants, 3, 4, 91, 160, 169, 171, 177, 179, 181, 185, 186
Hyalophacus, 16, 46, 197, 198
caecus, 46, 75
eyespot, 143
flagellar swelling, 145
ocellatus:
notes and drawings of, 46, **47**
phylogeny, 75
possible meiosis in, 92, 94, **94**
relationships, 29, 45, 73, 75
"*Hyalotrachelomonas*," 29, 36, 38, 197
flagellar swelling, 145
leucoplasts, 184
relationships, 73, 75
Hydrodynamic theory, and swimming of euglenoids, 142
Hydroxyechinenone, in euglenoid eyespots, 143

I

Ingestion, by euglenoids, 34, 55, 57, 60, **61,** 64, 66, 121, 190, 192, 194
Ingestion organelle (apparatus, rods), of euglenoids, 190–195
form in particular species, 60, **61, 63, 65,** 69, 192
in phylogeny, 73, 74, 190
relation to cell symmetry, 104

Ingestion organelle (*cont.*):
as a taxonomic feature, 9, 34, 52–71, 196, 197, 198
ultrastructure, **191, 193,** 194, 195
Interphase, 81 (*see also* Nucleus, of euglenoids)
Intracellular transport:
by endoplasmic reticulum, 115
by microtubules, 99, 100, 126
Ion absorption, by mitochondria, 163
Ionizing radiations, effect on euglenoids, 87
Iron, effect on euglenoid ornamentation and envelopes, 18, 36, 100, 114

J

Janus green B, 203
Jenningsia, 69, 198
diatomophaga, notes on, 69

K

Keratin, possible constituent of euglenoid pellicle, 99
Key to euglenoid genera, 196
Khawkinea, 16, 27, 38, 197, 199
eyespot, 143
flagellar swelling, 145
possible leucoplasts in, 184
quartana:
contractile vacuole, **149**
flagellar bases, **129**
living, **129, 149**
notes and drawing of, 29, **30**
relationships, 18, 29, 73, 75
Klebsiella, 16, 40, 197, 199
alligata, notes and drawing of, **39,** 40
chloroplasts, 171
envelope, 110
flagellar swelling, 145
relationships, 75

L

Lactoflavin, 147
Laminarase, from *Euglena* extracts, 186
Laminarin, 3, 185, 186
Latin diagnoses of euglenoid orders, 204–205
Lepocinclis, 8, 16, 43, 197
apical canal opening, 120
chloroplasts, 171
flagellar swelling, 145
ovum:
chromosome orientation during mitosis, 85
notes and drawing of, 43, **44**
relationships, 50, 73, 75
Leptodactylus, *Hegneria* in tadpoles of, 67, 197

Leucine, incorporation by *Euglena* ribosomes, 116
Leucine-H^3, labelling experiments on *Ochromonas*, 140n
Leucoplasts, 36, 184
Leucosin, 3, 14, 53, 71, 185n
Leucostigma, of *Distigmopsis*, 14, 16, 196
Lipid, 79, 115, 143, 155, 166, 169
in euglenoids:
in particular species, **30–65, 162, 164**
patterns in *Euglena*, 181
in pellicle of *Euglena*, 99
globules, in chloroplasts, 169, 177
of euglenoids, **117, 123,** 177, **178**
Lipofuscin granules, in aging cells, 167, 168
Lithodesmium, "9 + 0" flagellar pattern in, 128n
Locomotion (*see* Flagella, Locomotor apparatus, Swimming)
Locomotor apparatus, of euglenoids (*see also* Eyespot, Flagella, Flagellar swelling)
evolution of, 73, 74
form in particular species, **20–44**
replication, 104, 140–141, 145n
Loxophyceae, 4
Lutein, in euglenoid eyespots, 143
Lysosomes, **152,** 166–168

M

Manganese, effect on euglenoid ornamentation and envelopes, 36, 38, 100, 114, 197
Marsupiogaster, 71, 198
Mastigonemes, 139
Mastigophora, 5
Meiosis, 7, 46, 81, 160
euglenoid, 92–95, **94**
Membranes, 79, 96, 115, **117,** 143, 151, 169, 175, 176, 179, **180,** 194 (*see also* Unit membrane)
Menoidium, 46, 50, 53, 198
apical canal opening, 120, **122, 162**
bibacillatum:
living, **122, 162**
notes and drawings of, 50 **51,** 52
cytoplasmic streaming in, 117, **162**
relationships, 75
"Metaboly," 99n (*see also* Euglenoid movement)
Metachromasia, of phospholipid vesicles, 166
Metachromatic bodies, 166
Metaphase (*see* Mitosis, euglenoid, metaphase)
Metaphosphates, in *Euglena*, 166
Methamycin, non-permanent "bleaching" of *Euglena* by, 184

Methanol, 203
Methylene blue, 202
Micelles, in paramylon, 186
Micromonas pusilla, division of organelles, 161
Microscopical techniques:
  electron microscopy, 203
  light microscopy, 11, 202, 203
Microtubules, 79, 127
  contractile function, 99, 126, 194
  in euglenoids:
    around the canal, 99, 116, **117,** 120,
      121, **123, 124,** 126, **136**
    around the reservoir, 121, **125,** 126,
      136, 144, 153
    in association with pellicle, 97, 99,
      100, 102, 126, **178, 193**
    in flagella, **130, 131, 134,** 139, **152**
    in ingestion rods, 194
    in mitotic nuclei, 89
  skeletal function, 99, 116, 126
Mitochondria, 79, 148, 160–163
  autonomous movement, 160, 161
  division, 160, 161, 163
  of euglenoids, 104, 163–165
    autonomous movement, 16, 35, 50,
      119, 163
    cristae, 7, 161, 163
    DNA, 164–165
    form in particular species, 12–66,
      149, 156, 162
    genetic continuity, 163–164
    living, **149, 156, 162**
    respiration by, 165
    ultrastructure, **123, 124, 136, 154,**
      161, 193
  function, 163
  ontogeny, 160, 163
Mitosis, 81, 87, 128, 160
  euglenoid, 67, 83–92, 95, 104, 187 (*see*
    also Chromatids, Chromosomes,
    Endosome)
    anaphase, 83, 85, **86,** 87, **88,** 89, 90, **93**
    diagnostic features, 6
    duration, 85, 89, 90
    mechanism, 6, 83, 87, 89
    metaphase, 6, 83, **84,** 85, **86,** 90
    nature of, 87, 89
    periodicity of, **90,** 91
    prophase, 83, 84, **84,** 85, 90
    significance of, 89
    telophase, 83, 85, 90
Molluscs, paramylon digestion by enzymes
  from, 186
Monsters, 27, **106,** 107
Morphological varieties, of euglenoid
  species, 21, 25, 43
"Mouth," of *Peranema*, 192
Muciferous bodies, of euglenoids, 3, 7, 97,
  102, 108–114, 115, 116, 121, 202

Muciferous bodies (*cont.*):
  canals, 97, 99, 100, **100, 110, 124**
  form in particular species, 12–66, **108**
  living, **108, 109**
  relation to ornamentation, cysts and
    envelopes, 100, 110, 114
  as a taxonomic feature, 9, 12–60, 99
  ultrastructure, 97, **100,** 109, **110,** 116,
    117, 123, 124, 136, 178, 191, 193
Mucigenic bodies, 108 (*see also* Muciferous
  bodies)
Mucilage, 97, 99, 100, **101,** 108, **109,** 110,
  112, 114, 116, **178**
Mucopolysaccharide, 108, 166
Myelin figures, in phospholipid vesicles, 166
Myonemes, 126
Myxophyceae, 3 (*see also Cyanophyta*)
Myzostomum, "9 + 0" flagellar pattern in,
  128n

N

Neoxanthin, in euglenoid chloroplasts, 179,
  182
Neutral red, 14, 15, 16, 108, 202
Nicol prisms, 186
"9 + 0 pattern," of flagella, 128n
"9 + 2 pattern," of flagella, 127, 128,
  130, 132, **134**
Nitrates, as nitrogen source, 201, 202
Nitrofurantoin, permanent "bleaching" of
  Euglena by, 184
Notosolenus, 52, 57, 197
  apocamptus, notes and drawing of, 57, **58**
  flagellar activity, 141
  phagotrophy, 190
  relationships, 75
Nuclear membrane, 82n (*see also* Nucleus,
  envelope)
Nuclease, 87, 166
Nucleic acids, 166, 182, 183, 184, 202
  (*see also* DNA, RNA)
Nucleolus, 6, 81, 87 (*see also* Endosome)
Nucleoplasm, 80, 81, 82, 160
Nucleotide ratios, of *Euglena* ribosomes, 116,
  183
Nucleus, 79, 80, 81, 115, 161
  division, 3, 81, 83, 87, 174 (*see also* Ami-
    tosis, Meiosis, Mitosis)
  envelope, 80, 81, 82, 155, 160, 164, 183
  of euglenoids, 81–95, 104, 119, 158
    envelope, **13, 22, 65,** 82, **82, 83,** 85,
      87, 115, **116**
    form and position of interphase nucleus
      in particular species, **13–70, 109,**
      129, 149, 156, 162, 167, 172, 174,
      175
    fragmentation, 92 (*see also* Amitosis)

Nucleus, of euglenoids (*cont.*):
   interphase (chromosome studies), 81–82, **82, 83,** 87, **91**
   migration, 84, 89, 187
   as a taxonomic feature, 4, 9, 10, 34, 71
Nutrition of euglenoids, 201–202 (*see also* Heterotrophy, Osmotrophy, Phagotrophy)
   as a taxonomic feature 9, 12–71, 196–198

O

Ochromonas:
   flagella, 139, 140*n*
   flagellar swelling, 147
O-methylthreonine, permanent "bleaching" of *Euglena* by, 184
Opalinata, 5
Opalinids, relationship to euglenoids, 5
Osmium tetroxide, 203
Osmoregulation, 148, 153
Osmotrophy, in euglenoids, 200, 201, 202
   as a taxonomic feature, 9, 14–71, 196–198
Ottonia, 69, 198
Oxidative phosphorylation, 163, 165

P

Palmellae, of euglenoids, **113,** 114
   formation or not as a taxonomic feature, 9, 12–69
Paraflagellar rod, of euglenoids, **125, 130, 131,** 132, **133,** 134, **134,** 145*n*, **152, 191**
Paramylase, 186
Paramylon, 3, 104, 119, 185–189
   chemistry, 185
   diagnostic form, 6, 185, 186, 187
   digestion of, 186
   formation of granules, 187, 188, 189
   form in particular species, **13–70, 97, 103, 135, 149, 156, 162, 167, 176, 186,** 187, **187, 188, 189**
   helical organisation, 6, 36, **178,** 187, 189, **189**
   pyrenoid sheath (cap), 171, **173,** 177, **180,** 185, **186,** 187, **187, 189**
   structure of granules, 186, 187, **188,** 189, **189**
   as a taxonomic feature, 9, 12–71, 185, 187
Paramylon centre, 12, **13,** 25, **26,** 171, **174, 175,** 186
Paraphysomonas, division of Golgi body in, 155
Parasitic habit of euglenoids, 6, 14, 29, 66, 67, 149, 196, 197, 199
Parmidium, 46, 52, 198.
   circulare, 52

Parmidium (*cont.*):
   relationships, 52, 75
   scutulum, notes and drawing of, **51, 52**
Particulate food, 190, 201, 202 (*see also* Ingestion)
Pellicle, of euglenoids, 7, 96–107, 119, 120, 122, 126, 163, 192, 194 (*see also* Euglenoid movement)
   articulations, 96, 99, **100,** 105, 116, **193**
   chemical composition, 99
   diagnostic form, 6
   elasticity, 72, 99, 104
   form in particular species, 12–67, 96, **97, 98, 100, 102**
   growth, 104–107
   ornamentation, **19, 97, 98,** 100, **103, 105,** 203
   striations, 12–67, 96, **97, 101,** 104, 105, **106,** 108, **123** (*see also* S-helix, Z-helix)
   taxonomic use of features, 43–71, 196
   ultrastructure, 96, 97, **100, 101, 102, 105, 124, 136, 144, 191, 193**
Pellicular strips, 96, 97, **98,** 99, 100, **100,** 105, **105,** 107, **110,** 120, 121, 126, **178, 191, 193**
Pentamonas, 71, 198
   flagellar activity, 141
   spinifera, notes on, 71
Pentose phosphate pathway, in *Astasia* and *Euglena,* 165
Peranema, 59, 60, 196
   euglenoid movement, 99, 192
   Golgi bodies, 159
   ingestion by, 190
   relationships, 60, 62, 75
   trichophorum:
      flagellar activity, 141, 142
      flagellar growth, 140
      flagellar structure, 132
      ingestion by, 192
      ingestion organelle, 192, 194
      mitosis, 84, 85, **86**
      notes and drawings of, 60, **61,** 62
      nutritional requirements (and culture), 201, 202
Peranemeae, 9
Peranemopsis, 59, 60, 62, 66, 198
   flagellar activity, 141
   inflexum, notes and drawing of, 62, **63**
   ingestion by, 190, 194
   relationships, 69, 75
Perinuclear space, 82, 115, 116, **116**
Periodate-Schiff reagent, 185
Periplast, 4, 46, 104, 192 (*see also* Pellicle)
Petalomonas, 8, 52, 55, 198
   flagellar activity, 141
   ingestion by, 56, 190
   relationships, 71, 72*n* 75

Petalomonas (*cont.*):
  scutulum, 52 (*see also Parmidium scutulum*)
  tricarinata, notes and drawings of, **54, 56**
Phacotaceae, 69
Phacus, 8, 16, 45, 197
  cell cleavage, 104–105
  chloroplasts, 171
  flagellar swelling, 145
  paramylon studies on, 187
  pyrum, 45
    flagellar structure, **130**
    long chromosome, 95
    meiosis, 92–94
    mitosis, 84, 85, **86**
  relationships, 45, 46, 73, 75
  splendens, 45
  triqueter:
    chloroplasts, **172**
    notes and drawing of, **44,** 45
Phaeophyceae, 3, 4 (*see also Phaeophyta*)
Phaeophyta, 4, 143, 175, 185
Phagocytic vacuoles, 166 (*see also* Food
  vacuoles)
Phagotrophy, in euglenoids, 186, 190–195,
  201, 202
  in phylogeny, 8, 73, 74
  as a taxonomic feature, 9, 17–71, 196,
    197, 198
Phase segregation, in contractile vacuoles,
  148, 153
Pheophytin, 181
Phosphate condensations, 166
Phospholipid vesicles, 166–168
  in particular euglenoid species, **13–44,
    167**
  ultrastructure, **158, 161**
Photophosphorylation, 169
Photoreception, by euglenoids, 126, 146,
  147
Photoreceptor, of euglenoids, 6, 146, 147
  (*see also* Flagellar swelling)
Photosynthesis, 169
  by euglenoids, 25, 179, 182, 186
Phototactic responses, 143
  by euglenoids, 35, 46, 67, 146
Phototaxis, by euglenoids, 146, 183
Phototrophy, in euglenoids, 163, 181, 200,
  201, 202
  as a taxonomic feature, 9, 12–66
Phylogenetic scheme, 42, 73, 74, 75
Phylogeny, of euglenoids, 8, 10, 72–75, 179,
  183, 190
Phytoflagellates, 5
Phytomastigophorea, 5
Picromycin, non-permanent "bleaching"
  of *Euglena* by, 184
Pigments:
  carotenoid:
    in droplets, 43

Pigments, carotenoid (*cont.*):
  in euglenoid eyespots, 16, 143
  in euglenoid chloroplasts, 25, 179, 181–
    182, 184
  in eyespots, 143
  in phospholipid vesicles, 166, 168
  photosynthetic, 3, 169
Pinocytosis, 122, 153, 168
Pinocytotic vacuoles, 166
Plant kingdom, taxonomic position of
  euglenoids in, 3
Plasmalemma, 79, 127, 148
  in euglenoids:
    relation to contractile vacuole, 151,
      153
    relation to pellicle, 96, 100, **105,** 116,
      144, 178, 193
    relation to reservoir, 120, 121, 122
Plasma membrane, 79, 99, **134,** 153 (*see
  also* Plasmalemma)
Plastid continuity, 164, 183
Plastidome, 171 (*see also* Chloroplasts)
Plastids, 79, 143, 164, 174, 175, 177, 179,
  183, 184 (*see also* Chloroplasts,
  Leucoplasts)
Ploeotia, 71, 198
  vitrea, notes on, 71
Polyphosphates, 166
Polyploidy, of euglenoids, 12, 92, 94
Polysaccharides, 171, 185, 189 (*see also*
  Carbohydrate reserves)
Potassium permanganate, 203
Prasinophyceae, 4
Predatory behaviour, of *Peranema*, 192
Prey, capture of by euglenoids, 190, 192,
  194
"Primitive euglenoid flagellate," 73
Procaryota, 4
Procaryotic cell, 175
Prolamellar body, of chloroplasts, 181
Promitochondria, 160
Prophase (*see* Mitosis, euglenoid, prophase)
Proplastids, 179, 181, 182
Protaspis, 71, 141, 198
  obovata, drawing of, 70
Proteins, 79, 81, 99, 116, 128, 141, 153, 155,
  166, 171, 183, 192, 201
Protein synthesis, 115, 116, 155, 181, 182,
  183
Protista, 89, 126, 148, 166
Protochlorophyll *a*, 181, 182
Protochlorophyllide *a*, 181, 182
Protoeuglena, 69, 198
Protoplasm, 79n
Protoplast, 79, 148
Protozoa:
  contractile vacuoles, 166
  skeletal organelles, 194

Protozoa (*cont.*):
    taxonomic position of euglenoids in, 3, 5, 6
Pseudamoeba, 71
    planktonica, notes on, 71
"*Pseudastasia longa*," 32 (*see also Astasia longa*)
"*Pseudoperanema*," 60
Pseudopodia, of euglenoids, 71
Pyrenoids, 169, 171
    of euglenoids, 170, 171, 174, 175, 177, 179, 185, 186, 187
        form in particular species, 22–42, 173, 186, 187
        paramylon sheath (cap), 171, 173, 177, 180, 185, 186, 187, 187, 189
        as a taxonomic feature, 9, 12–67, 114, 170, 171
    ultrastructure, 177, 180
Pyrrophyta, 4, 71

Q

Quinones, in *Euglena* chloroplasts, 179

R

Rana, *Euglenamorpha* in tadpoles of, 67, 197
Reservoir (of euglenoids), 120–126
    diagnostic form, 6
    form in particular species, 13–70, 121, 122, 129, 135, 144, 162, 172
    insertion of flagella, 128, 129, 135, 135, 136, 140, 144
    microtubules, 99, 121, 125, 126, 136, 139, 144
    relation to contractile vacuolar function, 120, 122, 149–154
    relation to ingestion, 190, 194, 195
    relation to pinocytosis and chemoreception, 122
    ultrastructure, 125, 134, 144, 152, 154, 191
Respiration, 160
    by euglenoids, 165
Rhabdomonadales, 10, 46, 55, 73, 204
    flagellar activity, 141
Rhabdomonadina, 10, 46 (*see also Rhabdomonadales*)
Rhabdomonas, 46, 48, 198
    costata, notes and drawing of, 48, 49
    relationships, 75
    spiralis, 48 (*see also Rhabdospira spiralis*)
Rhabdospira, 46, 48, 198
    relationships, 75
    spiralis, notes and drawing of, 48, 49
Rhaphidophyceae, 4
Rhizaspidaceae, 71
Rhizaspis, 71, 141, 198
    simplex, drawing of, 70

Rhizopodia, of euglenoids, 70, 71
Rhodophyceae, 3, 4 (*see also Rhodophyta*)
Rhodophyta, 4, 175, 185
Rhynchopodaceae, 71
Rhynchopus, 71, 141, 198
    amitus, notes and drawing of, 70, 71
RNA (Ribonucleic acid):
    in chromosomes and nucleoli, 81
    in euglenoid chloroplasts, 117, 182, 183
    in euglenoid endosomes, 87
    messenger RNA, 115, 183
    transfer RNA, 115
Riboflavin, requirement for in *Peranema*, 202
Ribosomes, 79, 115
    in euglenoids, 115–117, 117, 121, 123, 154, 179, 183, 184
Rostral tube, microtubular construction of, 194
Ruthenium red, 108, 202

S

Saprotrophy, in euglenoids, 9, 201 (*see also* Heterotrophy, Osmotrophy)
Sarcodina, 5
Sarcomastigophora, 5
Scytomonas, 71, 198
    conjugation, 92
    klebsii, notes on, 71
Scytosiphon, flagellar swelling in zoospores of, 147
Seaweeds, euglenoids in association with, 40, 199
Secretory products, 79, 155
Sexuality (Sexual process):
    absence of in euglenoids, 7, 8, 92
    in *Scytomonas*, 71, 92
S-helix, of euglenoid pellicle, 12, 43, 45, 48, 50, 60, 64, 67, 100, 101, 102
Silicoflagellida, 5
Siphon (*see* Ingestion organelle)
Size varieties, of euglenoid species, 8, 18, 21, 27, 32, 34
Slime sheath, of euglenoids, 18, 21, 27, 48, 110, 114
Solenotus, 57 (*see also Notosolenus*)
Species concept in euglenoids, 8
Spermatozoids (Spermatids), 127, 128, 147, 160
Sphenomonadales, 10, 52, 71, 73, 74, 204
    flagellar structure, 129
    phagotrophy, 190, 195
Sphenomonadina, 10, 52 (*see also Sphenomonadales*)
Sphenomonas, 52, 53, 69, 141
    flagellar activity, 141
    laevis, notes and drawing of, 53, 54
    relationships, 55, 69, 75
Spherosomes, 166, 167

"Sphincter," 126
Spindle, 81
  apparent absence of in euglenoids, 6,
    87, 89
Sporozoa, 5
Stalks, of Colacium, 41, **42**, 43, 100, 110,
  111
Starch, 169, 171, 185, 186, 187, 192
Stenostomum, *Khawkinea* parasitic in, 29
Stigeoclonium, alveolate vesicles in, 153
Stigma, 143 (*see also* Eyespot)
Streptomycin:
  effect on euglenoid eyespot and flagellar
    swelling, 146
  permanent "bleaching" of *Euglena* by,
    163, 183, 184
Strombomonas, 8, 16, 38, 197
  australica, envelope, **39**
  chloroplasts, 171
  conspersa, notes and drawing of, 38, **39**
  envelope formation, 110
  flagellar swelling, 145
  pungens, envelope, **39**
Surface replicas, 96, **101**, 104, 107, 189
Swimming, of euglenoids, 72, 141, 142, 146
  flagellar and body movements in partic-
    ular species, 12–66
Symmetry, of euglenoids:
  bilateral, 72, 73, 104, 120
  dorso-ventral, 43, 45, 46, **47**, 50, **51**, 57,
    59, 104, 120
  helical, 6, 46, **49, 54, 65,** 66, 69, 96, 102,
    104, 119
Systole, 148, 149, 151, 153 (*see also* Contractile vacuole, of euglenoids, activity)

T

Tadpoles, euglenoids endozoic in, 66, 67,
  197
Taxonomy of euglenoids:
  ordinal, generic and specific characters,
    11–71
  position in the plant and animal king-
    doms, 3–5
  problems of classification, 8–10
Telophase (*see* Mitosis, euglenoid, telophase)
Tetraedron, ingestion of by *Euglenopsis*, 34
Thiamin (*see* Vitamin B₁)
Thylakoids (in chloroplasts), 169, 175, 176,
  177, **178**, 179, **180**, 182
Toluidine blue, 166
Tonoplast, 79
Trachelomonas, 8, 16, 35, 36, 197
  bulla, envelope structure, **111, 112**
  chloroplasts, 36, 171
  envelope formation, 100, 110, **112,** 114

Trachelomonas (*cont.*):
  flagellar structure, 129
  flagellar swelling, 145
  Golgi bodies, 159
  grandis:
    locomotory flagellum, **132**
    mitosis, 85, **88**
    notes and drawing of, 36, **37**
    paramylon (pyrenoid caps), **187, 189**
  horribilis, envelope, **37**
  inner pyrenoids, 27, 36, 171, **187**
  lychenensis, envelope, **37**
  muciferous bodies, 109
  relationships, 36, 38, 73, 75
  reticulata:
    mitochondrial reticulum, 162
    notes and drawing of, 36, **37**
  vestita, envelope, **37**
  volvocina, astaxanthin in eyespot of, 143
Transhydrogenase, photo-induction of in
  Euglena, 181
Triangulomonas, 71, 198
  rigida, notes on, 71
Tribonema, *Ascoglena* epiphytic on, 41
Tricarboxylic acid cycle, 163, 165
Trichocysts:
  of ciliates, 108
  of euglenoids, 3, 9n, 25, 62, 109, **191, 193**
Trichomonas, axostyle, 194
Trichonympha:
  flagellar basal bodies, 139
  rostral tube, 194
Tritiated acetate, flagellar regeneration of
  Astasia in, 141
Tropidoscyphus, 52, 56, 197
  caudatus, notes and drawing of, 56, 57, **58**
  flagellar activity, 141
  phagotrophy, 190
  relationships, 55, 71, 75

U

Ultraviolet irradiation, of *Euglena*, 181n,
  182, 183, 184
Ulva, *Klebsiella* in samples of, 40
Unio, paramylon digestion by enzymes
  from, 186
Unit membrane, 79, 82, 127, 148, 151,
  155, 161, 166, 189, **193**
Unna Pappenheim reaction, 87
Urceolopsis, 62 (*see also* Urceolus)
Urceolus, 59, 62, 198
  flagellar activity, 141
  macromastix, notes and drawings of, **63,** 64
  phagotrophy, 190
  relationships, 75
Uridylic acid, proportion in *Euglena* RNA,
  183

V

Vacuole, 79
Vibratile projection, of *Rhynchopus*, **70,** 71
Vital staining, 160, 202
Vitamin B₁ (Thiamin), requirement for in euglenoids, 202
Vitamin B₁₂ (Cobalamin), requirement for in euglenoids, 202
Volutin granules, 166
Volvocales, 69
Volvocida, 5

W

Warts, of *Euglena spirogyra*, **19, 97, 98,** 100, **105,** 114 (*see also* Pellicle, of euglenoids, ornamentation)

X

Xanthophyceae, 3, 4, (see also *Xanthophyta*)
Xanthophyta, 4, 143, 175
X-irradiation, of *Euglena*, 87n
X-ray diffraction studies of paramylon, 185
X-rays, destruction of mitochondria by, 160

Y

Yeasts, as food for *Peranema*, 192, 201

Z

Z-helix, of euglenoid pellicle, 50, 67, 69, 100, 104
Zooflagellates, relationship to euglenoids, 5
Zoomastigophorea, 5
Zoophytic habit, of *Colacium*, 41
Zoospores, 127, 143, 147, 148, 153